Introduction to Energy Analysis

Introduction to Energy Analysis

Kornelis Blok

Techne Press, Amsterdam

Kornelis Blok is a professor at the Copernicus Institute for Sustainable Development and Innovation, Utrecht University and co-founder and Managing Director of Ecofys, an influential consultancy on energy and climate change.

Introduction to Energy Analysis / by K. Blok
2007, Amsterdam, 256 pages
ISBN-13: 978-8594-016-6
ISBN-10: 90-8594-016-8
Keywords: Energy analysis, energy systems, energy demand, energy supply, energy efficiency, life-cycle energy analysis

Cover Illustration: Sven Geier -- www.sgeier.net/fractals
Cover Design: Ontwerpstudio Rood, Amsterdam, The Netherlands
www.ontwerpstudiorood.nl

Published and distributed by Techne Press, Amsterdam, The Netherlands
www.technepress.nl

Preface

The energy supply and demand system has been, still is, and will probably always be of great importance for society, from the economic, the social, and the ecological viewpoint. The continuously changing world of energy systems remains an important area for study, academic research, and professional work.

This textbook intends to provide an introduction into energy analysis for those students who want to specialise in this challenging field. In comparison to other textbooks, this book provides a balanced treatment of complete energy systems, covering the demand side, the supply side, and energy markets. The emphasis is very much on presenting a range of tools and methodologies that will help students find their way in analysing real world problems in energy systems.

The book is meant for students at the near graduate or graduate level and assumes that the student has a substantial basis in natural sciences. This book may also be useful for professionals dealing with energy issues, as a first introduction into the field and the methods applied there.

Acknowledgements

In the course of the years, I have worked in energy analysis together with a lot of colleagues. I wish to thank Jeroen de Beer, Jacco Farla, André Faaij, Chris Hendriks, David de Jager, Dian Phylipsen, Kees Vringer, Ad van Wijk, Ernst Worrell, Wim Turkenburg and many others from the Department of Science, Technology and Society of Utrecht University, from Ecofys and from other organizations. Without this cooperation and their contributions to energy analysis, this textbook could not have been written. Reviews by these colleagues and Maarten Neelis, Suzanne Joosen, Robert Harmsen, Monique Voogt, Martin Patel and Martijn Rietbergen prevented a number of errors entering the text.

I want to thank Evert Nieuwlaar, not just for providing the raw material for Sections 9.2 and 9.3, but also for providing me – in the course of the years – with many theoretical insights in energy analysis. I thank José Potting (Section 9.2), Jeroen de Beer (7.3 and 7.4) and Saskia Hagedoorn (4.1) for letting me use their texts. A special thanks goes to Sander van Egmond who helped in a lot of ways, but especially to improve the accessibility of the text. Thanks also to Dan Birkett for his help in the final preparation of the textbook, and Sören Johnson for improving the quality of the English.

Finally, I would like to thank Heleen Gierveld from Techne Press for her support and for bringing this book to the market.

Utrecht, October 2006
Kornelis Blok

Contents

Introduction

What is energy analysis?

Energy analysis – or energy systems analysis – is the study of energy use, energy production and energy conversion in society. It is an attempt to explain historic developments of energy use and energy production, to explore possible future developments, and to consider how such developments can be influenced.

The total body of interdisciplinary knowledge that has developed around these questions since the early 1970s can be referred to as *energy analysis*. It is important to realize that we build on the vast body of knowledge available in various other disciplines. First of all, energy analysis depends on knowledge from natural science and technology, and we will often refer back to the basic mechanisms that govern the conversion and use of energy. Next, we use knowledge from economics, including cost-benefit analysis and input-output analysis. Finally, we also use other social science disciplines, including policy science.

In order to advance our knowledge of energy systems in a systematic way, we need to use more or less standardised analytical methods. The main focus of this textbook is to help you understand these methods and learn how to use them.

Energy systems

An energy system consists of a number of stages. Figure 1 shows a very simple energy system consisting of just one simple chain.

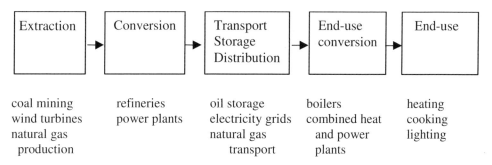

Figure 1. Schematic representation of a simple chain from extraction to end-use within an energy supply system.

The first stage in the energy supply system is the extraction of energy carriers. This can be the mining of coal or uranium, the extraction of oil or natural gas, the extraction of energy from wind by a wind turbine, or the cultivation of biomass for energy purposes. The energy produced in such a way is often not suitable for a specific application, so conversion is needed. Major energy conversion processes include power plants that convert fossil fuels to electricity and refineries that convert crude oil to a range of products, like petrol, naphtha and heavy fuel oil. Many other energy conversion processes exist and new ones will be developed in the future.

Having energy in the right form does not mean that it is available in the right place at the right time. A lot of activities in the energy system, like transport, storage and distribution, are needed to bring energy to the end user when it is needed. Once the user has acquired the energy, it may still not be in the right form, and further conversion may be needed, for example, converting fuel to heat in a boiler. This is known as end-use conversion.

When the energy is finally in its ultimate form, it can provide a certain service (or function) for the user. Such services include heating or lighting a room, transporting a person in a car, or making steel or clothes. All of these services are used, to varying degrees and in different ways, by people in different societies.

Energy analysis is interested in the total energy chain depicted in Figure 1. It is especially interested in the forces that drive the demand for energy services. In energy analysis, we are interested in how this demand for energy services can be met by various sorts of equipment with different energy inputs. We are also interested in how the user chooses this equipment and what influences this choice. Finally, we are interested in how the resulting end-use energy demand can be delivered in various ways using a range of primary energy sources with differing social, economic, and ecological consequences.

What can be expected in this book?

The text book starts with two introductory chapters. Chapter 1 briefly recollects main elements of thermodynamics, which forms the ever-present background for all energy analysis; next, Chapter 2 gives an introduction to measuring energy.

Chapters 3 to 6 are descriptive in character; first, Chapters 3 to 5 give an overview of energy demand systems, energy supply systems, and the energy markets that connect both. Chapter 6 provides looks at the broader social context of energy systems.

Chapters 7 – 15 each provide an overview of basic tools that are used in energy analysis. Chapter 7 provides methods to analyse energy use for individual sites. Chapter 8 is dedicated to the conversion of final energy use to primary energy (initial energy extraction) and emissions. Chapter 9 describes life-cycle energy analysis: how can we determine total energy use for specific commodities and products. Chapter 10 describes how energy efficiency is measured. Chapter 11 describes how future prospects of individual energy technologies can be analysed, whereas Chapter 12 focuses on the aggregate analysis of technologies. Chapter 13 describes how the past development of energy use can be decomposed into the underlying factors: economic growth, structural change, and energy efficiency. Chapter 14 looks forward and describes how energy scenarios can be built and what tools are available to do so. Finally, Chapter 15 describes how policies influence energy systems and how such policies can be evaluated.

1

Thermodynamics: the basis of energy analysis

1.1   The first law of thermodynamics

Energy exists in many forms, including:
- kinetic energy
- potential energy
- chemical energy
- nuclear energy
- electromagnetic radiation
- electricity
- heat

Many conversions exist between these various forms of energy. The first law of thermodynamics, also called the *law of conservation of energy,* states that energy can neither be created nor destroyed, but can only be converted from one form to the other (or from several forms combined to one or more other forms). This well-known law forms the basis for energy analysis, and this concept is implicitly used in many types of analysis. The law of conservation of energy also provides the background for the construction of energy balances, both for individual energy users and for countries.

1.2   Energy and enthalpy

The energy content can be determined for a given substance (e.g., an amount of coal, a certain volume of hot water). This energy content is dependent on conditions like pressure and temperature, and is always determined in comparison to a reference state. The energy content is then the amount of energy it takes to bring the substance from the reference state to the actual state. In energy analysis, we generally use an *environmental reference system,* with the reference state for each chemical element being the most stable naturally-occurring compound of that element (e.g., for carbon the reference is CO_2, and for hydrogen the reference is liquid H_2O). Reference temperatures and pressures are not always the same. For instance, for fuels, the energy of combustion is determined using a reference temperature of 25 °C and standard atmospheric pressure (101.325 kPa). For water and steam, the reference for the energy content is the triple point of the liquid (0.01 °C). In most cases we are only interested in energy *changes*, which makes the exact positioning of the reference level irrelevant.

In practice, two slightly different concepts of energy content are used:
- (internal) energy
- enthalpy

The change in internal energy of a substance is measured by adding (or removing) energy under constant volume; the change in enthalpy is measured by adding (or removing) energy under constant pressure.

Added energy can be stored in the substance in various ways: in kinetic energy of the molecules making up the substance, or in chemical bonds between atoms. The internal energy can be interpreted as the total amount of energy stored in the substance. In practice, enthalpy is usually used rather than the internal energy. Especially for solids and liquids, it is much easier to measure enthalpy, as measuring under constant pressure is easier than measuring under constant volume. In contrast to energy, enthalpy is not a conserved quantity (there is no 'law of conservation of enthalpy').

The relation between internal energy E and enthalpy H is as follows:

$$H = E + p \cdot V \qquad [1.1]$$

where:

H = enthalpy
E = internal energy (also often indicated with the letter U)
p = pressure
V = volume

For solids and liquids, the difference between H and E is very small, but for gases the difference cannot generally be neglected.

1.3 The second law of thermodynamics

There are several different formulations of the second law of thermodynamics. The Kelvin-Planck formulation reads as follows: "It is impossible for any system to operate in a thermodynamic cycle and deliver a net amount of energy by work to its surroundings while receiving energy by heat transfer from a single thermal energy reservoir". In simple words: heat cannot be fully converted into work.

We will calculate how much of the energy extracted from a thermal energy reservoir[1] can be converted into work. To this end, the entropy concept is introduced. The entropy change ΔS associated with the extraction of an amount ΔQ of heat from a reservoir with temperature T is (by definition):

---

[1] A thermal energy reservoir is a theoretical concept. It indicates a system in which the temperature remains constant if heat is extracted. A thermal energy reservoir is also often referred to as a 'heat reservoir'.

$$\Delta S = \frac{\Delta Q}{T} \qquad\qquad [1.2]$$

where:

ΔS = entropy change

ΔQ = heat extraction

T   = temperature

We will use one of the other ways of expressing the Second Law of Thermodynamics, namely: "in any process the total entropy of a closed (isolated) system cannot decrease".

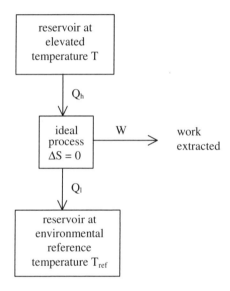

Figure 1.1. Schematic representation of energy flows in a process where the maximum amount of work is produced through the extraction of heat from a hot reservoir. The process is ideal in the sense that no entropy is generated ($\Delta S = 0$).

We will now calculate the amount of work that can be extracted from a thermal energy reservoir with constant temperature (see Figure 1.1), by combining the first and the second law of thermodynamics. According to the first law of thermodynamics (the law of conservation of energy) the following relation is valid:

$$Q_h - Q_l = W \qquad\qquad [1.3a]$$

where:

Q_h = the heat extracted from the high temperature reservoir

Q_l = the heat added to the low temperature reservoir

W   = the amount of work delivered.

According to equation [1.2], the entropy change ΔS associated with the extraction of an amount of heat ΔQ from a reservoir with temperature T is ΔS = ΔQ/T. So, the total entropy change of the process depicted in Figure 1.1 will be:

$$\Delta S = \frac{Q_h}{T} - \frac{Q_l}{T_{ref}}$$
[1.3b]

The second law says that the total of entropy changes in such a closed system is larger than or equal to zero. Now, let us first assume that we have an ideal process, where the entropy does not increase: ΔS = 0. Using the equations [1.3a] and [1.3b], one can easily derive that, for the ideal process:

$$W = \left(1 - \frac{T_{ref}}{T}\right) \cdot Q_h$$
[1.4]

From this we can conclude that for this ideal process, the maximum amount of work produced is always smaller than the heat extracted from the reservoir, which brings us back to our first formulation of the second law of thermodynamics.

Note that, for a given amount of heat and a given T_{ref}, the amount of work to be extracted increases with increasing T. For non-ideal processes (i.e., ΔS > 0), W will be smaller than the amount calculated with equation [1.4].

1.4   Exergy

The topic discussed in the previous section is of great relevance for energy analysis. We can convert 1 joule of electricity into 1 joule of heat (e.g., in the form of hot water), but we cannot convert 1 joule of heat contained in hot water into 1 joule of electricity. The concept of exergy is one way of dealing with this fundamental difference between various energy carriers.

The exergy content of an energy carrier is the **maximum amount of work** that can be extracted from it. More precisely, the exergy content of an energy carrier is defined as the maximum amount of work that can be obtained when the energy carrier is brought into equilibrium with the natural environment (i.e., when it is converted to the conditions of the environmental reference system).

What is the exergy content B of different energy carriers if the energy content is E?
- As electricity is work, by definition the exergy content of an amount of electricity is equal to the energy content. Thus B = E

- For fuels, the exergy content is more or less equal to the energy content. Thus $B \approx E$
- Big differences may occur in the case of heat: the exergy content of heat flows is smaller than the energy content: $B < E$

For heat extracted from a thermal energy reservoir, the exergy content B can be calculated, using the following expression (see equation [1.4]):

$$B = \left(1 - \frac{T_{ref}}{T}\right) \cdot Q_h \qquad [1.5]$$

where:

T   =   the absolute temperature of the thermal energy reservoir (kelvin)
T_{ref} =   the reference temperature (temperature of the environment), for
            instance 283 K (10 °C)
Q_h =   the heat extracted from the thermal energy reservoir
B   =   the exergy content of the heat

The factor $(1 - T_{ref}/T)$ is called the Carnot factor. This is the maximum efficiency of producing work out of heat when extracting heat from one thermal energy reservoir and transferring it to another thermal energy reservoir.

Expression [1.5] is used quite often, but in fact it is only valid for a thermal energy reservoir, which is a theoretical construct. It is a constant temperature heat source, whereas most actual heat sources, like an amount of steam or hot water, decrease in temperature as soon as heat is extracted. This means that the exergy content should be calculated by integrating over the temperature range. This results in the following, somewhat more complicated, expression, which is only valid if the specific heat of the substance containing the heat is constant over the temperature range

$$B = \left[1 - \frac{T_{ref}}{T - T_{ref}} \cdot \ln\left(\frac{T}{T_{ref}}\right)\right] \cdot Q \qquad [1.6]$$

where:
Q = the amount of heat that can be extracted from the substance

Note that in all cases the temperature (e.g., in [1.5] and [1.6]) needs to be given in absolute terms – i.e. in kelvin.

In Figure 1.2, the exergy is given as a function of the temperature according to equation [1.6]. The temperature of warm water for space heating is in the range of 75 °C to 120 °C (under pressure), so the exergy-energy ratio varies from 0.10 to 0.15. The exergy-energy ratio for industrial steam is more difficult to calculate, since equation [1.6] can not be used, as the specific heat is not constant over the temperature range. Steam tables are therefore needed to determine the exergy/energy ratio. Depending on the condition of the steam, the B/Q ratio is 0.3 to 0.4.

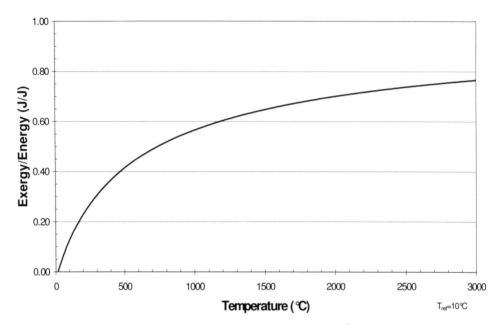

Figure 1.2. The exergy factor B/Q as a function of the temperature, based on equation [1.6]. The reference temperature T_{ref} used in this case is 10 °C. The picture is only valid for substances with a constant specific heat.

So far, we have focused on the conversion of heat to work. However, the concept of exergy has a broader use and can be utilized to determine the maximum conversion efficiency for all types of energy conversion. The exergy content of energy carriers can be calculated using the basic thermodynamic properties of substances. See Box 1.1 for the general definition of exergy.

Box 1.1. General description of the concept of exergy.

The concept of exergy is not only used for energy in the form of heat but can also be used for all energy flows. In thermodynamics, the maximum amount of work that can be extracted from a substance by converting it to the thermodynamic reference state is called the Gibbs free energy ('free' means 'free to do work'). It is defined as:

$$G = H - T \cdot S \qquad [1.7]$$

where:
G = Gibbs free energy
H = enthalpy of the substance
S = entropy of the substance
T = absolute temperature of the substance

The definition of exergy only differs from that of the Gibbs free energy with respect to the choice of the reference system: in the environmental reference system the most stable compounds occurring in nature are used, rather than the elements.

$$B = H_B - T_{ref} \cdot S_B \qquad [1.8]$$

where:
B   = exergy
T_{ref} = environmental reference temperature (absolute).

The subscript B (base) indicates that the environmental reference system is used. The use of T_{ref} instead of T in the exergy formula originates from the fact that all heat lost in the process disappears in the environment.

Further reading

Y.A. Çengel, M.A. Boles: Thermodynamics – An Engineering Approach, McGraw Hill, New York, 5th edition, 2006.

M.J. Moran, H.N. Shapiro: Fundamentals of Engineering Thermodynamics, John Wiley & Sons, Hoboken, NJ, USA, 5th edition, 2004.

E. Nieuwlaar: Developments in energy analysis, Ph.D. Thesis, Utrecht University, 1988.

J.M. Smith, H.C. van Ness: Introduction to Chemical Engineering Thermodynamics, McGraw-Hill, New York, 4th edition, 1987.

Final achievement levels

After having studied Chapter 1 and the exercises, you should:
- know the first and second laws of thermodynamics
- be able to explain the difference between energy and enthalpy and the practical consequences
- be able to derive the maximum amount of work or heat to be generated from various configurations of heat and work input (e.g., equation [1.4])
- know the definition of exergy and be able to use the concept for simple energy conversion processes

Exercises Chapter 1

1.1. A piece of wood
A piece of wood with a weight of 1 kg falls from the tenth floor (from a height of 30 meters). When the wood touches the ground, the energy is converted to heat. Assume that all the heat is added to the wood.
a. What is the kinetic energy of the piece of wood just before it touches ground? What is the speed? Neglect air resistance.
b. How much does the temperature of the wood increase after touchdown?
c. How much heat would be released if the wood were completely combusted?
d. What do you learn from these findings?
The specific heat of wood is 2.7 kJ/kg·K. The heat of combustion of wood is 18 MJ/kg.

1.2. Energy and enthalpy
Calculate the difference between the enthalpy and internal energy of a litre of gasoline under standard conditions. The energy content of gasoline is 33 MJ per litre.

1.3. Ocean thermal energy conversion
The temperature of the water in the deep ocean can be considered as an infinite reservoir of heat with a temperature of 5 °C. Consider the atmosphere as a thermal energy reservoir with a temperature of 25 °C. Ocean thermal energy conversion (OTEC) uses this temperature difference to produce electricity.
What is the maximum theoretical efficiency of this OTEC concept - i.e., how much work can one extract per unit of heat added to the deep ocean? Use an approach, comparable to the one in section 1.3.

1.4. The ideal cooling machine
The relation between work and heat has two directions. As described in section 1.4, the maximum efficiency of transferring heat into work is given by the Carnot factor. An ideal cooling machine extracts heat from a cold reservoir and transfers it to a warm reservoir.
a. Derive a formula comparable to the Carnot factor for an ideal cooling machine. In other words, how much heat can be removed per unit of work?
b. Calculate the theoretical maximum efficiency for a refrigerator and a freezer (temperature inside fridge 5 °C; inside freezer -18 °C; room temperature 20 °C).

1.5. Derive equation [1.6]

1.6. The exergy of steam
Calculate the energy content, the exergy content and the exergy/energy ratio of:
a.   saturated steam with a pressure of 10 bar (1.0 MPa) and a temperature of 180 °C;
b.   so-called superheated steam with a pressure of 10 bar and a temperature of 320 °C.
Such steam can be produced by first heating hot water from 10 °C to 180 °C (average specific heat 4.24 kJ/kg·K), then evaporating the steam at 180 °C (evaporation heat 2015 kJ/kg) and, if necessary 'superheating' the steam to 320 °C (average specific heat of the steam 2.26 kJ/kg·K).

For the superheating trajectory, you need an adapted version of the equation [1.6], as the heating trajectory does not start at the reference temperature. For a medium with constant heat capacity that is heated from T_l to temperature T_h the relation between the exergy addition B and the heat addition Q is given by:

$$ B = \left[1 - \frac{T_{ref}}{T_h - T_l} \cdot \ln\left(\frac{T_h}{T_l}\right) \right] \cdot Q \qquad [1.9] $$

1.7. Exergy change during combustion
What is the exergy/energy ratio for:
a.   Unburned natural gas
b.   The combustion products in a flame of natural gas (2200 °C)
c.   Diluted combustion air of 500 °C
d.   A certain amount of water at 90 °C
Describe some consequences of your calculation results.

1.8. Very efficient boilers
In a boiler for a domestic central heating system, a fuel is burned to heat the circulation water that is used for space heating. Modern natural-gas fired boilers are very efficient: 97% of the energy content in the natural gas is transferred to the circulating water. Assume that the return water from the central heating system enters the boiler at a temperature of 30 °C and is heated to 80 °C.
a.   Calculate the energy flows per litre of boiler water throughput
b.   Calculate the exergy flows per litre of boiler water throughput
The specific heat of water is 4.18 kJ/kg·K.
What conclusions can you draw about these efficient boilers?

2

What is energy use?

Before we can start with energy analysis, we should first clarify what we mean by energy use, and how it is measured. The contents of this chapter may have a somewhat technical character, but before one can continue with energy analysis, it is important to be clear about the definitions of energy use and how to measure energy use.

2.1   Units of energy

The standard unit of energy in the *Système Internationale* (SI) is the joule (J). One joule is one $kg \cdot m^2/s^2$. Many other units of energy are used: some refer to specific energy carriers like oil, coal or electricity, whereas others are used in specific regions. An overview is given in Table 2.1.

Table 2.1. Overview of units of energy use and their conversion to the SI-unit joule.

Unit	Conversion to joules (multiply by ...)	Remarks
calorie (cal)	4.1868	Old unit for quantities of heat
ton-of-oil-equivalent (toe)	$41.868 \cdot 10^9$	Defined as 10^7 kcal. The toe is widely used in international energy statistics
barrel-of-oil-equivalent (boe)	approx. $6.1 \cdot 10^9$	Conversion values range from 6.06 to $6.12 \cdot 10^9$
ton-of-coal-equivalent (tce)	$28.6 \cdot 10^9$	Used as the main unit of energy in China
kilowatt-hour (kWh)	$3.6 \cdot 10^6$	Used mainly for electricity
British-thermal-unit (BTU)	$1.055 \cdot 10^3$	Used in the USA; other units include the therm (10^5 BTU) and the quad (10^{15} BTU)
watt-year (Wyr)	$31.5 \cdot 10^6$	Useful unit for analytical applications; if one uses 1 W on average, one uses 1 Wyr in a year

The amount of one joule is too small to work with in energy analysis. In energy analysis we generally come across processes with a minimum amount of energy input or output of 10^6 J per year. This is referred to as one megajoule (MJ). Another extreme encountered in energy analysis is the total current world energy consumption, which is about $450 \cdot 10^{18}$ J, or 450 exajoule (EJ). See Table 2.2 for an overview of scales of energy use.

Table 2.2 Scales of annual energy use (in terms of primary energy).

	Category	Scale	Example
Companies	Countries	$100\ EJ = 10^{20}\ J$	450 EJ/yr World energy use
		$10\ EJ = 10^{19}\ J$	100 EJ/yr US energy use
		$1\ EJ = 10^{18}\ J$	3 EJ/yr Netherlands' energy use
			1 EJ/yr energy use of Royal Dutch Shell
		$100\ PJ = 10^{17}\ J$	300 PJ/yr energy use of Ghana
		$10\ PJ = 10^{16}\ J$	30 PJ/yr energy use of a 500 MW coal power plant
		$1\ PJ = 10^{15}\ J$	
		$100\ TJ = 10^{14}\ J$	680 TJ/yr energy use of a large university complex
		$10\ TJ = 10^{13}\ J$	
	Individuals	$1\ TJ = 10^{12}\ J$	1 TJ/yr energy use of a small book shop
		$100\ GJ = 10^{11}\ J$	150 GJ/yr energy use of an EU citizen
		$10\ GJ = 10^{10}\ J$	10 GJ/yr energy use of an Indian citizen
Household appliances		$1\ GJ = 10^{9}\ J$	2 GJ/yr energy use of a refrigerator
		$100\ MJ = 10^{8}\ J$	500 MJ/yr energy use of a lamp
		$10\ MJ = 10^{7}\ J$	40 MJ/yr energy use of a toaster
		$1\ MJ = 10^{6}\ J$	

The annual primary energy consumption of countries typically lies in the order of exajoules. For individuals it lies in the order of gigajoules. Companies have a much wider range, which of course depends on the size and type of company. Their consumption generally lies in the order of petajoules or terajoules per year.

2.2   Power

Another important quantity in energy analysis is power: energy production, throughput, or use per unit of time. The SI unit is the watt (J/s). An older unit is horsepower (1 hp = 0.7457 kW). A variety of alternative units can also be encountered: e.g., kcal/hr or BTU/hr.

The nominal power (or capacity) can be determined for many types of equipment. This can be the power output, (e.g., a power plant that produces 600 MW of electricity), or the power input (e.g., an incandescent lamp that consumes 60 W of electricity).

For equipment with a constant power input or power output, the relation between energy and power is straightforward:

$$E = P \cdot t \qquad\qquad [2.1]$$

where:
E = energy input (or output)
P = power input (or output)
t   = time in use

If power is given in kW and time in hours, then the result is in kWh, which gives us the energy unit already mentioned in Table 2.1.

2.3   What are energy carriers?

There are many substances that are generally considered as energy carriers. Table 2.3 gives the energy content of these energy carriers.

Many other substances, like food, plastics and metals, contain energy. However, in energy analysis, these are generally not considered as energy carriers. The standard convention in energy analysis is that a substance is considered an energy carrier *if the substance is predominantly used as a source of energy*. So, coal is an energy carrier, but potatoes are not.

In line with this definition, waste is not considered an energy carrier, although the use of waste as an energy source is increasing. Wood is increasingly considered an energy carrier, as the use of biomass for energy production increases. Other commodities such as methanol and hydrogen, which are now mainly used as a feedstock in the chemical industry, may be used more and more as energy carriers in the future.

Products that are derived from crude oil but whose primary aim is not combustion, like lubricants and bitumen, are not considered as energy carriers. However, because they are produced in oil refineries, their production is often reported in energy statistics.

Table 2.3 Energy content for a number of energy carriers. The energy content is given on the basis of the lower heating value (see section 2.4), if applicable. Source: IEA statistics.

Fuel type	Energy content (MJ/kg unless indicated otherwise)
Hard coal (coking coal and bituminous coal)	24 – 31
Brown coal (sub-bituminous coal and lignite)	7 – 20
Crude oil	42 – 44
Ethane, LPG	47.3
Gasoline/petrol	44.8 (33 MJ/litre)
Jet fuel	44.6
Kerosene	43.7
Diesel fuel	43.3 (36 MJ/litre)
Heavy fuel oil	40.2
Natural gas	31 – 38 MJ/m^3
Electricity	3.6 MJ/kWh
Hot water 90 °C (reference 10 °C)	0.34
Steam, depending on pressure and temperature (reference liquid water 10 °)	2.7 – 3.5

2.4 Higher and lower heating value of fuels

The energy content of a fuel can be defined as the amount of heat that is produced during combustion. It is calculated by taking the difference in enthalpy between the substance and its combustion products, both at 25 °C and 1 bar.

An important distinction that should be made is the one between higher and lower heating value. This distinction is relevant for fuels like coal, oil products, natural gas and biomass, which contain hydrogen in one form or another. Hence water is formed during combustion of the fuel. In the case of higher heating value (HHV), the heat content of the water that is the product of the combustion process is measured in the liquid form. In the case of lower heating value (LHV), the water is in the gaseous form. Alternative terms are net calorific value (NCV) for LHV, and gross calorific value (GCV) for HHV.

So, the difference between the higher heating value and the lower heating value is equal to the condensation heat (evaporation heat) of the water that is the result of combustion (the original water content of the fuel is not taken into account). The higher heating value is larger than the lower heating value. The relation between the two is given by the following formula:

28

$$E_{LHV} = E_{HHV} - h \cdot E_{w,evap} \cdot m_{H2O} \qquad\qquad [2.2]$$

where:

E_{LHV}	= the lower heating value of the fuel (MJ/kg)
E_{HHV}	= the higher heating value of the fuel (MJ/kg)
$E_{w,evap}$	= the heat of evaporation of water (2.26 MJ/kg at 25 °C)
h	= the fraction of hydrogen in the fuel (on a mass basis)
m_{H2O}	= the mass of water created per unit mass of hydrogen (8.9 kg/kg)

Table 2.4 shows typical values for the ratio between the higher and lower heating value for some fuels.

Table 2.4. Typical values for the ratio between higher
and lower heating values for some fuels.

Fuel type	HHV/LHV ratio
Hard coal	1.03
Petroleum products	1.06
Natural gas	1.10

The higher heating value gives the best indication of the utilisation possibilities of fuels. It indicates the total amount of heat that can be generated through combustion of the fuel.

The rationale for using the lower heating value is that in many cases it is not feasible to utilise the latent heat of the gaseous form of water that is present in the combustion gases of a fuel. The exhaust gases from combustion often leave the chimney at temperatures of 100 °C or more, and at such temperatures there is virtually no water in the liquid form. However, this argument is outdated: In modern natural-gas fired boilers for low-temperature heat production, the exhaust gases are cooled to such a degree that a substantial part of the water in the flue gases condenses and the associated heat can be utilised, for example for heating the building.

Despite this, lower heating values are used in many parts of the world, except for the USA, Canada, Japan and Australia. International statistics also use lower heating values.

For biomass fuels, which contain substantial amounts of water, additional conventions are in use (see Box 2.1).

Box 2.1. Higher and lower heating values for biomass fuels.

For biomass fuels (like wood) a different convention is used for determining the lower heating value. Biomass fuels often contain substantial amounts of water. To determine the lower heating value of the biomass, this amount of water is also assumed to be in the gaseous form after combustion. The higher and lower heating value of biomass fuels can therefore be calculated as follows:

$$E_{HHV,wb} = E_{HHV,dry} \cdot (1 - w) \qquad [2.3a]$$

$$E_{LHV,wb} = E_{HHV,wb} - h \cdot E_{w,evap} \cdot m_{H2O} \cdot (1 - w) - E_{w,evap} \cdot w \qquad [2.3b]$$

where:
$E_{HHV,wb}$ = the higher heating value of the fuel on a wet basis
$E_{HHV,dry}$ = the higher heating value of the fuel on an oven dry basis
$E_{LHV,wb}$ = the lower heating value of the fuel on a wet basis
$E_{w,evap}$ = the energy required for evaporation of water (2.26 MJ/kg at 25 °C)
h = the fraction of hydrogen in the oven dry fuel (by weight)
m_{H2O} = the mass of water created per unit mass of hydrogen (8.9 kg/kg)
w = the fraction of water in the biomass on a wet fuel basis.

One generally distinguishes oven dry ($w = 0$), air dry ($w = 20 - 35\%$), and harvested (e.g., for wood: $w = 50\%$). For woody biomass, E_{HHV} is typically 20 MJ/kg (oven dry).

2.5 Accounting energy use of individual energy users

Energy use can be measured at various levels, first of all for individual entities (like households or company sites). These entities are called energy users.

What can be measured most easily is the amount of energy that enters such an entity; we call this *purchased energy*. However, purchased energy is not equal to the total amount that such an entity uses. In addition to the purchased energy, an entity may extract energy itself in one form or another: e.g., a household with a solar domestic hot water system, or a firm that runs a hydropower plant. An entity may also sell energy of which it has an excess: e.g., a farmer with a wind turbine may sell excess energy to the grid. Furthermore, an entity may add energy carriers to its stocks or extract energy carriers from its stocks. Taking these matters into account, we define *net available energy*:

Net available energy = Purchased energy – Sold energy + Own extraction
+/- Stock changes [2.4]

(For an illustration, see Box 2.2.)

Although net available energy is an important characteristic of energy users, it is not the quantity most frequently used. The term used most is *final energy use*. The idea behind using this term is that also energy users may operate energy conversion processes. An important energy conversion process is electricity generation, e.g. in the form of combined generation of heat and power (CHP). Consequently, final energy use is defined as the net available energy, corrected for the conversion that takes place in these own conversion processes (see Box 2.3).

Final energy use = Net available energy − Input to own conversion processes

+ Output of own conversion processes   [2.5]

Box 2.2. A farmer with a wind turbine: illustration of net available energy.

Assume that in a certain year a farmer buys 1000 GJ of energy. His windmill produces 600 GJ in that period, of which 400 GJ is sold to the electricity company. He withdraws 100 GJ of gasoline from a storage tank. How much energy was available for the farmer?

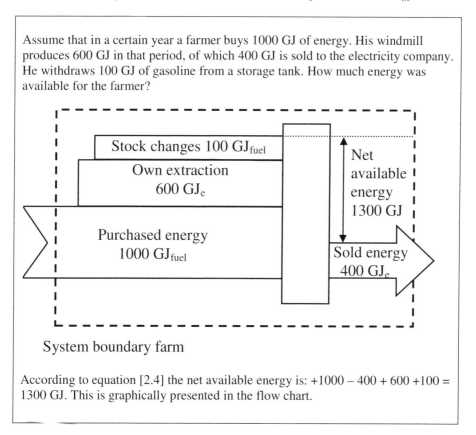

According to equation [2.4] the net available energy is: +1000 − 400 + 600 +100 = 1300 GJ. This is graphically presented in the flow chart.

Not all energy conversion processes are taken into account when calculating final energy use. For instance, boilers for heat production are rarely taken into account. This means that final energy is still not equal to the energy in its last stage of conversion. Therefore, analysts also use the term *useful energy* (or end-use energy) to indicate the amount of energy that is left after the last stage of conversion: e.g., the heat output of the central heating system that is supplied to heat a house.

Box 2.3. A hospital with a CHP plant: illustration of final energy use.

A hospital operates a combined generation of heat and power plant (CHP). In the CHP plant natural gas is converted into electricity and heat. The CHP plant of the hospital produces 5 TJ of heat and 3 TJ of electricity per year. The electricity is sold to the utility company; the heat is used for heating the hospital. The yearly input of the CHP plant is 10 TJ. Besides this 10 TJ, another 2 TJ is bought for direct use. What is the final energy use of the hospital?

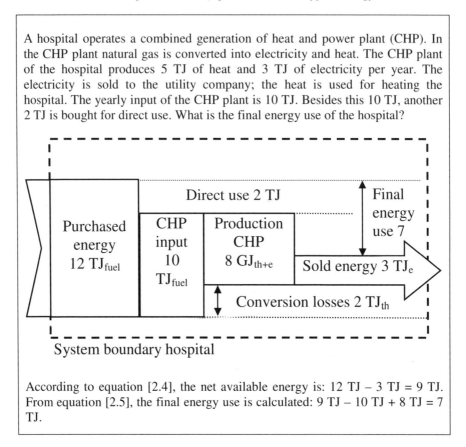

According to equation [2.4], the net available energy is: 12 TJ – 3 TJ = 9 TJ. From equation [2.5], the final energy use is calculated: 9 TJ – 10 TJ + 8 TJ = 7 TJ.

2.6   Energy balances and energy statistics

Just as we distinguish different forms of energy use for an individual energy user, we do the same at a higher aggregation level for a country (or a group of countries).

Information on energy use for a country is often given in the form of an energy balance. An energy balance is a matrix in which each row represents a sector, and each column represents an energy carrier. Each matrix element presents the amount of energy carrier that is used (or produced) in that sector. In cooperation with the United Nations, the International Energy Agency (IEA) compiles energy balances on an annual basis for countries all over the world. Examples of energy balances are given in Tables 2.5a, 2.5b and 2.5c.

An important row in the energy balances is the one presenting the total primary energy supply (TPES), which is generally considered as *the* indicator for a country's total energy use. This is more or less analogous to the net available energy from equation [2.4].

$$TPES = \text{indigenous production} + \text{imports} - \text{exports}$$
$$- \text{international marine bunkers}^1 +/- \text{stock changes} \qquad [2.6]$$

The five components that make up the TPES are listed above the TPES row in the energy balances.

The various energy conversion sectors are listed below the TPES row. Energy conversion sectors both have energy as an input (negative) and output (positive). After all energy conversion sectors[2] have been taken into account, the total final consumption (TFC) is left over:

$$TFC = TPES - \text{inputs to conversion processes}$$
$$+ \text{outputs of conversion processes} \qquad [2.7]$$

This is more or less analogous to the final energy use from equation [2.5]. The total final consumption is also the sum of the final consumption in all the end-use sectors listed in the rows below the TFC row in the IEA energy balances.

Different energy carriers are distinguished in the columns of an energy balance. For fuels, each column may contain both the original fuel and its derivatives. Another option is to organise the fuels by phase (solids, liquids, gases).

The columns are totalled by adding all energy carriers together (see last column). This is a straightforward aggregation of all energy carriers, irrespective of their differing values. This summation is useful for statistical purposes, but it cannot generally be used for other purposes such as comparing energy use between sectors or countries (see next section and Chapter 8).

---

[1] The category 'international marine bunkers' covers the amount of energy delivered to sea-going ships that leave the country. This category is excluded from the national consumption figures, as consumption cannot be attributed to a specific country. Energy use by inland shipping is included in the TPES and total final consumption of a country. Note that international aviation is also included in the TPES and total final consumption of a country.

[2] The treatment of combined generation of heat and power (CHP, see section 4.5) is as follows. CHP plants produce both heat and electricity. In IEA energy statistics, private CHP plants are artificially split into two parts: an electricity producing plant that is included as one of the conversion sectors and a heat producing plant that is included in the final energy use sectors.

The IEA balances are published annually by the International Energy Agency (IEA) and the Organization for Economic Cooperation and Development (OECD) in Paris. Though these energy statistics can be considered the best available, international energy statistics (and energy statistics in general) should be handled with care. Errors can occur for a variety of reasons, including different fuel and sector classifications in use in various countries, different definitions, as well as more general statistical problems, such as incomplete coverage of statistical surveys and erroneous reporting by companies and countries.

A distinction is generally made between energy balances and energy statistics. Energy statistics contain the basic information, generally in the original, physical units for the various energy carriers, whereas energy balances give all quantities in the same unit (e.g., J or toe).

Non-energetic energy use. A specific category of energy demand is the so-called non-energetic use of energy carriers: i.e., the use of energy carriers in products. An important example is the use of naphtha and other refinery products as a feedstock for the production of chemicals like ethylene in the petrochemical industry (shown in the IEA statistics as *feedstocks*). Other non-energetic uses are waxes, lubricants, bitumen, and graphite electrodes (shown in IEA statistics as *non-energy use*). It is important to note that the definition of non-energetic use of energy carriers differs from country to country.

2.7   Primary energy

An important distinction should be made between *primary energy* and *secondary energy*, and between primary energy carriers and secondary energy carriers. Primary energy is energy found in its original or natural form, so coal, natural gas, and crude oil, as they are extracted from the Earth's crust are primary energy carriers. Crude biomass, like harvested wood, is also considered a primary carrier.

Energy that is the product of an energy conversion process is called secondary energy. Heat and electricity are the most important secondary energy carriers. If secondary energy is converted into another form of energy, like the conversion of electricity into heat in an electrical boiler, it is still called secondary energy.

The conversion of energy can cause substantial energy losses. For instance, production of electricity in a power plant typically has a conversion efficiency of around 40%. So, 100 joules of a primary carrier, like coal, are needed to produce 40 joules of electricity. If an energy user uses both coal and electricity, it therefore does not make sense to combine coal energy and electricity together as if they were equal[3]. We often solve this problem by determining the primary energy use of such an energy user. In this case, the primary energy use is not measured but calculated. For an energy user that consumes both fuels and electricity, the primary energy can be estimated in the following simple way:

$$E_p = F + \frac{E}{\eta_e} \qquad [2.8]$$

where:
E_p = primary energy use
F = fuel use
E = electricity use
η_e = conversion efficiency of the electricity production system.

The problem of calculating primary energy use will be treated in more detail in Chapter 8.

Determining the amount of primary energy is problematic in the case of non-fossil fuels. For instance, in the case of wind energy, should one take the energy in the wind, or the energy extracted from the wind through the turbine blades? In the case of uranium, various definitions are also possible. In energy statistics, ad hoc decisions are taken to characterise the energy content of these sources (see Box 2.4).

Box 2.4. Primary energy in the case of nuclear and renewable energy.

For nuclear and renewable energy sources, it is hard to determine primary energy; default factors are therefore used for the conversion from electricity to primary energy. In the IEA energy balances these are:
- electricity produced by non-thermal means (hydropower, wind energy etc.): 1 MJ electricity equals 1 MJ primary energy
- nuclear electricity: a 33% conversion efficiency is assumed: i.e., 1 MJ electricity equals 3.03 MJ primary energy
- geothermal electricity: a 10% conversion efficiency is assumed: i.e., 1 MJ electricity equals 10 MJ primary energy.

2.8   Energy use or energy consumption?

The terms energy *use* and energy *consumption* are used interchangeably. Considered from the point of view of the first law of thermodynamics (the law of conservation of energy),

---

[3] By giving the unit joule an extra index, one is aware of the different quality of the different types of energy. By 1 J_e, we indicate one joule of electricity. The index "fuel" is used for fuels like natural gas, coal or oil. The index "p" is used to indicate primary energy. For heat, the index "th" (thermal) is used, so 1 J_{th} is 1 joule of heat. By giving the unit an extra index, we avoid mixing up different types of energy.

the term energy consumption is less suitable: energy may be converted to other forms, but it never really gets lost. Of course, in the case of specific forms of energy, one may speak of consumption: e.g., electricity consumption or coal consumption.

Although the term energy consumption should be dismissed from the point of view of thermodynamics, it may be justified from other points of view. In the economic meaning of the word, energy *is* actually consumed; in general, the energy left after it has been used no longer has any economic value and can be considered as consumed. The use of the term 'energy consumption' is widespread, for instance in energy statistics.

2.9 Load factors and load duration curves

Useful concepts in energy analysis are the *load factor* and the *load duration curve*. They provide links between the (instantaneous) power uptake and the (annual) energy use.
The load factor – or capacity factor – is defined as the annual output (or input) of a system divided by the output (or input) that would have been achieved if the system had run at the nominal capacity for the full year (8760 hours in a non-leap year). A 1000 MW power plant producing 6000 GWh per year has the following load factor:

$$load\ factor = \frac{6000\,GWh}{1000\,MW \times 8760\,hours} = 68\%$$

An alternative definition for the load factor is the annual output divided by the nominal capacity. In this case, we also talk about the equivalent operation time. The power plant mentioned above has a load factor or equivalent operation time of 6000 hours. This does not mean that the power plant runs 6000 hours per year: it may run longer, but not always at the nominal capacity.

The load factor is determined by various factors. Maintenance periods and forced outages limit the load factor. Also, the demand for output limits the load factor (e.g., in the case of power plants, the demand for electricity). Also, input limitations can have a reducing effect on the load factor, for instance in the case of wind energy systems and solar energy systems.

The load factor provides a measure of the total use of the equipment, but does not show how the use varies over time. In many cases, it is important to know how the use of energy or the production of energy varies over time. Time series are often recorded, in order to get an understanding of how energy use or production varies over time. Examining these time series recordings can give a good understanding of important characteristics of energy use. For instance, time series of office building energy use often indicate substantial energy use at night and over the weekend, although there are no activities in the building then.

Examining long time series is cumbersome. For instance, if one sampled energy use in hourly steps, this would mean 8760 data points per year. One way of representing time variation of energy use in a well-organized way is a so-called load duration curve. In a load duration curve, the data on energy use per time period (e.g., per hour) are sorted from high to low. The time is given on the horizontal axis (e.g., from 0 to 8760 hours in a year), and the energy use that is exceeded during the given number of hours is depicted on the vertical. Figure 2.1 gives an example of a load duration curve. Load duration curves form the starting point for further analysis, such as investment optimisation.

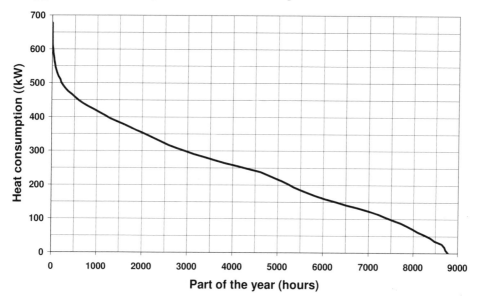

Figure 2.1. Example of a load duration curve. The curve represents the heat demand (space heating, hot water) for a hotel.

Table 2.5a. Energy Balance of OECD Europe, 2003. Data are in PJ unless indicated otherwise (bottom rows). Source: IEA, 2005.

SUPPLY AND CONSUMPTION	Coal	Crude Oil	Petro-leum	Gas	Nuclear	Hydro	Geoth. Solar Wind	Combus. Renew.	Elec.	Heat	Total
Production	8644	12783	-	10722	10704	1680	551	3224	-	13	48321
Imports	6276	27127	11283	12118	-	-	-	50	1142	0	57995
Exports	-1240	-9952	-10159	-4964	-	-	-	-13	-1071	0	-27399
Intl. Marine Bunkers	-	-	-1950	-	-	-	-	-	-	-	-1950
Stock Changes	220	-93	-110	106	-	-	-	0	-	-	124
TPES	**13901**	**29865**	**-936**	**17982**	**10704**	**1680**	**551**	**3261**	**70**	**13**	**77091**
Transfers	-	1281	-1211	-	-	-	-	0	-	-	71
Statistical Differences	-50	228	119	-90	-	-	-	1	-	-	208
Electricity Plants	-7270	-	-897	-2470	-10385	-1680	-382	-388	10027	-	-13446
CHP Plants	-2768	-2	-561	-2448	-319	-	-36	-514	2043	1369	-3236
Heat Plants	-201	-	-45	-223	-	-	-7	-114	-11	463	-139
Gas Works	-23	-	-8	17	-	-	-	-	-	-	-13
Petroleum Refineries	-	-31909	32126	-	-	-	-	-	-	-	217
Coal Transformation	-1024	2	-75	-2	-	-	-	0	-	-	-1099
Liquefaction Plants	-	-	-	-	-	-	-	-	-	-	-
Other Transformation	0	536	-553	-5	-	-	-	-4	-	-	-24
Own Use	-254	0	-1731	-637	-	-	-	-5	-1010	-94	-3732
Distribution Losses	-28	0	0	-90	-	-	-2	0	-853	-126	-1101
TFC	**2282**	**1**	**26228**	**12033**	**-**	**-**	**124**	**2237**	**10265**	**1624**	**54795**
INDUSTRY SECTOR	1742	1	4744	4750	-	-	8	706	4265	407	16622
Iron and Steel	804	-	76	438	-	-	-	1	503	14	1836
Chemical and Petrochem.	133	1	2865	1462	-	-	-	22	733	177	5392
of which: Feedstocks	-	0	2470	542	-	-	-	-	-	-	3012
Non-Ferrous Metals	37	-	59	132	-	-	0	3	383	7	620
Non-Metallic Minerals	231	-	469	729	-	-	-	44	311	6	1790
Transport Equipment	10	-	37	155	-	-	0	0	168	17	387
Machinery	22	-	121	322	-	-	0	1	384	15	863
Mining and Quarrying	8	-	44	25	-	-	2	0	53	4	137
Food and Tobacco	98	-	231	593	-	-	0	30	394	25	1371
Paper, Pulp and Printing	52	-	118	407	-	-	-	444	525	26	1573
Wood and Wood Products	7	-	18	16	-	-	-	117	85	2	245
Construction	59	-	175	36	-	-	0	3	55	2	331
Textile and Leather	10	-	78	174	-	-	0	3	180	7	451
Non-specified	272	-	453	260	-	-	5	37	494	106	1628
TRANSPORT SECTOR	0	-	15212	57	-	-	-	76	275	-	15620
International Aviation	-	-	1669	-	-	-	-	-	-	-	1669
Domestic Aviation	-	-	410	-	-	-	-	-	-	-	410
Road	-	-	12723	19	-	-	-	76	-	-	12818
Rail	0	-	115	-	-	-	-	0	225	-	340
Pipeline Transport	-	-	0	38	-	-	-	-	4	-	42
Domestic Navigation	-	-	291	-	-	-	-	-	-	-	291
Non-specified	-	-	5	0	-	-	-	-	46	-	52
OTHER SECTORS	514	-	4670	7226	-	-	117	1456	5725	1216	20924
Agriculture	40	-	874	173	-	-	3	48	193	13	1344
Comm. and Publ. Services	67	-	1014	1450	-	-	5	63	2564	247	5410
Residential	405	-	2733	5309	-	-	95	1338	2937	887	13704
Non-specified	2	-	49	294	-	-	13	7	30	70	466
NON-ENERGY USE	26	-	1603	-	-	-	-	-	-	-	1628
in Ind./Transf./Energy	20	-	1460	-	-	-	-	-	-	-	1480
in Transport	-	-	116	-	-	-	-	-	-	-	116
in Other Sectors	5	-	26	-	-	-	-	-	-	-	32
Electr. Generated - TWh	*1009.29*	-	*164.95*	*610.81*	*980.47*	*466.59*	*53.72*	*65.62*	-	-	*3351.44*
Electricity Plants	*768.32*	-	*110.20*	*403.61*	*951.59*	*466.59*	*52.64*	*31.18*	-	-	*2784.14*
CHP plants	*240.97*	-	*54.75*	*207.21*	*28.88*	-	*1.08*	*34.44*	-	-	*567.31*
Heat Generated - PJ	*737.88*	-	*93.68*	*669.42*	*3.56*	-	*13.52*	*298.48*	*3.22*	*24.82*	*1844.57*
CHP plants	*575.13*	-	*55.49*	*519.20*	*3.56*	-	*8.54*	*206.65*	*0.76*	*3.99*	*1373.31*
Heat Plants	*162.75*	-	*38.18*	*150.22*	-	-	*4.99*	*91.84*	*2.46*	*20.83*	*471.26*

What is energy use?

Table 2.5b. Energy Balance of the United States of America, 2003. Data are in PJ unless indicated otherwise (bottom rows). Source: IEA, 2005.

SUPPLY AND CONSUMPTION	Coal	Crude Oil	Petro-leum	Gas	Nuclear	Hydro	Geoth. Solar Wind	Combus. Renew.	Elec.	Heat	Total
Production	22032	14691	-	18701	8598	1003	460	2857	-	-	68342
Imports	693	23454	3568	3888	-	-	-	-	109	-	31713
Exports	-1068	-145	-1972	663	-	-	-	-	-86	-	-3935
Intl. Marine Bunkers	-	-	-805	-	-	-	-	-	-	-	-805
Stock Changes	586	-211	5	-186	-	-	-	-	-	-	195
TPES	**22243**	**37789**	**796**	**21741**	**8598**	**1003**	**460**	**2857**	**23**	**-**	**95510**
Transfers	-	-2003	2013	-	-	-	-	-	-	-	10
Statistical Differences	283	-518	21	161	-	-	-	-	-	-	-54
Electricity Plants	-19965	-	-1071	-3703	-8598	-1003	-366	-467	13317	-	-21856
CHP Plants	-738	-	-277	-1981	-	-	-	-525	1284	347	-1891
Heat Plants	-	-	-	-	-	-	-	-	-	-	-
Gas Works	-80	-	-	-	-	-	-	-	-	-	-80
Petroleum Refineries	-	-35268	35993	-	-	-	-	-	-	-	725
Coal Transformation	-322	-	-	-	-	-	-	-	-	-	-322
Liquefaction Plants	-	-	-	-	-	-	-	-	-	-	-
Other Transformation	-	-	-	-	-	-	-	-	-	-	-
Own Use	-94	-	-1958	-1789	-	-	-	-191	-1085	-58	-5175
Distribution Losses	-	-	-	-	-	-	-	-	-1025	-52	-1077
TFC	**1326**	**-**	**35517**	**14429**	**-**	**-**	**94**	**1674**	**12514**	**237**	**65791**
INDUSTRY SECTOR	1228	-	4227	5662	-	-	5	1202	3860	188	16372
Iron and Steel	144	-	50	463	-	-	-	-	234	7	897
Chem. and Petrochem.	229	-	3302	2529	-	-	-	51	892	108	7111
of which: Feedstocks	-	-	3021	635	-	-	-	-	-	-	3656
Non-Ferrous Metals	-	-	14	352	-	-	-	-	303	3	672
Non-Metallic Minerals	315	-	83	388	-	-	-	18	142	0	946
Transport Equipment	9	-	78	186	-	-	-	0	203	5	479
Machinery	5	-	70	399	-	-	-	-	454	3	930
Mining and Quarrying	-	-	-	..	-	-	-	-	108	-	108
Food and Tobacco	139	-	102	536	-	-	-	37	290	22	1126
Paper, Pulp and Printing	186	-	156	550	-	-	-	804	469	10	2182
Wood and Wood Products	1	-	71	87	-	-	-	201	106	10	475
Construction	-	-	70	..	-	-	-	-	-	-	70
Textile and Leather	13	-	45	136	-	-	-	2	121	5	321
Non-specified	187	-	187	35	-	-	5	90	540	11	1054
TRANSPORT SECTOR	-	-	25834	669	-	-	-	48	16	-	26566
International Aviation	-	-	699	-	-	-	-	-	-	-	699
Domestic Aviation	-	-	2622	-	-	-	-	-	-	-	2622
Road	-	-	21906	18	-	-	-	46	-	-	21970
Rail	-	-	431	-	-	-	-	-	16	-	447
Pipeline Transport	-	-	-	651	-	-	-	-	-	-	651
Domestic Navigation	-	-	137	-	-	-	-	2	-	-	139
Non-specified	-	-	38	-	-	-	-	-	-	-	38
OTHER SECTORS	98	-	2590	8098	-	-	89	425	8638	49	19987
Agriculture	15	-	547	-	-	-	-	6	-	-	569
Com. and Publ. Services	82	-	727	3118	-	-	16	59	4029	49	8079
Residential	-	-	1316	4981	-	-	73	360	4609	-	11339
Non-specified	-	-	-	-	-	-	-	-	-	-	-
NON-ENERGY USE	-	-	2866	-	-	-	-	-	-	-	2866
in Ind./Transf./Energy	-	-	2858	-	-	-	-	-	-	-	2858
in Transport	-	-	8	-	-	-	-	-	-	-	8
in Other Sectors	-	-	-	-	-	-	-	-	-	-	-
Electr. Generated - TWh	*2082.78*	-	*137.56*	*670.19*	*787.82*	*278.61*	*26.72*	*70.67*	-	-	*4054.35*
Electricity Plants	*2023.41*	-	*113.88*	*436.46*	*787.82*	*278.61*	*26.72*	*30.95*	-	-	*3697.85*
CHP plants	*59.37*	-	*23.68*	*233.73*	-	-	-	*39.72*	-	-	*356.50*
Heat Generated - PJ	*53.77*	-	*17.74*	*250.71*	-	-	-	*24.35*	-	-	*346.57*
CHP plants	*53.77*	-	*17.74*	*250.71*	-	-	-	*24.35*	-	-	*346.57*
Heat Plants	-	-	-	-	-	-	-	-	-	-	-

Table 2.5c. Energy Balance of China, 2003. Data are in PJ unless indicated otherwise (bottom rows).
Source: IEA, 2005.

SUPPLY AND CONSUMPTION	Coal	Crude Oil	Petro-leum	Gas	Nuclear	Hydro	Geoth. Solar Wind	Combust. Renew.	Elec.	Heat	Total
Production	38529	7112	-	1516	473	1022	-	9171	-	-	57824
Imports	523	3812	2232	52	-	-	-	0	48	-	6666
Exports	-2947	-340	-702	-52	-	-	-	-	-48	-	-4090
Intl. Marine Bunkers	-	-	-448	-	-	-	-	-	-	-	-448
Stock Changes	-219	-26	3	-	-	-	-	-	-	-	-241
TPES	**35886**	**10557**	**1085**	**1516**	**473**	**1022-**		**9172-**	**-**		**59711**
Transfers	-	-	-	-	-	-	-	-	-	-	-
Statistical Differences	-1709	-178	-78	-41	-	-	-	-	-	-	-2006
Electricity Plants	-16708	-39	-569	-109	-473	-1022	-	-36	6997	-	-11959
CHP Plants	-	-	-	-	-	-	-	-	-	-	-
Heat Plants	-2050	-5	-165	-61	-	-	-	-21	-	1773	-527
Gas Works	-242	-	-36	201	-	-	-	-	-	-	-77
Petroleum Refineries	-	-9985	9766	-	-	-	-	-	-	-	-219
Coal Transformation	-2683	-	-	-	-	-	-	-	-	-	-2683
Liquefaction Plants	-	-	-	-	-	-	-	-	-	-	-
Other Transformation	-	-	-	-	-	-	-	-	-	-	-
Own Use	-1467	-242	-685	-374	-	-	-	-	-1057	-352	-4177
Distribution Losses	-	-	0	-29	-	-	-	-	462	-20	-512
TFC	**11027**	**108**	**9317**	**1104**	**-**	**-**	**-**	**9115**	**5478**	**1401**	**37550**
INDUSTRY SECTOR	7620	102	2551	707	-	-	-	-	3522	1008	15510
Iron and Steel	2470	-	149	14	-	-	-	-	593	136	3362
Chem. and Petrochem.	1067	62	1448	579	-	-	-	-	706	446	4309
of which: Feedstocks	-	62	1236	289	-	-	-	-	-	-	1587
Non-Ferrous Metals	206	-	54	15	-	-	-	-	386	88	747
Non-Metallic Minerals	2127	-	307	25	-	-	-	-	371	13	2844
Transport Equipment	88	-	30	10	-	-	-	-	102	28	257
Machinery	314	-	118	52	-	-	-	-	399	36	920
Mining and Quarrying	131	-	40	-	-	-	-	-	136	14	321
Food and Tobacco	392	-	41	-	-	-	-	-	130	52	614
Paper Pulp and Printing	233	-	31	-	-	-	-	-	140	66	471
Wood and Wood Products	55	-	6	-	-	-	-	-	25	9	95
Construction	116	-	130	3	-	-	-	-	68	2	320
Textile and Leather	279	-	64	4	-	-	-	-	235	90	672
Non-specified	142	40	134	5	-	-	-	-	229	29	579
TRANSPORT SECTOR	227	-	3750	8	-	-	-	-	66	-	4050
International Aviation	-	-	180	-	-	-	-	-	-	-	180
Domestic Aviation	-	-	222	-	-	-	-	-	-	-	222
Road	-	-	2495	8	-	-	-	-	-	-	2503
Rail	227	-	451	-	-	-	-	-	66	-	744
Pipeline Transport	-	-	15	0	-	-	-	-	-	-	16
Domestic Navigation	0	-	386	-	-	-	-	-	-	-	386
Non-specified	0	-	-	-	-	-	-	-	-	-	0
OTHER SECTORS	2751	6	2170	390	-	-	-	9115	1889	392	16714
Agriculture	421	-	719	-	-	-	-	-	278	1	1419
Comm. and Publ. Serv.	235	-	738	43	-	-	-	-	443	24	1484
Residential	1913	-	714	346	-	-	-	9115	840	337	13265
Non-specified	181	6	-	-	-	-	-	0	328	30	546
NON-ENERGY USE	429	-	846	-	-	-	-	-	-	-	1275
in Ind./Transf./Energy	429	-	846	-	-	-	-	-	-	-	1275
in Transport	-	-	-	-	-	-	-	-	-	-	-
in Other Sectors	-	-	-	-	-	-	-	-	-	-	-
Electr. Generated - TWh	*1542.50*	*-*	*57.60*	*13.31*	*43.34*	*283.68*	*-*	*2.47*	*-*	*-*	*1942.89*
Electricity Plants	*1542.50*	*-*	*57.60*	*13.31*	*43.34*	*283.68*	*-*	*2.47*	*-*	*-*	*1942.89*
CHP Plants	*-*	*-*	*-*	*-*	*-*	*-*	*-*	*-*	*-*	*-*	*-*
Heat Generated - PJ	*1563.78*	*-*	*142.17*	*54.57*	*-*	*-*	*-*	*12.48*	*-*	*-*	*1773.00*
CHP Plants	*-*	*-*	*-*	*-*	*-*	*-*	*-*	*-*	*-*	*-*	*-*
Heat Plants	*1563.78*	*-*	*142.17*	*54.57*	*-*	*-*	*-*	*12.48*	*-*	*-*	*1773.00*

Further reading

The following publications are issued every two years by the International Energy Agency (IEA) and the Organisation of Economic Cooperation and Development (OECD), Paris, France:

Energy balances of OECD Countries
Energy balances of Non-OECD Countries

In addition, a number of more detailed publications on energy supply and use are available from these organizations (coal, oil, natural gas, electricity, renewable energy).

A quick reference guide is:
Key World Energy Statistics (can be ordered free of charge, but also downloadable from www.iea.org, under Publications – Energy Statistics – Key Statistics)
Note that all energy quantities in these statistics are given in tonnes-of-oil-equivalent (toe).

Virtually all countries publish national energy statistics. In most cases, these have their own national characteristics, and formats often deviate from the balances published by the IEA/OECD.

BP Statistical Review of World Energy, BP, London, June, annual publication. This publication is available much earlier than the IEA Statistics. It is mainly supply-side oriented, and is not necessarily compatible with the statistics from the IEA.

Final achievement levels

After having studied Chapter 2 and the exercises, you should:
-   be able to indicate whether certain substances are considered energy carriers
-   be able to explain the difference between higher and lower heating value and to convert from one to the other
-   know the concepts net available energy, final energy use and be able to determine these for concrete situations
-   be able to work with energy balances, and know the meaning of the concepts total primary energy supply and total final consumption
-   understand the concept primary energy use and be able to calculate this in a simple way
-   be able to discuss why one should or should not use the term energy consumption

Exercises Chapter 2.

2.1. Forms of energy

Check that the well-known equations for the kinetic energy of a moving object, the potential energy in a gravity field, and the heat content of a substance all lead to outcomes with the unit joule $(kg \cdot m^2/s^2)$.

Calculate the following energy quantities:

a.   The kinetic energy of a car with a speed of 100 km/h.
b.   The heat content of a bathtub with 100 litres of water at a pleasant temperature.
c.   Your potential energy after you have climbed two flights of stairs.

Choose your reference levels and make estimates for the missing data.

2.2. Power consumption and energy use of household equipment

Make estimates of the annual energy consumption of household equipment: e.g., a TV set, a vacuum cleaner, a lamp, a microwave heater, a desktop computer.

The power consumption can often be found on the equipment; make an estimate of the number of hours the equipment is in use.

2.3. HHV versus LHV

In international energy statistics the Lower Heating Value is often used instead of the Higher Heating Value.

a.   A coal-fired power plant has an electrical efficiency of 40% based on the LHV. What is the efficiency on an HHV basis?
b.   A natural-gas fired boiler has a conversion efficiency of natural gas to heat on HHV of 97%. What is the efficiency on LHV basis?
c.   Why would energy analysts prefer to use the HHV rather than the LHV?

2.4. Combustion of wood

The Higher Heating Value of oven dry wood is typically 20 MJ/kg. The chemical composition of wood is roughly $(CH_2O)_n$.

a.   Calculate the LHV for oven dry wood.
b.   Calculate the HHV and the LHV for air dry wood and harvested wood (for data see box 2.1).

2.5. Water heating

A natural-gas fired boiler has a heat storage tank with a storage capacity of 100 litres.

a.   How much energy is needed to heat the tank to 70 °C, if you fill it with cold water? The efficiency of the boiler is 80%.
b.   Now suppose that the storage tank is heated by electric resistance heating ($\eta_{th} = 100\%$). How much electricity is then needed?
c.   What is the primary energy use in both cases, and what do we learn from this?

2.6. Conversion efficiency of energy conversion sectors

The energy conversion efficiency of an activity can be calculated as the total energy output, divided by the total energy input. Using Table 2.5a, calculate (for OECD Europe) the conversion efficiency of:

a. public electricity plants (also distinguish by fuel, see figures at the bottom of the tables)
b. public CHP plants (also separate electrical and heat efficiencies)
c. oil refineries

2.7. Primary energy use of nuclear power plants and hydro power plants
In Tables 2.5a and 2.5b, examine the share of nuclear power and hydro power in total primary energy supply. Also examine the actual electricity production of both. What is the effect of the IEA convention in converting both to primary energy?

2.8. Share in total final consumption
With the help of equation [2.8], you can calculate the primary energy use associated with the total final consumption of a country. Calculate the share of the industry sector, the transport sector, the residential sector, the service sector, and agriculture in this primary energy use (in OECD Europe).
Use the energy conversion efficiencies for electricity plants calculated in exercise 2.6.

2.9. Load factor of a boiler
The capacity of the boiler in your house is 20 kW of heat. The boiler uses 2000 m^3 of natural gas per year (heat content 35 MJ/m^3 HHV). The conversion efficiency of the boiler is 95% HHV. What is the load factor of the boiler (in percentage and in equivalent operation time)?

2.10. Load duration curve
Examine the load duration curve in Figure 2.1.
a. What is the maximum heat demand, what is the minimum heat demand?
b. The heat for the system is delivered by a combined heat and power (CHP) system and boilers. The CHP system is much more efficient, but only attractive if it can run for at least 4000 hours per year. What is the heat production capacity of the CHP system and of the boilers to be selected? To be on the safe side, total heat production capacity should be 10% higher than the maximum demand.
c. What is the share of the CHP system in total heat production capacity? What share of the heat will be delivered by the CHP system (no precise answer is required)?

3

Energy services and energy demand

The energy system can roughly be broken down into an energy demand system and an energy supply system (see Figure 3.1). This chapter deals with the energy demand system, and the following chapter looks at the supply part of the energy system.

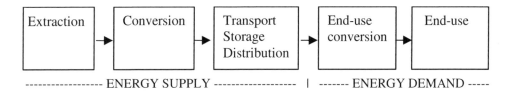

Figure 3.1 Energy supply system and energy demand system.

Energy is currently used by three major end-use categories: buildings, manufacturing industry, and transportation. Typically, each of these sectors accounts for about 30% of demand on primary energy use, but there are strong differences between countries. Other end-use categories are agriculture, mining and construction, but in developed economies these are much less important than the first three. The main aim of this chapter is to present an overview of energy use in these three categories. In our approach, the relation between the energy use and the physical and technological characteristics of a sector is an important building block for energy analysis. These characteristics will therefore be treated in detail for a number of key energy functions. Of course this is not exhaustive, and there are many more important mechanisms and processes, but the set described in this chapter can be considered as a first step.

Before we move to the three major sectors, the concept of *energy function* will be introduced.

3.1 Energy functions / energy services

Energy is used in society to satisfy certain human needs, like the need for a warm or cool living environment, the need for material products, and the need to move from one place to another. An energy service or an energy function is defined as a result of human activity obtained through the use of energy and satisfying a human need. Examples of energy functions are heating or lighting a certain area of working space, travelling a certain distance by car, or producing a certain amount of steel.

As indicated, the two terms energy function and energy service are used interchangeably. In economics, a service is defined as a product of human activity (e.g., transport, research) meant to satisfy a human need, but not constituting an item of goods. The latter aspect makes the term 'energy service' less suitable. To complicate things further, the term energy service is also used for intermediate energy carriers (e.g., delivered heat). However, in energy analysis, the term energy service is more frequently used than energy function. The term 'function' is also used in environmental life-cycle assessment, with a more or less comparable meaning (see Chapter 9).

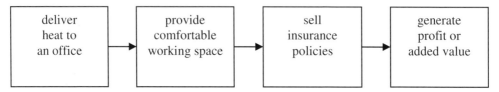

Figure 3.2. A hierarchy of energy functions.

It is important to recognise that energy services or energy functions can be defined on different hierarchic levels. For instance, heating an office in an insurance company is not an aim in itself, but is derived from a hierarchically 'higher' need, delivering insurance services to people (see Figure 3.2). Car transportation serves the need of moving from one place to another, which in turn serves other needs, for example visiting friends.

In energy analysis, the energy function is generally chosen in such a way that there is a fairly direct physical relation between the energy function and the technological characteristics of energy use. For example, in the case of the insurance company, the relation between energy use and the area of office space will be fairly direct. On the other hand, the relation between the number of insurance policies sold and energy use is much less straightforward.

Important energy functions that are often distinguished in energy analysis include:
- space heating, expressed as the area or volume that is heated;
- industrial production, expressed as the volume of a specific product, for instance, in tonnes of product;
- transportation performance, for example expressed in person-kilometres or tonne-kilometres.

Closely related to the concept of energy function is the concept of *specific energy use*. Specific energy use is the amount of energy needed per unit of energy function provided: e.g., the amount of energy used to heat one square metre of home area for one year ($MJ/m^2 \cdot yr$), the amount of energy used to produce one tonne of steel (MJ/tonne), or the amount of energy used to transport one person one kilometre (MJ/person-km).

For end-use sectors, specific energy use, or specific energy consumption (SEC), is the most important quantity for measuring energy efficiency. The lower the specific energy use of a certain application, the better the energy efficiency. We will elaborate on measuring energy efficiency in Chapter 10.

3.2   Energy use in buildings

Energy use in buildings can be broken down into residential energy use and energy use in the service sector. The service sector comprises both commercial services (e.g., retail and wholesale trade, catering industry, banking and insurance companies) and public services (e.g., schools, hospitals, government). The residential sector is typically responsible for about two-thirds of the demand on primary energy in the building sector, but the precise share differs from country to country.

Space heating represents far and away the dominant energy function in the residential sector in countries in temperate and cold climate zones. This function is responsible for about half of the demand on primary energy for buildings. In most industrialized countries, local heat sources (stoves) have to a large extent been replaced by central heating systems, where the heat is provided by a boiler. The dominant energy carriers are fossil fuels (natural gas, light fuel oil, and sometimes coal), but in some countries electricity or wood also make substantial contributions. Due to the extensive application of wall, floor and roof insulation, double-glazing, and the application of heating systems with improved conversion efficiencies, the energy use for space heating has fallen in many countries over the past decades.

Another important energy function is the production of hot water, most of which is used for showering and bathing. This hot water is supplied by a range of electrical, gas or oil-fired equipment, either stand-alone or in combination with a central heating system boiler. In a few countries, solar domestic hot water systems already deliver a substantial contribution.

The rest of the energy use in the residential sector is scattered over a range of energy functions, which include:
- lighting
- refrigeration and freezing
- clothes washing and clothes drying
- dish washing
- air conditioning
- cooking
- TV and video
- information (computers and peripherals)

In the services sector, space heating is also a dominant energy function. However, in this sector, space conditioning is a better term, as heating, mechanical ventilation, and air conditioning (HVAC) often form an integrated system meant to maintain a comfortable working environment. The other important energy functions are lighting and office appliances (mainly computers). In some specific sub-sectors like hospitals, food retail shops, and the catering industry, other energy functions play a role as well.

We will now have a closer look at the energy needs for space heating.

Space heating: heat losses of buildings

Energy for heating homes and offices is generally needed if the temperature of the environment is lower than the desired temperature inside the building. Heat is lost from the building to the environment in two ways:
- transmission of heat through the solid parts of the building construction (walls, roofs, windows); and
- ventilation, the exchange of air between the building and the environment. This exchange can be either natural (through slits and open windows) or forced (through mechanical ventilation).

There are three basic mechanisms of heat transfer:
- conduction: thermal energy is transferred by interactions between atoms or molecules, but there is no transport of the atoms or molecules themselves;
- convection: heat is transported through the macro-scale transport of material;
- radiation: thermal energy is transported in the form of electromagnetic radiation.

Transmission through solid walls. Within the wall, conduction is the main mechanism for heat transport, driven by a temperature difference. The general law describing heat transport through conduction is:

$$q = -\lambda \cdot \frac{dT}{dx}$$
[3.1]

where:

q $\quad$ = heat flow density (W/m^2)
λ $\quad$ = thermal conductivity (W/m·K)
dT/dx $\quad$ = temperature gradient (K/m)

Values for the thermal conductivity of some materials are given in Table 3.1.

Formula [3.1] describes the local relation between temperature differences and heat flow, but, for practical applications, the relation needs to be modified to include macro-quantities. As heat transport through a building envelope generally has a one-dimensional character,

Table 3.1. Thermal conductivities of some materials.

Material	Thermal conductivity (W/m·K)
Concrete	1.3
Building brick	0.4 – 0.5
Glass	0.8
Wood	0.3 – 0.5
Mineral wool	0.04
Extruded polystyrene foam	0.027
Steel	~ 50
Plastics	~ 0.2

the expression of the stationary heat transport through a flat wall with a surface area A and a constant composition takes the following form:

$$Q = \lambda \cdot \frac{\Delta T}{d} \cdot A = k \cdot \Delta T \cdot A \qquad [3.2]$$

where:
Q = the heat flow through the wall (W)
ΔT = the temperature difference across the wall (K)
d = the thickness of the wall (m)
k = heat transmission coefficient (or unit thermal conductance) = λ/d (W/m²·K)
A = surface area of the wall (m²)

The inverse of the heat transmission value k is the thermal resistance R (m²·K/W). The thermal resistances of the individual layers of a wall consisting of a number of layers can be counted together to obtain the total thermal resistance of the wall. For a wall consisting of three layers with thermal resistances R_1, R_2 and R_3 and heat transmission coefficients k_1, k_2 and k_3, the total thermal resistance R_{tot} and the total heat transmission coefficient k_{tot} become:

$$R_{tot} = R_1 + R_2 + R_3 \qquad [3.3a]$$

and:

$$k_{tot} = \frac{1}{\dfrac{1}{k_1} + \dfrac{1}{k_2} + \dfrac{1}{k_3}} \qquad [3.3b]$$

Up to now we have only discussed heat transmission *within* the wall. In addition to this, heat is transferred to and from the wall. Both convection and radiation are mechanisms for this transfer, but at ambient temperatures convection is most important. The heat transfer is given by:

$$Q = \alpha \cdot \Delta T \cdot A \qquad [3.4]$$

where:

Q = the heat flow to or from the wall (W)

ΔT = the temperature difference between the wall surface and the room or the environment (K)

α = heat transfer coefficient (W/m²·K)

A = surface area (m²)

The heat transfer coefficient α depends on many factors, like the orientation of the wall, surface structure and composition, and wind speed; values may range from 6 – 30 W/m²·K.

The thermal resistance for heat transfer to and from the wall can be described as 1/α. The total thermal resistance or the total heat transfer coefficient of the three-layer wall discussed earlier can now be described as:

$$R_{tot} = \frac{1}{\alpha_i} + R_1 + R_2 + R_3 + \frac{1}{\alpha_o} \qquad [3.5a]$$

$$k_{tot} = \frac{1}{\dfrac{1}{\alpha_i} + \dfrac{1}{k_1} + \dfrac{1}{k_2} + \dfrac{1}{k_3} + \dfrac{1}{\alpha_o}} \qquad [3.5b]$$

where:

α_i = heat transfer coefficient at the inside of the wall

α_o = heat transfer coefficient at the outside of the wall

The heat transfer through a solid wall is mainly limited by the thermal resistance of the solid parts; the heat transfer through a window is limited by the heat transfer to and from the surfaces.

Ventilation. The heat loss through ventilation depends on the amount of air that is exchanged between the building and the environment and the temperature difference between the inside of the building and the outside environment:

$$Q_v = c_p \cdot m \cdot \Delta T \qquad [3.6]$$

where:

Q_v = the heat loss through ventilation (W)

c_p = the specific heat of air (J/kg·K)

m   = the amount of air exchanged with the environment (kg/s)

ΔT = the temperature difference between the inside of the building and the environment (K)

The ventilation rate is the number of times the total volume of air in the building is exchanged with the environment per hour. For residential buildings and regular office buildings, a ventilation rate of about once an hour is generally sufficient to keep the indoor air fresh and healthy. In specific cases, higher air exchange rates are required: for example, if cooling needs to be provided, if rooms are crowded, or if harmful substances have to be removed (e.g., in laboratories).

Boilers. The equipment often used to supply heat is a boiler. In a modern natural-gas fired boiler, fuel is combusted in air that is introduced into the boiler by a fan. The heat is transferred to a piping system that contains water, which is distributed to the central heating system using a circulation pump.

The energy efficiency of a boiler is defined as the ratio of the heat transferred to the water and the energy content of the fuel. Losses in the flue gas account for the main energy losses. These are determined by two factors: the amount of flue gas and the flue gas temperature. The amount of flue gas (given the amount of fuel combusted) is determined by the air excess ratio: the amount of air used compared to the minimum required amount to reach stoichiometric combustion. Air excess ratios are typically 1.1 – 1.2. Flue gas temperatures exiting the boiler range from 50 °C – 250 °C. Conventional boilers with flue gas exit temperatures above 100 °C have efficiencies of 80 – 85% (HHV).

In conventional boilers, water in the flue gas exit is still in the gaseous form. So-called *condensing boilers* have extra heat exchanger capacity, leading to lower flue gas exit temperatures. These lower temperatures allow a substantial part of the water vapour to condense, permitting the latent heat of condensation to be recovered. This allows condensing boilers to reach efficiencies of 90 – 97% (HHV). Unburned fuel and radiation losses represent small loss factors. More important are the auxiliary energy use (fan, pump, control), losses due to operation of the boiler at partial load and as a result of starting and stopping the equipment.

Heat pumps. Alternative ways of supplying heat are combined generation of heat and power (CHP) and heat pumps. (CHP will be treated separately in Section 4.5.) A heat pump extracts heat from the exterior of the house and transfers it to the inside. The heat source can be the outside air, the ground, ventilation exhaust air, surface water, etc. Heat pumps driven by electricity are the most common. The conversion efficiency of a heat pump is generally expressed as the coefficient-of-performance (COP): the ratio of the supplied heat to the electricity input. Typical values for the COP of heat pumps range from 4 – 5. Heat pumps can also be driven by a high-temperature heat source or natural gas. For an analysis of the primary energy use of heat pumps, see Box 3.1.

Box 3.1. Heat pump efficiency.

Electrical heat pumps are efficient producers of heat. Assume a heat pump with a COP of 3.5. To produce 100 J of heat, $100/3.5$ J $= 28.6$ J_e of electricity is needed. The 28.6 J_e of electricity has to be produced as well. The electric efficiency of an average power plant is about 40% (LHV). So 28.6 $J_e/40\% = 71.4$ J of fuel is needed to produce 100 J of heat. This is summarized in the following picture.

So with 71 J of fuel, like natural gas, one can *produce* 100 J of heat. This looks like an impossible machine, but it is not. This is why the efficiency of heat pumps is expressed in coefficient-of-performance (COP) and not as an efficiency to avoid misunderstanding.

Although the energy efficiency lies above 100% the exergy efficiency is much lower than 100%, in line with the laws of thermodynamics.

To compare: to produce 100 J_{th} of heat with a very efficient boiler with an efficiency of 107% (LHV), the natural-gas requirement would be 93 J_p.

3.3   Energy use in manufacturing industry

The manufacturing industry comprises all the companies that produce material goods out of raw materials or intermediate products. Due to the enormous diversity of activities in manufacturing industry, this sector is a nightmare for energy analysts.

However, a substantial part of the energy use in manufacturing industry is used by so-called energy-intensive industries, industries where the energy use per unit of value is high. The cut-off is somewhat arbitrary, but can be put at about 20 MJ per € of value added (for a further treatment of the concept 'energy intensity', see Chapter 10). In these sectors energy costs are typically more than 3% of total production costs. The following industries are energy-intensive:
- iron and steel production;
- production of non-ferrous metals (of which aluminium production is the most important);
- basic chemical production (e.g. petrochemicals, ammonia, chlorine);
- non-metallic mineral production (e.g. cement, building bricks and tiles, glass); and
- pulp and paper production.

These industries all produce intermediate materials out of primary materials (though secondary materials are also frequently used as an alternative input). These industries are often referred to with the term 'heavy industry', but this is not entirely correct, as 'heavy industry' formally means capital-intensive. Though most energy-intensive industries are capital-intensive, not all are.

In energy-intensive industries, much energy is used for material conversion processes, generally involving a chemical conversion. Many of these processes must be conducted at high temperatures (800 – 1500 °C) because of chemical equilibrium, or because the reaction kinetics are more favourable then, or just because it is convenient to have the products in the liquid phase. In many cases, the energy supply is in the form of combustion of fuel; sometimes the fuel even takes part in the reaction as well as delivering the heat.

In some processes, the chemical conversion is performed using electrolysis (aluminium, chlorine). In addition to the major conversion steps, energy is used for pre-treatment of the raw material input, or for separation and treatment of the intermediate products. By comparison the energy required for heating and lighting in energy-intensive sectors is relatively small.

Other types of industry are often referred to as 'light industry'. They cover a large variety of sectors, most of them not energy intensive, including:
- the food and drugs industries (a sector which includes energy-intensive sub-sectors, like starch production and sugar production);
- the textiles and leather industries;
- production of cars and other equipment for transportation;
- the machinery industry; and
- the wood and wood products industries.

These sectors generally have diverse product mixes. In many cases, heating and lighting take up a substantial part of the energy use. Furthermore, a variety of processes play a role.

Some important components of industrial energy systems are steam systems, heat exchangers, motor drives and separation systems. These systems will be discussed first, and a number of specific processes will be described later.

Steam systems. Steam is an important intermediate energy carrier in manufacturing industry. Steam is most frequently generated centrally in boilers[1]. Fuels are combusted in the boiler to generate heat, which is transferred to pipes. In most boilers these pipes are organized in three sections:
- an economiser, where the water is preheated to near the evaporation temperature;
- an evaporation section where the water is evaporated, resulting in saturated steam; and

---

[1] An alternative way of generating steam is in CHP-plants (see Chapter 4.6). Steam is also generated by heat recovery from production processes.

- a superheater, where the steam is further heated to the required temperature.

The steam is distributed to the places where the heat is required in the industrial site through steam pipes. Heat is transferred to the production processes through condensation (the steam is normally only slightly superheated), and the condensate is recycled to the boiler. High pressure superheated steam can also be used for driving rotating equipment, using steam turbines, though this application is losing importance.

Heat exchangers. Heat exchange between two flows occurs in industrial processes very often. A simple example is a process where the heat of the hot outgoing flow can be transferred to a cold incoming flow.

There are many types of heat exchangers, but the plate heat exchanger (see Figure 3.3) is common. The amount of heat transfer is proportional to the heat exchanger surface area and the temperature difference between the flows (see also section 3.2). When the temperature difference is constant, the heat transfer rate is given by:

$$q = k \cdot A \cdot \Delta T \qquad\qquad [3.7]$$

where:

q   = heat transfer rate (W)
k   = heat transfer coefficient (W/m^2·K)
A   = heat exchange surface area (m^2)
ΔT = temperature difference across heat exchanger (K)

Typical values for the heat transfer coefficient are 8 – 10 W/m^2·K for heat exchange between air and air; 12 – 13 W/m^2·K for heat exchange between water and air; 325 – 350 W/m^2·K between water and water; and 1050 – 1150 W/m^2·K between condensing steam and water. From these numbers, we see that heat exchange between two liquid flows requires much less heat exchange surface area than between two gas flows. The heat transfer coefficient depends on the physical properties of the fluid media, the surface characteristics of the heat exchanging area, the fluid velocities, etc.

Motor drives. Electricity in manufacturing industry is predominantly used for motor drives. The three main types of equipment that are driven by these motors are:
- fans: used for the transportation of gases (without a substantial pressure increase);
- compressors: used for bringing gases to elevated pressures; and
- pumps: used for the transportation of liquids.

Electric motors have high conversion efficiencies; the conversion efficiency for industrial motors is generally above 90%. However, further energy losses occur in fans, compressors and pumps, in the control of such equipment and in the associated system (e.g. piping).

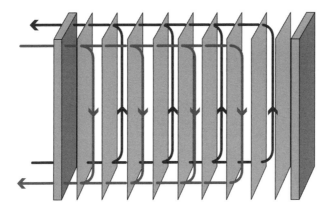

Figure 3.3. Plate heat exchanger with the heat flows illustrated. Source: Spirax Sarco Learning Center, http://www.spiraxsarco.com/learn/.

Separation processes. Separation processes are important in many sectors, especially in the food and drugs industries and in chemical industries. These processes include:

- Evaporation: the evaporation of water or another liquid from a mixture or solution in order to make the latter more concentrated. An example of an evaporation process is the production of concentrated milk out of raw milk (e.g., as a first step to make powdered milk). Simple evaporation would be very energy consuming: the energy requirement would be equal to the heat of vaporization of water (approx. 2.5 GJ/tonne). However, in practice evaporation is done in a number of stages, with the water vapour in one stage used to heat the next stage through condensation. In theory, the heat required for an n-stage evaporation process is 1/n-th of the heat required for a single-stage process (see Box 3.2).
- Drying: further evaporation in order to completely (or almost completely) remove the remaining liquid. An example is the further drying of condensed milk in order to get powdered milk. This is done in drying towers where the condensed milk is sprayed into heated air.
- Distillation: separation of components of a mixture of liquids and gases, making use of differences in evaporation temperatures of the substances that constitute the mixture. Distillation is used, for instance, by the petrochemical industry in refineries to separate crude oil into fractions (see section 4.7). An important – very low temperature – separation process is the production of oxygen through air separation.
- Membrane separation: an emerging separation process that may require less energy than alternatives. Membrane separation is used, for instance, to separate a mixture of carbon dioxide and hydrogen.

Box 3.2. A multi-stage evaporation process.

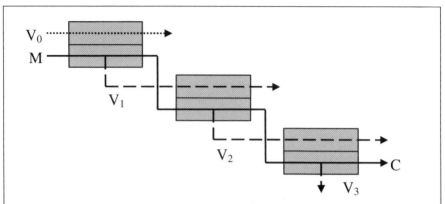

Illustration of a multi-stage evaporation process. V_0 is the primary steam flow. M is the stream to be concentrated. The vapour V_1 produced in the first stage is used – through condensation – to drive the further evaporation of M in the second stage. In a similar way, the vapour V_2 produced in the second stage is used to drive the third stage. C is the concentrated product.

In a single-stage evaporation process, one tonne of steam can be used to evaporate approximately one tonne of water. In the multi-stage evaporation process depicted here, one tonne of steam evaporates about three tonnes of water.

Four important industrial processes will now be treated in more detail: production of iron and steel, petrochemicals, ammonia, and cement.

Iron and steel production

Although the relative importance of steel within total manufacturing energy use is declining, it is still the most important energy-using sector within manufacturing industry, having a share of about 5% of world energy use.

The most important way of producing steel is in so-called integrated steel mills, where steel is mainly produced from iron ore (see Figure 3.4). The core of such an iron and steel plant is the blast furnace. Iron ore (mainly Fe_2O_3), coke, and limestone ($CaCO_3$) are added to the blast furnace from the top. At the bottom, hot compressed air (the 'blast') is blown into the furnace. The reduction of iron ore takes place in two stages, the gasification of carbon to CO, and the reduction of ore by this carbon monoxide. The main reactions that occur in a blast furnace are (with the hottest zones at the bottom of the furnace):

150 – 600 °C	$3\,Fe_2O_3 + CO \rightleftharpoons 2\,Fe_3O_4 + CO_2$
	$2\,CO \rightleftharpoons C + CO_2$
600 – 1000 °C	$Fe_3O_4 + CO \rightleftharpoons 3\,FeO + CO_2$
	$FeO + CO \rightleftharpoons Fe + CO_2$
1000 – 1400 °C	$FeO + C \rightleftharpoons Fe + CO$
	$CO_2 + C \rightleftharpoons 2\,CO$
1400 – 2000 °C	$C + O_2 \rightleftharpoons CO_2$
	$2\,C + O_2 \rightleftharpoons 2\,CO$ [3.8]

The so-called pig iron leaves the blast furnace in liquid form at the bottom. The carbon monoxide that is formed at the bottom is gradually converted to CO_2, but not completely (check how this evolves through the blast furnace). An important by-product is thus the blast furnace gas: a mixture of gases (mainly N_2, CO and CO_2) that still has substantial energy content.

The main energy source for the blast furnace is coal. Not all coals can be used for iron-making: only so-called metallurgical coal (other coals are called 'steam coal'). Coal is converted to coke in a coke oven: volatile and sulphur-containing compounds are removed with limited oxygen. This results in a sturdy and porous material with a high carbon content. Increasingly, modern blast furnaces feed the coal directly to the blast furnace instead of first converting it to coke. Coal and coke are needed both for the reduction process and for heating.

The second important process is the steel making process, where carbon and other impurities, like silicon and manganese are removed. The dominant technology for steel making is the basic oxygen furnace (the BOF plant shown in Figure 3.4). Oxygen is blown through a lance from the top into a converter containing the liquid iron, which oxidises the impurities. If the pig iron is fed to the basic oxygen furnace in a liquid form, this process is a net energy producer. However, oxygen production implies an indirect energy need. Finally, the steel needs to be cast and rolled into the required shape. Rolling, in particular, is a process that requires substantial amounts of electricity.

The most efficient integrated steel mills currently use 19 GJ/tonne, but some plants use up to 40 GJ/tonne (both in terms of primary energy). As with many industrial processes, there is a *theoretical minimum* to the energy use. The theoretical minimum is equal to the difference in the exergy between the products and the raw materials. For iron-making, this theoretical minimum is 6.6 GJ/tonne (when the iron ore is Fe_2O_3).

Next to integrated steel production, we have secondary steel production in so-called mini-mills, whose main input is scrap. The scrap is fed into a so-called electric arc furnace. After the scrap has been melted, the molten iron is refined. An efficient electric arc furnace needs approx. 1.3 GJ of electricity per tonne of steel.

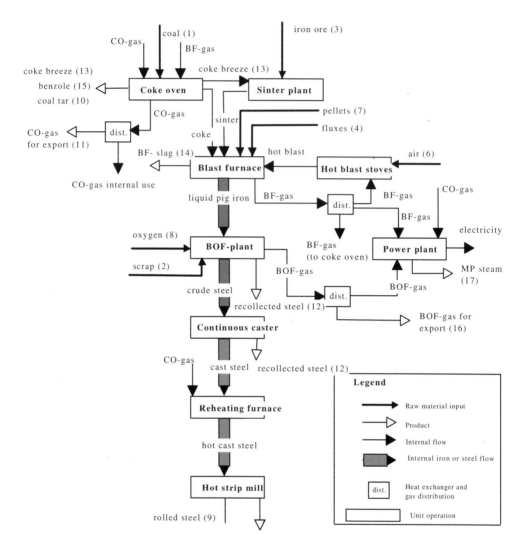

Figure 3.4. Flow sheet of an integrated steel mill.

Petrochemical production

An important energy-using activity within the chemical industry is the production of petrochemicals. Important petrochemicals are:
- olefines: ethylene (C_2H_4), propylene (C_3H_6) and butadiene (C_4H_8);
- aromatics: benzene (C_6H_6), toluene (C_7H_8) and xylenes (C_8H_{10}).

These petrochemicals form the building blocks of a lot of widely-used substances, in particular the polymers that are used as plastics, like polyethylene, polypropylene, polystyrene and polyvinylchloride.

Olefines and aromatics can be produced by one single process: steam cracking of hydrocarbons. The following paragraph describes the steam cracking of naphtha[2].

Naphtha is one of the lighter products of an oil refinery (see section 4.7) and consists of alkanes (C_nH_{2n+2}) with a chain length of 5 to 9 carbon atoms. A mixture of naphtha and steam is fed to a cracking furnace and externally heated to about 850 °C. At such a temperature, the alkanes break down into a variety of shorter, unsaturated compounds (compounds with a double bond between carbon atoms). After leaving the furnace, the gas mixture is rapidly cooled to about 400 °C. All the olefins and aromatics product compounds are already present in this mixture, but other compounds, such as hydrogen, methane and fuel oil are also present. The product composition is determined by the composition of the feedstocks, but also by what is called the severity: the higher the pressures and the temperature, the higher the severity. A higher severity leads to a higher fraction of ethylene in the product mix.

The next step is to separate the various compounds. First, the gas mixture is cooled to about 50 °C; this causes the benzene, toluene and xylene to condense. This mixture is called the BTX-fraction, or pyrolysis gasoline. Further separation takes place by a series of distillation steps at low temperatures and high pressures. This delivers the fraction C_4 (including butadienes), propylene and ethylene. After the monomers have been produced, they can be converted to polymers through a polymerisation reaction, for example from ethylene to polyethylene, to form long molecular chains:

$$n\ C_2H_4 \rightleftharpoons (CH_2)_{2n} \qquad\qquad [3.9]$$

This exothermic reaction takes place under high pressure (up to 300 bar) at a temperature of about 200 °C. Despite the fact that the reaction is exothermic, energy is still needed in real processes, mainly for compression and separation (approx. 6 GJ primary energy per tonne of product).

Naphtha cracking is an example of a process where energy is used for two purposes: as a feedstock (so-called non-energy use) and as an energy carrier. The energy use as a feedstock is about 40 GJ/tonne of product; the energy use as energy carrier is 10 – 13 GJ/tonne of product.

---

[2] In addition to naphtha, liquefied petroleum gas (a mixture of propane and butane) and heavier fractions can also be used. In some countries, like the USA and the UK, the most important feedstock is ethane, a by-product of oil and natural gas extraction.

Although the breakdown into non-energy use and energy use is often made – and also reported in statistics – it is important to recognize that there are various definitions. Some possible definitions are:

- all the material that is fed into the cracking furnace is considered as feedstock;
- only the energy use for which the carbon ends up in the product is considered as feedstock;
- the energy content of the product is considered as the non-energy use.

Ammonia production

Ammonia (NH_3) is an important feedstock for fertilizer. Ammonia production is the most energy-using part of the fertilizer industry. The two main steps in ammonia production are (see Figure 3.5):

- conversion of fossil fuel to hydrogen;
- reaction of hydrogen with nitrogen to produce ammonia.

Hydrogen can be produced out of different types of fossil fuels. Worldwide, the dominant production route is steam reforming of natural gas; this is the most common way to produce hydrogen as well as ammonia. First, natural gas is mixed with steam and fed to the so-called primary reformer. The following reactions take place:

$$CH_4 + H_2O \rightleftharpoons CO + 3\ H_2 \qquad\qquad [3.10a]$$
$$CO + H_2O \rightleftharpoons CO_2 + H_2 \qquad\qquad [3.10b]$$

The reaction rate is enhanced by a catalyst. The first reaction can be considered as partial combustion, generating heat that helps to form the right process conditions (800 – 900 °C).

To complete the conversion of the methane, a secondary reforming reactor is needed. To this end, air is added. The reactor works on a somewhat higher temperature (1000 °C):

$$2\ CH_4 + O_2 \rightleftharpoons 2\ CO + 4\ H_2 \qquad\qquad [3.10c]$$

The result of the reforming reactors is a mixture of (mainly) carbon monoxide, hydrogen and nitrogen. The carbon monoxide is converted in a so-called shift reaction:

$$CO + H_2O \rightleftharpoons CO_2 + H_2 \qquad\qquad [3.11]$$

The carbon dioxide is removed from the resulting mixture (mainly H_2, N_2 and CO_2). The remainder is the input for the actual ammonia synthesis:

$$N_2 + 3\ H_2 \rightleftharpoons 2\ NH_3 \qquad\qquad [3.12]$$

This reaction takes place at about 450 °C and is exothermic – i.e., it generates heat. The conversion to ammonia is only limited (about 15%), which means that after it exits the reactor, the product NH_3 needs to be removed, and the remaining N_2 and H_2 are recycled to the reactor.

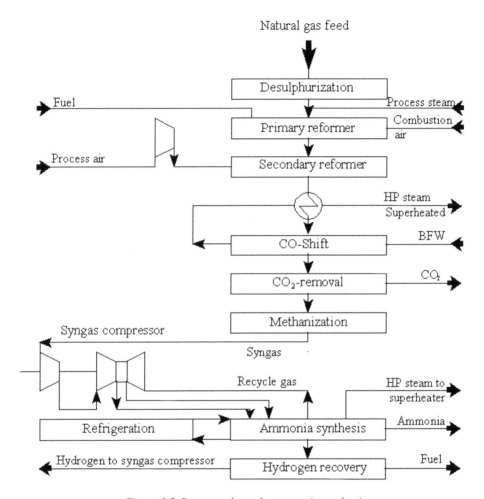

Figure 3.5. Process scheme for ammonia production.
BFW = boiler feed water

The energy demand for ammonia production varies from 30 – 45 GJ per tonne. The best processes now available use 28 GJ per tonne. The thermodynamic minimum energy use is about 20 GJ per tonne, depending on the feedstock.

Ammonia is used to produce a number of follow-up products, like nitric acid (HNO_3), ammonium nitrate (NH_4-NO_3) and urea (NH_2-CO-NH_2). These are predominantly used as fertilizer, but they are also widely used as feedstock for other chemicals.

Cement production

Within the non-metallic minerals industry (often also referred to as the building materials industry), cement production is the most important energy-using process. Cement production consists of two main steps:
- clinker production;
- blending into cement.

The first process uses the most energy. The main feedstock is limestone ($CaCO_3$), but silicon oxides, aluminium oxides and iron oxides are also used. In the modern so-called dry process, these raw materials are mixed, dried, ground and fed into a kiln. The clinker is formed in this kiln, at high temperatures (up to nearly 1500 °C). A variety of reactions occur, but the main reaction is:

$$CaCO_3 \rightleftharpoons CaO + CO_2 \qquad\qquad [3.13]$$

Note that this process not only leads to CO_2 emissions through the use of fossil fuels, but also through these so-called process emissions.

In the second process step, the clinker is blended with gypsum ($CaSO_4$) and other additives, such as fly ash from coal-fired power plants, slag from blast furnaces (see iron and steel production), and is then pulverized to form cement, which is used as a building material.

Specific energy consumption for cement production ranges from 3 – 5 GJ per tonne.

3.4   Energy use in transportation

Transportation considers both passengers and freight. On average, the breakdown in energy consumption between these two categories is about two-thirds to one third, but there are differences among countries.

In both cases, road transport is the dominant form, and road transport also accounts for most of the energy use: typically over 85% in both cases. For passenger transport, air transport is the second most important energy user in absolute terms, whereas public transport generally accounts for less than 5% of energy use.

Transportation is one of the sectors that has shown the largest growth in energy use, due among other things to the increased number of cars, larger distances driven per capita, and increased vehicle size. Car technology has improved gradually (with more efficient engines and better aerodynamics), but not enough to offset these factors for increase of energy use.

In general, passenger cars and aircraft require the most energy per passenger-km, whereas public transportation modes generally require less. We will come back to this later, but first we will take a closer look at the most important energy user in transportation: the passenger car.

The passenger car[3]

The driving force needed to drive a car at constant speed over a flat road is determined by the following components:
*   air resistance;
*   rolling resistance;
*   friction in the transmission;
*   power needed to run accessories.
Furthermore, starting and stopping and climbing and descending play a role.

The air resistance depends on the speed, the frontal area and the aerodynamic properties of the car. The rolling resistance depends on the weight of the car and the properties of the tyres and the road.

The mechanical power required to overcome the air resistance (P_a) and rolling resistance (P_r) is given by (in W):

$$P_a = \tfrac{1}{2} \cdot C_D \cdot A \cdot \rho \cdot v^3 \qquad [3.14]$$

$$P_r = C_R \cdot M \cdot g \cdot v \qquad [3.15]$$

where:
C_D = the drag coefficient for the car (state of the art values are around 0.3) (-)
C_R = rolling resistance coefficient (typical values 0.01 – 0.015) (-)
A   = the frontal area of the car (maximum cross section area perpendicular to the driving direction) (m^2)
ρ = the density of air (about 1.2 kg/m^3)
M   = the car mass (kg)
g   = the acceleration of gravity (m/s^2)
v   = the speed of the car (m/s)

At higher speeds, the air resistance becomes dominant; the specific energy use (in MJ/km) then becomes proportional to P_a/v (i.e., proportional to v^2). Weight is not only relevant for the rolling resistance, but is also relevant for the energy use needed for starting/stopping

---

[3] This description relies on Ross (1994).

and climbing/descending. A rule of thumb is that a 10% change in weight leads to a 5% change in specific fuel consumption. The efficiency in transmission is fairly high (typically about 90%). Power needed for accessories is limited but increasing, with the widespread introduction of accessories like air conditioning in cars.

The power in a car is generally delivered by an internal combustion engine. Two types of engines are in use: the spark ignition engine (Otto engine), which is the most common, and the Diesel engine.

Engine efficiency is determined by two factors:
- thermal efficiency: the fraction of the fuel energy that is converted to work by moving the pistons (this is determined by the thermodynamic characteristics of the cycle);
- mechanical efficiency: the fraction of this work that is delivered by the engine to the vehicle (the remainder is needed to keep the engine running).

Thermal efficiencies of state-of-the-art Otto engines are 38% (lower heating value).
Mechanical efficiencies are about 90% at full load. However, in absolute terms, the mechanical losses are fairly constant over the load range. Therefore, the mechanical efficiencies strongly decrease at lower loads. The average mechanical efficiency is no more than 50%, leading to a typical overall efficiency of Otto-engines of 20%. Diesel engines perform somewhat better.

Various new car propulsion systems are being considered. The only one that has been marketed so far is hybrid propulsion, which is a combination of a conventional engine, an electric engine, and a battery storage. These three components provide the possibility of optimising overall efficiency. For instance, at low speeds the electric engine is used. If the batteries are empty, the fuel engine is started, to drive the car, which recharges the batteries at the same time. The energy released through braking is also recovered and stored in the battery. Hybrid cars typically save 30 – 40% compared to conventional cars of similar size.

Other new propulsion systems are the electric engine and the fuel cell engine.

Energy use of different transportation modes

Table 3.2 provides an overview of typical specific energy use figures for different transportation modes. Note that these figures may strongly depend on local circumstances, like technology, driving habits, and vehicle occupancy. The comparison is not straightforward, as the different transportation modes have different detour factors.

Table 3.2. Comparison of energy use per passenger-kilometre for different modes of passenger transportation. Data are valid for the Netherlands, 2000. Source: Van Essen et al. (2003).

Transportation mode	Energy use per passenger-kilometre (MJ/p-km)
Passenger car, motorcycle	1.5 – 1.7
City bus, regional bus	0.9 – 1.1
Long-distance bus	0.3
Tram, subway, local train (electric)	0.8 – 0.9
Intercity train	0.5
High-speed train	1.1
Aircraft	2.5 (500 km distance) 1.5 (6000 km distance)

Table 3.3. Comparison of energy use per tonne-kilometre for different modes of freight transportation. Data are valid for the Netherlands, 2000. Source: Van Essen et al. (2003).

Transportation mode	Energy use per tonne-kilometre (MJ/tonne-km)
Van	8
Truck	2.8 (< 10 t) 0.8 (> 20 t)
Train	0.3 – 0.5
Aircraft	12 (500 km) 8 (6000 km)
Ship	0.15 – 1.0 (inland) 0.05 – 0.3 (sea-going)

Further reading

A. Chauvel, G. Lefebvre: Petrochemical Processes, Part 1 and 2, Éditions Technip, Paris, 1989.

C. Cleveland (ed.): Encyclopedia of Energy, Elsevier (6 volumes), St-Louis, MO, USA, 2004.

H. van Essen, O. Bello, J. Dings, R. van den Brink: To Shift or Not to Shift, That's the Question – The Environmental Performance of Freight and Passenger Transport Modes in the Light of Policy Making, CE, Delft, The Netherlands, 2003.

F. Kreith, M.S. Bohn: Principles of Heat Transfer, Harper and Row, New York, 1986.

M. Ross: Automobile Fuel Consumption and Emissions: Effects of Vehicle and Driving Characteristics, Annual Review of Energy and Environment, 19 (1994) pp. 75-112.

V. Smil: General Energetics, John Wiley & Sons, New York, 1991.

Final achievement levels

After having studied Chapter 3 and the exercises, you should:
- know the concept energy function or energy service and be able to use it
- have indicative knowledge of the breakdown of energy use in the most important energy functions in society (by sector and by application)
- be able to carry out calculations on the energy transmission of houses, the propulsion of a car, the efficiency of a boiler, a heat pump
- understand the relevance of the four main components of industrial energy use systems
- understand how the four important industrial process described in this chapter work

Exercises Chapter 3

3.1. Heat transport through a wall
A wall consists of concrete (10 cm thick), mineral wool (8 cm) and bricks (10 cm).
a.   Calculate the heat transmission coefficient of the wall. What is the energy flow through the wall if the outside temperature is 0 °C and the inside temperature is 20 °C?
b.   Depict the temperature profile through the wall
So far, only heat transfer within the wall has been taken into account. Now, take into account the transfer of heat from and to the wall. Assume that $\alpha_i = 8$ W/m^2·K and $\alpha_o = 20$ W/m^2·K.
c.   Can you explain why is α_i smaller than α_o?
d.   Calculate the heat transmission coefficient of the wall and the heat flow through the wall if you take into account the heat transfer to and from the wall (further assumptions same as above).
e.   Do the same as in the previous question for a single glass window; assume a glass thickness of 3 mm.

3.2. Switching off the heating at night?
In the seventies, the Californian energy company PG&E recommended keeping the central heating system on at night to save energy. 'Don't mess with the thermostat. You'll use more gas heating your house in the morning than you'll save overnight.' Discuss the usefulness of this recommendation.

3.3. Insulation of a refrigerator
a.   Calculate the annual heat loss through the walls of a refrigerator.
b.   Calculate the heat loss if the refrigerator is opened ten times per day and the complete volume of air is exchanged.
c.   How much electricity and primary energy is needed to compensate for the total heat loss of the fridge?
d.   What savings would be achieved if wall thickness were doubled? What if the COP were increased from 1.5 to 2.0?
Assumptions: inside temperature 5 °C, outside temperature 20 °C, insulation 2.5 cm foam insulation, total wall surface 6 m^2, volume 0.8 m^3, COP of cooling machine 1.5.

3.4. Exergetic efficiency of a heat pump
Consider the heat pump chain depicted in Box 3.1.

a. Calculate the conversion efficiency in exergy terms of i) the heat pump; ii) the power plant; and iii) the combination of both. Assume that the heat pump heats water from 30 °C to 50 °C.
b. Check that the chain does not conflict with the first and the second law of thermodynamics

3.5. Conversion efficiency of a boiler

In a boiler, natural gas is burned to heat water from 30 °C to 80 °C. The flue gases are cooled to 120 °C.

a. Calculate the stoichiometric air requirement for combustion.
b. Calculate the efficiency of the boiler. Assume that the only loss is the heat content of the flue gases leaving the boiler.
c. Calculate the effect on the conversion efficiency if the flue gases are cooled to 60 °C.
d. In a high-efficiency boiler, the flue gases are cooled even further, e.g. to 40 °C. Determine the gain in conversion efficiency. Take into account two effects: i) the flue gases are cooled further; ii) part of the water vapour in the flue gases condenses (about 55%).
e. Indicate why it is not possible to realize such high conversion efficiencies in industrial boilers that generate steam.

Assume that the natural gas is pure methane: heating value is 39.8 MJ/m^3 (HHV) or 35.9 MJ/m^3 (LHV). Composition of air: 78.1% N_2, 21.0% O_2, 0.9 Ar. Air excess ratio: 1.1. Assume a specific heat of the combustion gases of 1.36 kJ/m^3·K (this excludes the heat of water condensation).

3.6. Heat exchanger

A process releases 10 cubic metres hot water flow per minute at 90 °C. A heat exchanger is used to transfer part of the heat to an incoming water flow of the same size. The cooling flow is heated from 10 °C to 70 °C.

a. Make a diagram of the system.
b. What is the temperature of the hot flow at the end of the heat exchanger, if both mass flows are equal? What is the heat transfer rate?
c. Determine the size of the heat exchanger (surface area and volume).
d. What heat exchanger size would be needed if the cold flow were be heated to 80 °C instead of 70 °C?

Specific heat of water 4.18 kJ/kg·K. Assume a surface area density of 800 m^2/m^3. Further, assume that the heat exchanger has no losses to the environment except for the two outgoing heat flows described in the introduction of this exercise.

3.7. Energy use of a car

a. Determine the energy use of a car at speeds of 60, 90 and 120 km per hour, both in MJ/km and litre per 100 km.
b. Examine the effect of reducing drag (by one third), reducing car weight (by 20%) and switching from Otto to Diesel engines (assume that the latter have 20% higher conversion efficiency). Consider only the 90 km/h case.

Assumptions: car weight 1200 kg, frontal area 2 m^2, power consumption of accessories 500 W, further assumptions, see section 3.4.

4

Energy extraction and conversion

This chapter will investigate the supply side of the energy system. First, non-renewable energy sources (4.1 and 4.2) and renewable energy sources will be examined (4.3). The following sections turn to energy conversion, looking first at the electricity sector: stand-alone power plants (4.4), combined generation of heat and power (CHP) (4.5), and electricity transmission and distribution systems (4.6). Finally, oil refineries will be considered in Section 4.7.

4.1 Non-renewable energy sources

The non-renewable energy sources currently in use are fossil fuels and uranium. The three main fossil fuels are coal, oil and natural gas. The so-called conventional variants will be discussed here (see also Section 4.2).

Coal is a sedimentary rock that is formed by chemical metamorphism of large amounts of plant debris, such as leaves, bark, and wood. Plant structures can still be identified when coal is examined under a magnifying glass. Other constituents of coal can include silicate, carbonate and sulphide minerals. the largest deposits of coal were formed during the Carboniferous period (280 to 345 million years ago).

The initial stage in coal formation is the accumulation of large quantities of plant remains in an oxygen-deficient environment such as stagnant swamps, which persist in lowland sedimentary basins. Complete decay of the plant material is not possible in such environments; instead, the plants are partly decomposed by anaerobic bacteria that liberate oxygen and hydrogen. During decomposition, acids are also released from the plant material, thereby reducing pH and partly killing the bacteria. For masses of undecayed organic matter to be preserved and to form economically valuable coal, the environment must remain steady for prolonged periods of time, and the waters feeding these peat swamps must remain essentially free of sediment. This requires minimal erosion in the uplands of the rivers. As time passes and more hydrogen and oxygen are released, the percentage of carbon gradually increases. This initial stage results in a layer of peat, which is a soft brown material with recognisable plant structures, a moisture content of up to 90%, and still a rather low energy content.

When peat is buried by sediments at shallow depths, it slowly changes to lignite, which is a soft brown coal with moderate energy content (7 – 20 GJ/tonne). Generally, to form a coal seam of 1 metre thick, between 10 and 30 metres of peat are required. Further burial increases temperature and pressure. Temperature increase causes chemical reactions in the plant material, during which water (dehydrogenation) and organic gases such as methane, ethane and propane (methanogenesis) are released. Though methane in coal can serve as a significant source of natural gas, it is dangerous, as it can cause coal seam explosions, especially in underground mines, and may cause the coal to spontaneously combust. Increased pressure causes the water and volatiles to be pressed out, and further compaction of the coal occurs. During this process, the carbon content of the remaining solid (fixed carbon) increases and the associated energy content of the fuel rises as well. In this stage lignite is transformed into harder, more compacted black rock called bituminous coal (24 – 31 GJ/tonne).

After this stage, the sedimentary rocks might be subjected to folding and deformation associated with mountain building and transformed into a very hard, shiny black metamorphic rock called anthracite (about 95% carbon purity). Though anthracite is a rather clean burning fuel with very high energy content (29 – 33 GJ/tonne), it is only mined in small amounts, as it is not widespread and it is more difficult and expensive to extract than sedimentary coal. Graphite is the end product of the conversion of plant matter into pure carbon.

Coal can be found both near the Earth's surface, where it is extracted in open-pit mines, and in deeper deposits where it needs to be recovered through deep mining. Coal reserves are spread widely across the globe. Important coal-producing countries are China, the USA, Australia, India and the Russian Federation.

Mined coal only requires limited treatment before it can be used as a fuel. The main processing is washing to remove dirt and part of the ash content and sulphur. The downside is that flue gases of coal combustion still need substantial treatment to remove fly ash and sulphur dioxide (SO_2).

Coal is used widely as a fuel, but the emphasis is on power generation. In countries like China and India, which have limited reserves of other fossil fuels, coal is also widely used in the industrial sector. Furthermore, coal remains the most important fuel for iron production (see Section 3.3) and other metallurgical industries. The latter industries use so-called metallurgical coal, which has to satisfy stringent requirements regarding heating values and composition. Coal used as a fuel is called 'steam coal' (because it is used to generate steam in power plants).

Petroleum and natural gas are found in similar environments and typically occur together, though their formation is complex and not completely understood. Nonetheless, it is known that they form from small particles of marine organic matter, mostly debris of small floating organisms, both plant and animal material that sinks to the seafloor and mixes with mud. These accumulations must occur in biologically active regions, such as near shore areas.

The formation of petroleum and natural gas also requires that burial proceed rather rapidly to create an oxygen-poor environment and prevent bacterial decomposition. As more and more material is buried over millions of years, it is exposed to elevated temperatures and pressures. Chemical metamorphism gradually transforms some of the organic matter into liquid and gaseous hydrocarbons.

In the first stages, kerogen is formed, which can be converted into hydrocarbons by the natural cracking process. As time passes and the hydrocarbons are subject to high temperatures (and pressures), maturation proceeds and natural gas can be formed. Generally, sediments that generate natural gas are buried deeper and at higher temperatures than those that give oil (1 – 6 km and 65 – 150 °C).

The hydrocarbon liquids and gases are mobile and start to migrate through pores and fractures due to the compacting pressure of overlying beds. Under the seabed, rock layers are saturated with water; however, oil and gas are less dense than water, so they migrate upwards through the water-filled pores of the host rock. Unless there is a structural and/or stratigraphical barrier that can serve as a trap, these fluids will eventually reach the surface. Economically significant amounts of oil and gas have two basic conditions in common: they need a porous, permeable reservoir rock that hosts the hydrocarbon fluids and makes drilling worth while, and they need a cap rock such as an impermeable shale.

Oil and gas accumulate under anticlines, which are up-arched series of sedimentary strata that contain impermeable layers. The rising oil and gas collect at the apex of the fold. Due to density differences, the gas is on top of the oil, which is on top of the water. Faults can form structural traps, as can salt domes. The impermeable salt blocks the upturned sedimentary beds containing oil and gas, thus trapping the upward moving fuels.

Petroleum, or crude oil, is a liquid fuel consisting of a mix of hydrocarbons. Alkanes (C_nH_{2n+2}) are the most important constituents. Primary production of crude oil is done by drilling wells to the underground reservoirs and pumping the crude oil out. After primary production decreases, the extraction of the crude oil can be enhanced by so-called secondary recovery. In this case the exploitation of the oil fields is improved by injecting steam or carbon dioxide into the reservoir. These substances increase the viscosity of the crude oil.

More than 60% of the world's proven reserves of conventional oil are in the Middle East. Major oil producing countries include Saudi Arabia, the Russian Federation, the USA, Iran, and Mexico.

Different qualities of crude oil exist, with API[1] gravity as the main distinguishing characteristic. API gravity is a function of the specific gravity of oil: the lower the specific gravity, the higher the API gravity. The measure distinguishes high, medium and low

---

[1] API = American Petroleum Institute, the organisation that developed the API gravity scale.

gravity, with crude oil with the highest API gravity having the highest market value. Another distinction is between sweet and sour oil, with sour crude oil containing more sulphur than sweet crude oil.

Crude oil is hardly suitable for direct utilization and needs to be refined (i.e., separated into various fractions through distillation, see section 4.7). Oil products are used in many sectors, but they are especially dominant in transportation. Oil products are also dominant in some industrial sectors, including refineries and the petrochemical industry.

Natural gas has methane (CH_4) as its most important constituent. A range of other components is also often present, like higher alkanes, nitrogen, carbon dioxide and hydrogen sulphide. Natural gas is also produced by drilling wells into the underground reservoirs. Initially, the pressure of the reservoir is enough to expel the natural gas. After some time, though, compressors need to be installed at the well head to keep production going.

The major reserves of conventional natural gas are found in the Middle East and the Russian Federation. The most important natural gas producing countries are the Russian Federation, the USA, Canada, Iran and Algeria.

The quality of natural gas depends on its heating value, with differences caused by differences in composition. High-calorific natural gas consists mainly of alkanes, but the presence of nitrogen or carbon dioxide can lead to a substantial decrease in heating value.

Natural gas requires limited treatment before it can be used. Normally, H_2S is removed, but high fractions of CO_2 are generally also removed. Natural gas is widely used as a fuel; it is very popular as a heating fuel in the residential and service sector, wherever a natural-gas grid is available, as is currently the case in many industrialized countries. The use of natural gas for large-scale application in power generation and industry is also rapidly increasing.

Uranium is present in the Earth's crust in the form of ores with a uranium oxide (U_3O_8) concentration ranging from 1% to 0.01%. Natural uranium consists of 0.7% ^{235}U, with the remainder ^{238}U. Only the first component is directly fissile.

Uranium is recovered both from open pit mines and underground mines. Reserves of uranium are distributed around the globe. The main countries that produce uranium ore are Canada, Australia, Kazakhstan, Niger and the Russian Federation.

Before uranium can be used as a fuel, a range of treatment steps is necessary. First the U_3O_8 is extracted from the ore by chemical leaching. The uranium oxide is then converted to UF_6, after which the uranium is enriched: the fraction of ^{235}U is increased (e.g., to 3%) through a gas diffusion process or in an ultracentrifuge. Subsequently, the enriched UF_6 is converted to uranium dioxide (UO_2) pellets and built into fuel rods, which are used in nuclear reactors. Apart from ^{235}U, a plutonium isotope (^{239}P) can also be used as fissile material. This isotope is produced from ^{238}U in nuclear reactors and can be extracted out of the spent fuel through reprocessing.

At present, in the energy sector, uranium is only used for power generation.

4.2 Reserves and resources

To characterize the size of the resources, several definitions are in use. The most important are (see Figure 4.1):

- proven reserves (or reserves): these are the occurrences of fuels that have been identified and measured and that are known to be technically and economically recoverable;
- ultimate resources (or resources): these are all occurrences of fuels, including those with less-certain geological assurance and/or with doubtful economic feasibility.

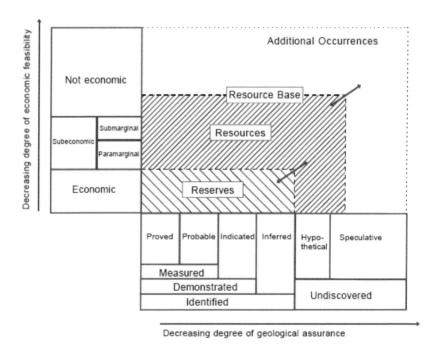

Figure 4.1 Classification of energy reserves and resources. Source: Rogner, 1997.

Reserves are those occurrences that have at least been identified, even though the exact size may have been estimated. However, in many parts of the world only limited exploration has been carried out. Resource occurrence may be estimated for these areas, for example on the basis of the geological structures. The distinction between reserves and resources is often fuzzy. An overview of resource estimates is given in Table 4.1. Note that coal reserves, in particular, are still very high.

Table 4.1 Overview of global fossil energy sources by fuel and by occurrence category in EJ ($=10^{18}J$). Source: World Energy Assessment, 2000.

	Consumption		Reserves	Resources	Resource base	Additional occur-rences
	1860-1998	1998				
Oil						
Conventional	4854	133	6000	6100	12,100	
Unconventional	285	9	5100	15,200	20,300	45,000
Natural gas						
Conventional	2346	80	5500	11,100	16,600	
Unconventional	33	4	9400	23,800	33,200	
Clathrates	-	-	-	-	-	930,000
Coal	5990	92	20,700	179,000	200,000	
Total fossil occurrences	13,508	319	46,700	235,000	282,000	975,000

A quantity widely used for characterizing the reserve position is the reserve/production ratio. The reserve/production ratio, or R/P ratio of a stock is defined as the amount of the stock divided by the annual extraction. It represents the number of years that the stock can be used at current extraction rates.

An important distinction must be made between conventional and unconventional resources. Unconventional oil reserves are oil shales, tar sands, and heavy crude oil. Unconventional natural gas reserves are coal-bed methane, tight-formation gas, and geo-pressured gas. A special, huge, category is the methane hydrides, or clathrates: crystallized ice-like mixtures of natural gas and water. Hydrates are stable in specific conditions; such as on the deep ocean floor. It is still uncertain whether these hydrates can be recovered on a large scale.

The proven reserves of richer ore uranium (0.01 – 1% uranium) are estimated to be 2000 – 3000 EJ, and ultimate resources are in the order of 10,000 EJ. The uranium resources in poor ores (20 – 50 ppm) and in ocean water may be a factor 100 larger than these figures.

4.3 Renewable energy sources and conversion

Most renewable energy sources depend on solar irradiation. The Earth intercepts only a tiny fraction of the solar radiation output, but this amount is still enormous: 3,850,000 EJ per year. Depending on the location on the Earth, the irradiation per square metre per annum is 4 – 10 GJ.

Biomass energy. Biomass energy is a generic term for all forms of energy derived from the biosphere (mainly plants), in a non-fossilised form. Wood is the most well-known example, and at present wood is the most abundantly used renewable energy source, as well as the most important source of energy for a large part of the world's population. Organic waste is an important source of biomass: e.g., domestic waste, manure, household and industrial wastewater, agricultural crop residues, and residues from forestry.

Biomass can also be cultivated specifically for energy purposes. Apart from wood, one can think of a range of other crops, including sugar cane, eucalyptus, sweet sorghum, miscanthus, and sugar beet. For energy purposes, the productivity in terms of dry mass per hectare is important. For most biomass crops, where water availability is not a limiting factor, productivity ranges from 10 – 30 tonnes of dry matter per hectare; this depends on the type of crop, soil conditions and climate. Especially in arid regions, productivities can be substantially lower, down to 2 – 4 tonnes per hectare. Even at a high productivity, the energy content of this biomass represents less than 1% of the incoming solar radiation.

Biomass can be applied directly for energy purposes. At present, direct combustion is still the most common way of using biomass. This may range from small stoves in developing countries, to large industrial boilers, for example for the combustion of residues in the pulp and paper industry. Flue gas clean-up may be necessary, but this depends, among other factors, on the composition of the biomass. In addition, a wide range of other technologies is under development, or has already been applied:

- Biological treatment. The most well-known is anaerobic digestion, a bacterial process – in a wet environment – in which organic waste is converted to a mixture of methane and carbon dioxide. Other processes include fermentation, which can be applied to crops like sugar cane and sugar beet to produce alcohol. Under development – and considered promising – is enzymatic hydrolysis to produce alcohol from wood.
- Thermal treatment. Gasification is the most promising new form of thermal conversion of biomass. Biomass is converted to a mixture of gases like methane, hydrogen and carbon monoxide under low-oxygen conditions. This gas mixture can be used as energy carrier, for example to produce electricity, but it can also be converted further, for example to produce hydrogen, methanol or synthetic gasoline. These fuels are suitable for automotive applications.

Hydropower. The second most important renewable energy source at present is hydropower. Hydropower utilizes the potential energy of water. The energy is used to drive turbines that generate electricity. The most important application is the construction of dams with large height differences (tens to hundreds of metres), which form large water reservoirs. The alternative is the run-of-river plant: a dam is constructed in a river, with a limited height difference (up to ten metres), and no substantial reservoir capacity.

Wind energy. Wind energy utilizes the kinetic energy in flowing air masses. The flow of kinetic energy through a vertical plane is proportional to the third power of the wind speed. This can easily be understood, considering that the kinetic energy in the wind is proportional to the square of the wind speed, and the mass flow through a wind turbine rotor is proportional to the wind speed. Using presently available wind turbines, the maximum theoretical amount of power that can be extracted is, according to Betz' theorem:

$$P = \frac{16}{27} \cdot \frac{1}{2} \rho v^3 \cdot A_t \qquad \text{[4.1]}$$

where:
P   = wind power (W)
ρ = specific mass of air (kg/m^3)
v   = wind speed (m/s)
A_t = swept rotor area of the wind turbine (m^2)

Modern wind turbines can produce up to 75% of this theoretical maximum. If the annual mean wind speed at hub height is 7 m/s, the energy that can be extracted per square meter of swept rotor area is about 4 GJ$_e$; at 10 m/s this is about 7 GJ$_e$ (depending on the frequency distribution of wind speeds and of course the wind turbine design).

In wind farms it is customary to install between 5 and 15 MW of wind turbine capacity per square kilometre land or sea area. Depending on the wind speeds, the annual energy output is between 0.05 and 0.25 GJ$_e$/m^2 of land area.

Solar energy. There are various ways of utilising solar irradiation directly:
- Heat production through solar collectors. A surface that is thermally isolated from the environment is heated by irradiation, and this heat can be taken away by water or air, among others. The most common application is hot water production, though space heating is also possible if the seasonal storage problem is solved. Typical conversion efficiencies from solar irradiation to useful heat are 30 – 60%.
- Electricity production through so-called solar thermal power plants. In this case, solar irradiation is concentrated by using mirrors, making it possible to generate high temperatures, for example hot air or steam, which can be used to produce electricity. Concentration is only possible when there is direct irradiation, which limits the application to sunny regions.
- Electricity production by use of the photovoltaic effect. In photovoltaic cells, solar irradiation is converted directly into DC electricity. Efficiencies for practical systems are now above 10%, but in the future efficiencies of 20% and above may be feasible. Photovoltaic (PV) power production is still among the most expensive renewable

energy sources, but it has the potential to become the most important in the long-term.

Geothermal energy. Geothermal energy is heat extracted from the Earth's crust. Geothermal energy is attractive when there is a high underground vertical temperature gradient, but this is only the case in a limited number of places. Geothermal energy is already applied for space heating (e.g., in Italy and France) and for power production (e.g., in Iceland and California). Strictly speaking, geothermal energy is not a renewable energy source as those discussed before: when a heat source is depleted, it will take thousands of years before the heat is replenished.

Marine energy. A number of renewable energy sources are lumped together as ocean energies or marine energy sources:
- Tidal energy can be utilized on a number of places on Earth where the difference between high tide and low tide is large enough. Like geothermal energy, tidal energy does not originate from solar irradiation.
- Wave energy can utilize the high power densities that occur in wind generated ocean waves.
- Ocean-thermal-energy-conversion (OTEC) makes use of the temperature differences between surface water and deep ocean water.

Overview renewable energy. Most renewable energy sources are developing rapidly. An overview of the current characteristics is given in Table 4.2. Most renewable energy sources except for large hydropower plants still produce secondary energy carriers at higher costs than most non-renewable energy sources do.

4.4 Electricity production – conventional power plants

Electricity has been produced from fossil fuels in more or less the same way since the end of the 19th century. During the first century of electricity production, the steam cycle was the dominant mode of electricity production. In the last decades of the 20th century, the so-called combined-cycle became more important. We will discuss both types of plants in this section.

Table 4.2. Overview of the worldwide status of renewable energy sources in 2000. Source: World Energy Assessment, 2004.

Technology	Increase in energy production 1997-2001 [%/yr]	Operating capacity end 2001	Load factor	Energy production 2001	Turnkey investment costs [$2001/kWh]	Current energy cost	Potential future energy cost
Biomass energy							
Electricity	~ 2.5	~ 40 GW$_e$	25 – 80	~ 170 TWh$_e$	500 – 6000	3-12 ¢/kWh	4-10 ¢/kWh
Heat	~ 2	~ 210 GW$_{th}$	25 – 80	~ 730 TWh$_{th}$	170 – 1000	1-6 ¢/kWh	1-5 ¢/kWh
Ethanol	~ 2	~ 18 bln litres		~ 450 PJ		(8-25 $/GJ)	(6-10 $/GJ)
Bio-diesel	~ 1	~1.2 bln litres		~ 45 PJ		15-25 $/GJ)	10-15 $/GJ)
Wind electricity	~ 30	23 GW$_e$	20 – 40	43 TWh$_e$	850 – 1700	4-8 ¢/kWh	3-10 ¢/kWh
Solar PV electricity	~ 30	1.1 GW$_e$	6 – 20	1 TWh$_e$	5000–18000	25-160 ¢/kWh	5 or 6-25 ¢/kWh
Solar thermal electricity	~ 2	0.4 GW$_e$	20 – 35	0.9 TWh$_e$	2500 – 6000	12-34 ¢/kWh	4-20 ¢/kWh
Low-temp solar heat	~ 10	57 GW$_{th}$ (95 mln m^2)	8 – 20	57 TWh$_{th}$	300 – 1700	2-25 ¢/kWh	2-10 ¢/kWh
Hydro energy							
Large	~ 2	690 GW$_e$	35 – 60	2600 TWh$_e$	1000 – 3500	2-10 ¢/kWh	2-10 ¢/kWh
Small	~ 3	25 GW$_e$	20 – 90	100 TWh$_e$	700 – 8000	2-12 ¢/kWh	2-10 ¢/kWh
Geothermal energy							1 or 2-8 ¢/kWh
Electricity	~ 3	8 GW$_e$	45 – 90	53 TWh$_e$	800 – 3000	2-10 ¢/kWh	
Heat	~ 10	11 GW$_{th}$	20 – 70	55 TWh$_{th}$	200 – 2000	0.5-5 ¢/kWh	0.5-5 ¢/kWh
Marine energy	-						
Tidal	-	0.3 GW$_e$	20 – 30	0.6 TWh$_e$	1700 – 2500	8-15 ¢/kWh	8-15 ¢/kWh
Wave	-	exp. phase	20 – 35	0	2000 – 5000	10-30 ¢/kWh	5-10 ¢/kWh
Tidal stream/ current	-	exp. phase	25 – 40	0	2000 – 5000	10-25 ¢/kWh	4-10 ¢/kWh
OTEC	-	exp. phase	70 – 80	0	8000–20000	15-40 ¢/kWh	7-20 ¢/kWh

The principle of the steam cycle is simple. Superheated steam (steam whose temperature is higher than the evaporation temperature at the steam pressure) is generated in a boiler. This steam is expanded through a turbine that is connected to a generator. After passing through the steam turbine, the steam is condensed in a condenser, which is cooled using surface water or cooling towers. A pump recirculates the condensate to the boiler. A modern steam cycle is much more complex than this simple description. In order to optimise the electricity production, a number of recycle loops are used in which the steam is reheated to the maximum achievable temperatures and subsequently further expanded (see Figure 4.2).

A typical steam-cycle plant has an efficiency of about 40%. However, with present technology, it is possible to build steam-cycle power plants with efficiencies over 45%. Though steam cycles can be fuelled with any type of fuel, worldwide the most commonly used fuel for this type of plant is coal, because the costs are lowest.

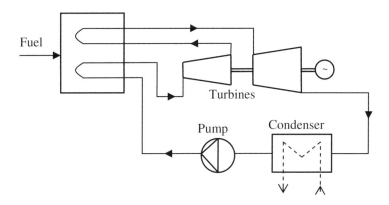

Figure 4.2. Simple representation of a steam installation.

As the name suggests, the combined-cycle combines two cycles: a gas turbine cycle and a steam cycle (see Figure 4.3). In a gas turbine, first air is compressed to 10 – 30 bar in a compressor, and fuel is combusted in this compressed air. The hot combustion gases (1100 – 1400 °C) are expanded through a turbine, which drives both the compressor and a generator. After the gases have left the turbine, their temperature (450 – 600 °C) is still high enough to produce steam, which is in turn used to drive a steam cycle. The total conversion efficiency of the best possible combined cycle power plant is nearly 60% (LHV) under full-load conditions.

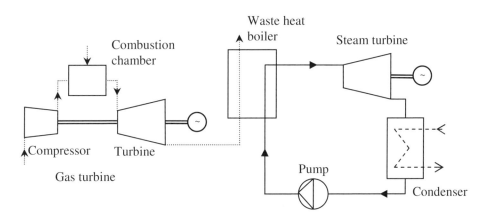

Figure 4.3. Simple representation of a combined-cycle installation.

The gas turbine has developed rapidly in the past decades. The most important change is the elevation of turbine inlet temperatures, which have increased to over 1400 °C. Turbine blade materials cannot withstand such temperatures, but contact between the hot gases and the turbine blades is avoided by using sophisticated air injection techniques. So far, only clean fuels such as natural gas or light fuel oil can be used, and these are more expensive than coal; however, since the investment costs of a combined-cycle power plant are lower than those of a steam-cycle power plant and the conversion efficiencies are higher, the natural-gas fired combined-cycle power plant is often an attractive option for power production.

For some of the characteristics of both types of power plants, see Table 4.3.

Table 4.3. Characteristics of different types of power plants.

Type of power plant	Conventional steam-electric	Combined-cycle
Dominant fuel	Steam coal	Natural gas
Unit size (MW$_e$)	400 – 600	250 – 400
Typical efficiencies (LHV)	40%	50 – 55%
Best available efficiencies (LHV)	47%	60%
Investment costs (€/kW)	1200	700
Operation and maintenance cost (€/kW)	40	15
Comments	Investment includes flue gas desulphurisation and selective catalytic reduction of NO$_x$	Units are often combined to power plants up to 2000 MW$_e$

4.5   Combined generation of heat and power

An increasing proportion of electricity and heat production is provided by plants for *combined generation of heat and power* (CHP). The reason for this is that combining electricity and heat production in one plant is often advantageous compared to separate production of these two commodities: it generally requires less primary energy, leads to lower emissions, and in some cases costs less.

Combined generation of heat and power is not new. In the past, steam engines, and later steam turbines, played an important role in industrial electricity production. Steam was extracted from these machines to supply industrial process heat. In the course of the 20th century, central electricity production was increasingly organized on a large-scale basis; industrial electricity production could not generally compete. This led to a decline of the share of CHP in power production below 10% in most countries by the 1960s. Renewed interest in CHP arose with the introduction of the gas turbine in the 1970s.

There are many configurations for CHP plants. For the combined production of electricity and industrial process steam, the following alternatives are available:
- Back-pressure steam turbines. High pressure steam is raised in a boiler and expanded to lower pressures (e.g. 3 – 30 bar) in a steam turbine. The extracted steam is used as a heat supply for the production processes.

- Extraction-condensation steam turbines. Similar to the previous type, but with a low-pressure steam turbine that can further expand the steam to low pressures. This provides higher flexibility: the mid-pressure steam can either be used directly in the production process or be expanded to generate additional electricity.
- Gas turbines with a waste heat boiler. Electricity is generated in a gas turbine. The exhaust gases with a temperature of 450 – 600 °C are fed to a so-called waste heat boiler, where the heat is transferred to generate steam. The (low-pressure) steam is then used for the production process (see Figure 4.4).
- Combined-cycle plants. Electricity is generated in a gas turbine. The exhaust gases are again fed to a waste heat boiler, but in this case to generate high-pressure steam. The steam is expanded through a steam turbine and the resulting low-pressure steam is used for the production process.

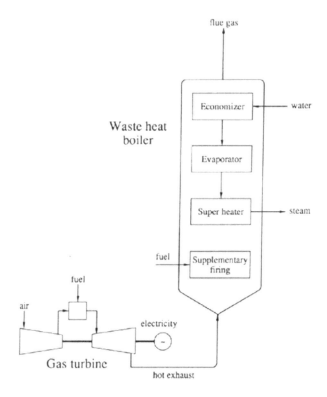

Figure 4.4. Schematic diagram of a CHP plant consisting of a gas turbine and a waste heat boiler.

The extraction-condensation steam turbine was the dominant form of CHP until 1960/1970. The latter two types are now most commonly applied in new situations. However, this equipment can only be used with the generally more expensive fuels, natural gas or light fuel oil, and when such fuels are not available, the first two options may still be interesting. Electricity produced in industrial CHP plants can either be used locally or delivered to the public grid.

For the combined production of electricity and low-temperature heat (e.g. water of 80 – 120 °C for space heating), we have the following equipment:

- Conventional power plants with heat extraction. This is a plant similar to the one in Figure 4.2. Steam is extracted from the low-pressure steam turbine and used to produce hot water.
- Combined-cycle plants. This is a plant similar to the one in Figure 4.3. Steam is extracted from the low-pressure steam turbine to produce hot water.
- Gas engine plants. A gas engine using the Otto-cycle drives a generator. Water is heated through heat exchange with the cooling water, the lubrication system, and the engine's combustion gases.

The first two types must be applied on a somewhat larger scale ('district heating plants'), whereas gas engines can be applied on a small scale, for hospitals, large offices, or greenhouses.

An overview of the characteristics of the state-of-the-art equipment is given in Table 4.4.

Table 4.4. Typical values for the characteristics of various types of combined heat and power facilities. Conversion efficiencies are given on the basis of the lower heating value of the fuel input. O&M = operation and maintenance.

Sector		Industrial heat			Low-temperature heat e.g. for space heating	
Type of equipment		Combined-cycle	Gas turbine		Combined-cycle district heating	Gas engine
Unit capacity	MW$_e$	25 – 100	10 – 50	1 – 10	100 – 250	0.1 – 2
Typical load factor	hrs/year	7500	7000	7000	4000	4000[2]
Efficiencies						
Electric efficiency	%	42	34	32	48	40[2]
Heat efficiency	%	32	48	46	36	50[2]
Costs						
Investment	Euro/kW$_e$	750	800	1300	1300[3]	500[2]
O&M costs	Euro/kW$_e$	30	40	60	50[3]	30[2]

Data adapted from: A.W.N. van Dril, F.A.M. Rijkers, J.J. Battjes, A. de Raad: Toekomst warmtekrachtkoppeling, Netherlands Energy Research Foundation ECN, Petten, 1999.

4.6   Transmission and distribution of electricity and natural gas

Energy transport and distribution represent an important part of energy systems, especially for grid based energy systems, namely electricity and natural gas.

---

[2] Numbers valid for plants > 0.5 MW
[3] This includes the costs of a district heat distribution system, which represents about half of the investment costs. The costs depend among other things on the heat demand density.

Electricity is often produced at a voltage of 10 kV, but needs to be transformed to 200 kV (AC) and more for transport. These high voltages are used to limit energy losses. The main function of the transport system is to transfer the electricity from the power plants to the areas where electricity is used. The system also transports traded electricity from one area to another. Finally, the transport system is needed in case of unexpected outages of power plants.

Near the consumer, the voltage is transformed down, first to 10 – 110 kV, and distributed to large consumers and city areas. In a further transformation step, the voltage is brought down to 110 – 230 V and fed to distribution grids that bring the electricity to households and other small consumers.

Energy is lost both in the transformers and in the power lines. Typical values for a well-designed system are:
- high-voltage transmission: 1%
- high-voltage distribution: 2%
- low-voltage distribution: 5%

These figures should not be counted together, as not all electricity consumers are connected to the low-voltage distribution grid. In well-designed systems with high density, average total losses amount to 4 – 5%, but in some situations losses can be as high as 15 – 20%. On average, transport and distribution of electricity is more costly than production of electricity.

Apart from the technical losses in the distribution system, losses also occur due to bad metering equipment, illegal tapping, other forms of theft, and non-payment. For some countries, these losses may amount to 20% of the electricity generated.

There is a similar system for natural gas. Transportation takes place at high pressures (e.g., 20 – 100 bar), and large consumers get their natural gas delivered at these pressures. For use in urban areas, the pressure is brought down and the gas is fed into the distribution grids. In general, the losses in gas transport and distribution are small, except for long-distance transportation (across continents).

4.7 Refineries

A modern refinery is a complex and integrated system separating and transforming crude oil into various products, including transport fuels, residual fuel oils and many other products. The simplest refinery type is a facility in which the crude oil is separated into lighter and heavier fractions through distillation. Modern refineries have developed into much more complex systems in which hydrocarbon compounds are not only distilled but are also further converted and blended into products.

The first step in oil refining is the crude distillation unit (CDU). The crude oil is heated to 315 – 370 °C, and subsequently fed into the distillation tower. This results in a number of fractions (see Table 4.5) each with their specific applications. The share of the various products depends on the crude oil type. In the distillation tower, the fractions are separated according to their boiling temperature, which is a good measure for the molecular weight or length of the carbon chain. The crude distillation unit is the largest energy user in refineries because of the large volumes of crude oil processed.

Table 4.5. Fractions resulting from the distillation of crude oil.

Fraction	Composition	Range of boiling temperatures (°C)	Applications
Liquefied petroleum gas (LPG)	Alkanes less than 4 carbon atoms	< 40	Boiler fuel Automotive fuel
Naphtha	Alkanes 5 – 9 carbon atoms	60 – 100	Petrochemical feedstock
Gasoline	Alkanes 5 – 12 carbon atoms and cycloalkanes	40 – 205	Automotive fuel
Kerosene	Alkanes 10 – 18 carbon atoms and aromates	175 – 325	Jet fuel
Gasoil or diesel oil	Alkanes more than 12 carbon atoms	250 – 350	Automotive fuel (Diesel engines)
Lubricating oil	Alkanes 20 – 50 carbon atoms, cycloalkanes, aromates	300 – 370	Motor oil Grease
Fuel oil	Alkanes 20 – 70 carbon atoms	370 – 600	Industrial fuel Shipping
Residuals	Multiple ringed compounds more than 70 carbon atoms	> 600	Asphalt Tar Waxes

Residues with a high boiling point are fed to the vacuum distillation unit (VDU), where the residues are further separated. Since the distillation product mix is different from what the market for oil products demands, further processing is needed, to make lighter or heavier compounds. Due to the increasing demand for automotive fuels, compared to other applications, there is a steady trend towards making lighter products ('a whiter barrel'). Some important conversion processes are:

- The gas oil mixture from the crude distillation unit (the heavy fraction) is further processed with help of a fluid catalyst. A Fluid Catalytic Cracker[4] (FCC) produces

---

[4] There are various other cracking processes. Thermal cracking uses high temperatures, but is increasingly being replaced by hydro-cracking, which is a catalytic process that uses hydrogen.

high-octane gasoline, diesel and fuel oil. FCC is the most common process for converting heavy fuel oils into gasoline and lighter products. Catalytic crackers are net energy users (using fuel and electricity), but produce energy as well, through heat recovery and power recovery.

- Naphtha can be processed in the catalytic reformer to produce gasoline. Reforming is undertaken by passing the hot feedstock through a catalytic reactor. The catalytic reformer consumes steam, fuels and electricity.

In addition to these operations, blending and refining is needed to bring the products to the required specifications.

Further reading

About fossil fuels and uranium:
Nuclear Energy Agency: Uranium 2001 – Resources, Production and Demand, OECD/NEA, Paris, 2002.
S.M. Stanley: Earth System History, W.H. Freeman and Company, USA, 1999.
H-H. Rogner: An Assessment of World Hydrocarbon Resources, Annual Review of Energy and Environment, 22 (1997) pp. 217-262.
E.J. Tarbuc and F.K. Lutgens: Earth, an Introduction to Physical Geology, Prentice Hall Inc., New Jersey, 6th edition, 1999.

About renewable energy sources:
G. Boyle: Renewable Energy, Oxford University Press, Oxford, UK, 2nd edition, 2004.
T.B. Johansson, H. Kelly, A.K.N. Reddy, R.H. Williams (eds.): Renewable Energy – Sources for Fuels and Electricity, Island Press, Washington, D.C., 1993.
World Energy Assessment, UNDP/UNDESA/WEC, United Nations Development Programme, New York, 2000 (Chapter 7). See: http://www.undp.org/energy /activities/wea/drafts-frame.html
Table 4.2 is taken from the updated version: World Energy Assessment 2004 Update, UNDP/UNDESA/WEC, United Nations Development Programme, New York, 2004.

A broad overview of energy extraction and conversion is given by:
C. Cleveland (ed.): Encyclopedia of Energy, Elsevier (6 volumes), St-Louis, MO, USA, 2004.
G. Boyle, B. Everett, J. Ramage (eds.): Energy Systems and Sustainability – Power for a Sustainable Future, Oxford University Press, Oxford, UK, 2003.

Final achievement levels

After having studied Chapter 4 and the exercises, you should:
-   know the difference between reserves and resources; between conventional and unconventional resources;
-   have indicative knowledge of the size of the various resources;
-   be able to discuss the functioning of the four most important renewable resources;
-   be able to explain – with help of a diagram – the operation of a steam cycle and a combined-cycle power plant;
-   have indicative knowledge of the electric efficiency of various types of power plants;
-   be able to explain what CHP or cogeneration is; be able to calculate energy savings achieved through CHP;
-   be able to explain how a refinery works.

Exercises Chapter 4

4.1. Reserve/production ratios
a. Calculate the R/P ratio for the different fossil fuels according to Table 4.1. Do this for both the reserves and resource base.
b. Roughly how long can the world depend on fossil fuels if we continue our current consumption?
c. Determine the proved reserve/production ratio for the USA, Europe and Eurasia, and China for the three major fossil fuel types (use for instance the BP Statistical Review of World Energy).
d. What do you conclude for each of these countries/regions?

4.2. Energy supply in history
a. Man started with only his own power and heat available. What is the total energy equivalent of food energy (recommended value is currently 2900 kcal/day)? What is the average power produced if all the food is converted to useful energy (either heat or power)?
b. What does 10 kg (as harvested) of wood per day for a five-person family add to the energy supply per capita?
c. What does a horse add, in terms of work, if it works 10 hours per day? Assume the capacity of a horse is 1 hp – although in practice it is generally somewhat less.
d. What does a 5 kW waterwheel for a community of 200 persons add to the energy supply per capita? Assume that the waterwheel runs half of the time.
e. It is said that modern man has fossil slaves. How many fossil slaves does an EU citizen have (see Table 2.2)?

4.3 Wind energy
A typical wind turbine has a capacity of 2 to 5 MW_e. This output power is achieved at a wind speed of 10 m/s. Typical load factors are 2000 hours per year (on land) and 3500 hours per year (at sea).
a. Calculate the rotor area needed for wind turbines of this size.

b.   Calculate the annual energy production of a 2 MW wind turbine on land and a 5 MW wind turbine at sea.
c.   How many households in your country can be supplied with electricity from these wind turbines?

4.4. Solar photovoltaic energy
A small solar system for a house has a capacity of 500 W (about 5 m^2)
a.   In moderate climates (e.g., Western Europe) the load factor of such a system is about 850 hours per year. How much energy does such a system produce per year?
b.   How does this contribute to the electricity production of a typical household? What size is needed to cover the total electricity consumption of a home?
c.   In the latter case, is the total electricity consumption really 'covered'?

4.5. Energy density of renewable energy sources
The maximum incoming solar radiation on Earth is about 1000 W/m^2. The load factor is very much dependent on the place on Earth and may range from 1000 – 2500 hours per year.
a.   Calculate the annual incoming solar energy per km^2 for this range.
b.   Calculate how much energy can be produced per km^2 through biomass energy, wind energy and solar energy (both heat and electricity).
c.   Discuss the comparability of the results of the previous exercise.
d.   What can you conclude about the various renewable energy sources?

4.6 Energy saving by CHP plants
a.   Investigate whether the CHP plants mentioned in Table 4.4 really save energy. Do this by assuming that if no CHP plant were built, the electricity would have been produced in power plants with an average conversion efficiency of 40%. The industrial heat would have been produced in boilers with a conversion efficiency of 90% and the low-temperature heat with a conversion efficiency of 100% (all on LHV basis).
b.   Investigate whether savings are still achieved if electricity is produced at a conversion efficiency of 55%.

4.7. Exergetic efficiencies of CHP plants
Compare the exergy efficiency of:
a.   Power plants with conversion efficiencies of 40% and 55%
b.   Boilers for raising steam (90% efficiency) or hot water (100% efficiency)
c.   The CHP plants given in Table 4.4.
Assume an exergy/energy ratio for hot water of 0.15 and for steam of 0.35.

4.8. Transportation losses for electricity
Argue why the use of higher voltages for transportation of electricity leads to lower energy losses caused by the transportation.

5

Energy markets

Energy is traded in many forms. At present the most important international energy market is the market in crude oil, though important developments are taking place in the markets for electricity and natural gas. Although there is a trend towards opening energy markets to more and more competition, government intervention and the presence of monopolies influences price formation for all energy carriers to some degree.

After a period of relative stability in the 1990s, prices have increased substantially since 2000, and have also become more volatile. As a result, the prices quoted in this chapter are only indicative. For up-to-date price information, see the websites quoted at the end of this chapter. All prices quoted in this chapter exclude taxes, unless indicated otherwise.

5.1 Oil and oil products

About 60% of crude oil production is traded internationally, so this energy market has a truly global character. The international oil market is strongly dominated by the members of the Oil Producing and Exporting Countries (OPEC). Most of these countries are in the Middle East, where over 60% of the world's proven oil reserves can be found.

In the early seventies, OPEC countries had a share of about 30% of world oil production. When a military conflict broke out between Israel and its Arab neighbours, the OPEC countries announced an oil embargo against some countries, including the USA, and limited their production. The conflict between Iran and Iraq from 1980 onwards also led to a limitation of oil production. Due to these two events, oil prices rose in two steps from approximately \$2 per barrel[1] (approx. 10 $_{2005}$/bbl) in the early seventies to over \$30 per barrel (approx. 80 $_{2005}$/bbl) in the early eighties; this led to a worldwide economic recession. After 1985, fuel prices dropped and have fluctuated between 15 and 30 $_{2005}$ per barrel (2.5 – 5 \$/GJ). At present, the market share and market power of OPEC countries is again increasing. A growing demand for oil combined with the disruption of production in several oil producing countries has led oil prices to increase in recent years, and they are now (2006) in the range of 60 – 75 \$ per barrel (10 – 12 \$/GJ).

The wide range of oil prices can be explained by the oscillation between two extremes: situations with temporary abundant supply or temporary scarcity. When oil supply is

---

[1] All prices in this chapter are US dollars (\$).

abundant, the oil is offered at its production price. The minimum oil price can be determined by constructing a supply curve for oil. Figure 5.1 gives a long-term supply curve for oil, gas and coal. Such a supply curve depicts how much oil can be produced below a certain level of production costs. From this curve we can conclude that it is still theoretically possible to produce oil at prices below $10/bbl for several decades (given the present use of oil of approx. 3 Gtoe per year). Of course, at any given moment in time the curve might look different, as actual production possibilities are limited by the availability of production installations.

On the other side, the maximum oil price is limited by the possibilities of applying alternatives. When oil demand exceeds supply, oil prices will increase. Then it becomes more attractive to save energy and to move away from energy-intensive activities. It is also possible to switch to alternative types of fuel, especially in the electricity production sector. However, both adaptations generally cannot be introduced instantaneously, so oil prices still can remain at high levels for some time. Given these extremes, it is extremely hard to make reliable projections of oil prices, and many price projections are no more than extrapolations of recent trends.

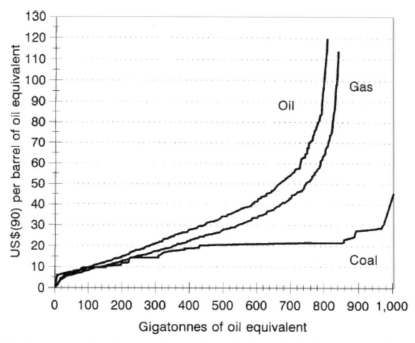

Figure 5.1. Supply curves for oil, coal and natural gas. On the vertical axis the price is shown below which the amount of fuel shown on the horizontal axis can still be produced (base year approx. 1995). Source: Rogner, 1997 (referenced in Chapter 4).

The prices of oil products differ from those of crude oil. Light fractions are more expensive, whereas heavy fuel oil is generally cheaper than crude oil. Gasoline, for example, is typically 50% more expensive than crude oil. In addition, automotive motor fuels are heavily taxed in some parts of the world, leading to prices for final consumers of 30 $/GJ and more.

5.2   Coal

The second important energy carrier is coal. International world coal trade accounts for only a small part – about 15% – of the total world coal production; most of the coal is consumed in the country where it is produced, often close to where it is produced (so-called mine-mouth coal). World hard coal prices are relatively stable, with prices in the range of 30 – 50 $ per tonne (1.1 – 1.8 $/GJ), though prices of 60 $ per tonne (2.2 $/GJ) and higher have occurred in recent years (2004 – 2006). These prices refer to the international market, but domestically consumed coal may have much lower prices (even half as low), especially when the coal is used at the mine-mouth.

In many countries, for instance in Europe, it is not possible to produce coal at costs that are competitive on world markets. However, production of coal is sometimes subsidized for social policy reasons (e.g., to provide employment).

5.3   Natural gas

The production of natural gas has been growing fastest of all fossil energy carriers and the level is already close to that of coal. Important producing countries are Russia and the USA. Over 20% of natural gas production is traded internationally, most of it transported through pipelines, such as those from Canada to the USA and from Russia to Western Europe. A typical average import price was 2 – 3 $ per GJ in the1990s, but in recent years prices have risen to 4 – 7 $ per GJ. About one quarter of the international trade is in the form of liquid natural gas that is transported by ship, for example to Japan; in that case, prices are about 1 $ per GJ higher.

The price of natural gas is to some extent connected to the price of crude oil and oil products. There are two reasons for this. First, natural gas and oil products can be easily substituted for each other, for example in boilers of conventional steam-electric power plants. In addition the natural gas market is regulated in many countries, and gas prices are then often based on the prices of oil products.

In the past, national natural gas markets were heavily regulated, but, just as with electricity markets, there has been a trend towards liberalization (see section 5.5). Natural gas prices for final consumers are higher than those for imported natural gas; industrial consumers and power generators pay the prices mentioned above, but households and other small consumers may pay double that price.

5.4 Electricity - planning and operational dispatch

In an electricity supply system without storage facilities, electricity production should be equal to the electricity demand at every moment. One of the main strategies to provide a sufficiently reliable electricity supply is to integrate a large number of power plants into a network. By now, these networks often span a number of countries.

An electricity supply system generally consists of various types of power plants: e.g., coal, oil and natural gas fired power plants, nuclear power plants, and power plants utilising renewable sources. Traditionally, we distinguish base load power plants, intermediate load power plants, and peak load power plants. Base load power plants have high capital costs and low variable operational costs (mainly fuel costs) and are hence suitable if they run for many hours a year (i.e., if they have a high load factor). For peak load power plants, the opposite is true; intermediate load plants are in between. Nuclear and coal-fired power plants are typically base load plants. Oil and gas-fired power plants are typically considered intermediate load. For peak load, gas turbines fired by natural gas can be used; these are not very efficient, but can be started very quickly.

These power plants are generally put into operation (dispatched) in such a way that the lowest possible costs of produced electricity are attained at each moment. In practice this means that power plants with the lowest variable production costs are put into operation first. Generally, the order is then: intermittent renewables, nuclear, coal, oil, and natural gas. However, depending on the design, these plants are limited in their operational flexibility. For example, it is difficult (and expensive) to shut some types of power plants down for just one night[2]. An example of how the fuel input can change over the day is given in Figure 5.2. Fluctuations also occur over the week (with lower demand in the weekend) and over the year (with generally lower demand in summer, except for regions where there is a high demand for electricity to run air conditioning).

Operational dispatch of power plants is done on a yearly basis, on a daily basis, and on an instantaneous basis. The required revision and maintenance is taken into account in the yearly planning. The daily planning is more detailed, taking into account unscheduled outages and demand projections, based on such things as expected weather conditions. Finally, the production is adjusted to the demand on an instantaneous basis, using the flexibility that most power plants have. Until recently, the electricity system was fully planned by a central authority, generally on the national or regional level. In liberalized electricity markets, planning is done by individual companies subject to market forces, with the grid operator acting as the only coordinating agent in place.

---

[2] Energy storage facilities complicate the picture. The only storage facility that is widely applied to 'store' large volumes of electricity is pumped hydro: water reservoirs are filled with help of cheap electricity at night; during the day, the stored energy is used to produce electricity again.

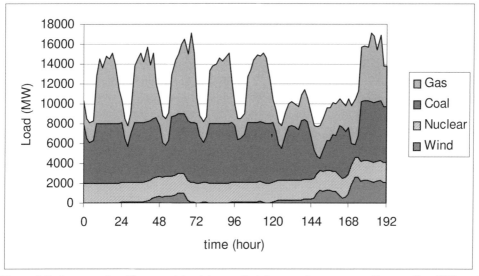

Figure 5.2. An example of how total load is supplied from various sources. Source: Van Wijk and Turkenburg, 1992.

Operational dispatch is only one aspect of planning; another is long-term investment planning. For a given load pattern, an optimum combination of base load, intermediate load and peak load power plants can be selected. The optimum cannot be absolutely determined, as the input parameters, notably future fuel prices, are uncertain. In the past, a central authority did the investment planning in most countries; this planning was not only based on the optimum combination of factors, but also often reflected national preferences with respect to fuel choice. More and more, the planning of electricity production systems is left to the free market.

5.5 Electricity markets

Throughout the 20th century, governments controlled electricity markets in most countries. In many countries national, regional or local electricity companies were owned by the government or were subject to government control. Costs of production, transport and distribution of electricity were imposed top-down by these companies, often on the basis of the costs associated with bringing electricity to the specific consumer. However, in a number of countries, mainly developing countries at present, cross-subsidizing takes place: for social reasons, households are given an artificially low price that leads to higher prices for other (i.e., industrial) electricity consumers; in some cases, the opposite occurs, when large industrial consumers get low prices to protect their competitive position.

As has already been said, many national electricity markets have gone through a process of liberalisation and privatisation. Liberalisation means that electricity consumers get a free choice between various suppliers of electricity. Privatisation means that electricity companies are no longer owned and controlled by governments. In general, the delivery chain in the electricity market has the following parts:

producers → traders → suppliers → consumers

Some companies focus on only one of these activities, but many of the large electricity companies combine production, trading and supply. Small consumers are free to choose between the various suppliers; large consumers negotiate with the suppliers about the delivery contracts. Contracts between suppliers of electricity and electricity users can either be closed bilaterally (so-called over-the-counter or OTC contracts) or via exchanges that specialize in electricity trading. Contracts for the delivery of electricity can be closed for the next day, but also for three years in the future.

The organizations that operate the electricity transportation and distribution grids still play an important role. These can be either in private hands or government owned. Apart from managing the technical operation of the grids, these organizations have to the balance supply and demand at all moments.

Even with liberalisation, a substantial degree of government regulation is still required, as there is generally only one electricity grid and all parties on the electricity market need to have the same access to the grid for a fair price. Most countries currently have a so-called regulator that is responsible for supervising the market.

In general both price allocation on the basis of top-down planning and price setting in a liberalised market lead to higher costs for small consumers than for large ones. The main reason small consumers pay more is that the distribution costs are much higher because of the fine distribution grid that is needed in residential or rural areas. Small electricity consumers also generally have lower load factors than large consumers. Typical electricity costs for large industrial consumers are 50 – 80 $/MWh (14 – 22 $/GJ$_e$); on average, households pay double this price.

Liberalisation often leads to a reduction of average energy prices. To some extent these decreases may be temporary, as they are caused by the present excess capacity on electricity markets. Figure 5.3 shows an example of how electricity prices develop in a specialized market (in this case, the Amsterdam Power Exchange). The price fluctuates significantly over time and follows more or less the same daily pattern.

Green electricity markets

A new phenomenon is a dedicated market for green electricity. In general, green energy is defined as energy produced from renewable sources (though electricity from CHP plants is sometimes also sold as green energy). Markets for green electricity already exist in many countries. Consumers can, either voluntarily or forced by government-set quotas, choose to buy part of their electricity from renewable sources. Of course it is not possible to physically provide green electricity to specific consumers, so the market sells certificates-of-origin instead.

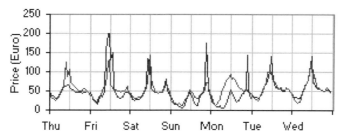

Figure 5.3 Spot prices of electricity in two subsequent weeks in April 2006 at the Amsterdam Power Exchange. Source: www.apx.nl

5.6 Heat markets

The most important market for heat is the district heat market, delivering low-temperature heat to consumers, mainly for space heating purposes. In general, prices on this market are fully regulated. This is necessary because of the monopolistic character of the heat supply. Occasionally, heat exchange also occurs among final energy consumers, such as between two industrial plants.

5.7 Price elasticities

In the treatment in this chapter so far, the demand for energy has been considered more or less as given. However, as we will see throughout this book, energy demand is determined by a number of factors, one of which is the price of energy. When energy prices increase, it is likely that demand for energy will fall, and vice versa. The relation between energy prices and energy demand can be described in the form of a demand curve (see Box 5.1).

The relation between energy use and energy price is often described by the concept price elasticity (α). Price elasticity of energy use is defined as the relative change in use, divided by the relative change in price (for small changes in price):

$$\alpha = \frac{dE/E}{dp/p}$$

[5.1]

where:
E = energy demand
p = energy price
α = price elasticity

Box 5.1. Supply and demand curves.

Economists describe markets for commodities with demand and supply curves. If prices of commodities increase, the demand will fall, as fewer and fewer buyers will find it attractive to buy the commodity. The consumer will look for alternatives (substitutes) or refrain from buying the commodity. If energy prices are high, energy users may decide to save energy (if an investment is required, this is a substitution of capital for energy), they may select a cheaper alternative energy carrier, or they may refrain from using the energy service.

In the same way, if prices of a commodity increase, the supply will increase. Producers will find it attractive to produce more of the commodity or to start producing the commodity. In case of increasing energy prices, for instance, oil fields that were unattractive to exploit may become attractive. Or electricity producers will start up power plants that run on more expensive fuels.

An imaginary – but typical – example of a supply and a demand curve for energy is given in the picture below. In an ideal market, the price and the volume produced will be determined by the intersection of the supply and demand curve (v_e, p_e) where the market is in equilibrium. But in many cases, markets are not ideal for a variety of reasons, including the presence of monopolies, lack of knowledge of some of the market players, and government intervention.

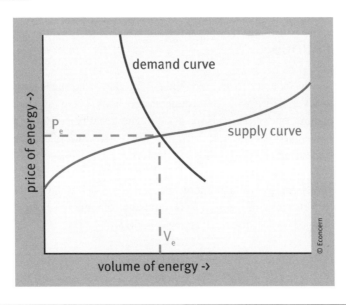

In other words, if the price of energy changes by x%, the energy use changes by $\alpha \cdot$ x%. For instance, if the price elasticity $\alpha = -0.2$, then an energy price increase of 1% will lead to a demand reduction of 0.2%. If the price elasticity is constant over a substantially wide range of energy prices, we can rewrite equation [5.1] as:

$$E = c \cdot p^{\alpha} \qquad [5.2]$$

where c and α are constants.

As energy demand decreases with increasing prices, the price elasticity α will normally be negative.

Short-term and long-term prices elasticities. A short-term price elasticity describes the effect of a sudden price change (e.g., within one year, or over a few years). Long-term price elasticity reflects the effect of long-term differences in prices (e.g., over decades). Long-term price elasticity is generally higher than short-term price elasticity, because energy users have more opportunity to adapt to changes in energy prices. Values for price elasticity are determined through econometric analysis (see section 13.3). Values found for the short-term price elasticity are relatively small, from -0.1 to -0.3, but for long-term price elasticity, values of -0.5 to -1.0 are reported.

Further reading

Information on prices of energy is published by the International Energy Agency (IEA):
 Energy Prices and Taxes, IEA/OECD, Paris, published quarterly.
 Longer time series of prices are available from the IEA on CD-ROM.
Extended information, mainly covering the USA, is provided by the Energy Information Administration of the US Department of Energy: http://www.eia.doe.gov/.
For European Union member states, data are available from the EU statistical agency, Eurostat: http://europa.eu.int/comm/eurostat – Environment and energy – (Tab "Tables") Energy – Prices.
Also the BP Statistical Review of World Energy provides energy price data.

Current prices of energy carriers are published in some newspapers and on various websites, e.g.:
 Bloomberg: www.bloomberg.com/energy
 WTRG Economics: www.wtrg.com
 European Energy Exchange: www.eex.de

J. Sloman: Essentials of Economics, Pearson Education, Harlow, England, 2nd edition, 2001.

Final achievement levels

After having studied Chapter 5 and the exercises, you should:
- be able to explain how prices of different energy carriers are established
- have indicative knowledge about the mutual relationships of the prices of different energy carriers
- know the differences between price formation in traditional electricity markets and liberalized electricity markets
- be able to describe how power plant planning and dispatch occurs

Exercises Chapter 5

5.1. Current energy prices
What is the current price of crude oil, some oil products, natural gas, coal and electricity? Give the prices both per physical unit (barrel, cubic metre, etc.) and per GJ.

5.2. Coal or natural gas?
In order to expand its capacity, a company needs to invest in new generating capacity. The choice is between natural gas and coal-fired capacity. Use the investment costs and typical efficiencies as quoted in Table 4.3. Assume that the annual costs for the investment with interest and depreciation (the so-called capital costs) are 15% of the investment. Assume a coal price of 2 €/GJ and a natural gas price of 5 €/GJ.
a. What are the fixed costs of the power plants per year (capital costs + operation and maintenance)? (express per kW)
b. What are the fuel costs per kWh?
c. If both types of power plants were already there, what plant would the company select to produce electricity?
d. If the company needs to build an additional power plant, what plant should the company select if the new plant is to run at base load (say 7000 hours per year)? And if the plant is mainly running during the daytime (say 3000 hours per year)?
e. How do the plants compare at current coal and natural gas prices? And how profitable is investing in new power generating capacity now, given the electricity prices?

5.3. Electricity in Wireland
In Wireland the electricity demand during the daytime (7.00 – 23.00) is 6000 MW and at night 3000 MW. This demand pattern is constant over the year. Furthermore, the electricity production system is made up of the following components:

Fuel	Annual fixed costs (€/MW)	Variable costs (mainly fuel costs) (€/MWh)	Capacity (MW)
Peat	200,000	10	2500
Wood	150,000	30	2500
Coal	150,000	20	2500

a. Depict the electricity consumption for one day, and also how the electricity is supplied by the different power plants
b. Why is the total generating capacity higher than the maximum demand?

98

c. Assume that the total electricity demand increased by 5000 MW (both during daytime and night times). How should the production capacity be expanded to cover the demand as cheaply as possible?

5.4. Dispatching electricity plants
A company has the following power plants:

	Size (MW)	Fixed cost per year[1] (€/kW/yr)	Fuel cost (€/kWh)
Nuclear	400	100	0.010
Coal-fired	1000	50	0.015
Natural gas-fired	1000	25	0.020

[1] Interest and depreciation plus operation and maintenance.

Assume that the demand during the day (7.00-19.00) is 2200 MW and during the night (19.00-7.00) is 1200 MW
The plants can all produce up to full load at any time.
a. What is the base-load, what is the intermediate load, what is the peak load?
b. Calculate the total fixed costs, the variable costs and the average kWh-price.
c. A potential new costumer from the aluminium industry asks for a tender. The plant is operational 24 hours per day, 365 days per year. What is the absolute minimum price you can offer them? Compare this with the average price.
d. It is expected that the demand for electricity will grow uniformly by 30%. What plants should the company build to get the lowest kWh-price?
e. Due to the liberalisation of the market there is a lot of uncertainty. The company doubts therefore whether their market share will also increase by 30%. Discuss how this uncertainty influences the choice made in answer d.

5.5. Spark spread and dark spread
Like many markets, energy markets have also led to the development of so-called derivatives, financial products that are used to reduce the risks of those operating in a market. One of these derivatives are spread options. A spread option gives the right to exchange one energy carrier (e.g., natural gas) for another (e.g., electricity). The spark spread is the difference between the price of electricity and the costs to generate it. Costs are only fuel costs and based on a conversion efficiency of 50%.
a. Calculate the spark spread at current energy prices (€/MWh).
b. Also calculate the dark spread. This is similar to the spark spread, but for coal instead of natural gas (conversion efficiency used is 38%).

5.6. Organisations in the electricity market
In the country where you live, what companies are responsible for electricity production, trade, and supply. Who is the regulator and who owns the transportation and distribution grids? Are there power exchanges?

5.7. Higher gasoline prices
Gasoline cost € 1.20 per litre, but due to changes in the crude oil market, the price has increased to € 1.40. What is the effect on the use of gasoline if the price elasticity of gasoline is –0.1 or –0.3?

6

Energy in the social context

Developments in society influence the energy system in many ways, but the energy system also affects society. This chapter will discuss the relations in economic terms (Section 6.1), social terms (6.2) and ecological terms (6.3). Finally, the concept of sustainable development will be introduced (6.4).

6.1   Energy and economy

There are two important relations between economic development and the energy system. First, increasing economic activity leads to an increase in energy consumption and production. Second, the energy sector is an important source of economic activity in itself.

As most human activities require energy, it is no surprise that economic growth leads to an increase in energy consumption. The amount of economic activity is generally expressed in terms of the gross domestic product (GDP). Figure 6.1 depicts primary energy use per capita and GDP per capita for the largest energy-using countries.

The growth of energy use, for instance expressed in total primary energy supply (TPES) is, in general, not proportional to the growth of GDP. Energy use may grow faster than GDP, but most often the growth of energy use is smaller than the growth of GDP, and this has especially been the case in recent decades.

There are two main reasons for the difference in growth rate between energy use and GDP:
  i.   Different economic activities have different energy intensities; for instance, it takes less energy for a bank to contribute 1$ to GDP than for a steel factory to contribute the same amount. In general, if the service sector grows more rapidly than the industrial sector, the growth of energy use will be smaller than the growth of GDP.
  ii.   Productivity (loosely defined as the economic output generated per unit of input) can increase at different rates for different sectors; energy productivity may not match the growth of productivity of capital and labour, though technological improvements lead to increases in productivity of all production factors.

These issues will be treated more quantitatively in Chapter 13. As already noted, in most of the cases, energy use grows slower than GDP. For instance, in IEA countries, the ratio of TPES to GDP declined by 32% in the period 1973 – 2000 (1.4% per year). Both of the reasons mentioned above play a role, but differently in different time periods. For instance, in the period 1973 – 1985 increasingly high energy prices and strong energy policies meant that increasing energy productivity was the most important factor.

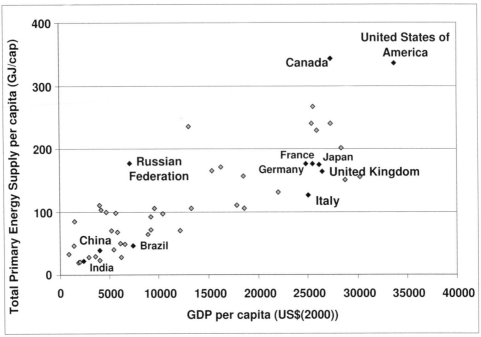

Figure 6.1. Energy use per capita and GDP per capita by country in 2000. Only countries with an energy use of more than 1 EJ are depicted. The GDP is purchasing power parity corrected. Source: Data World Resources Institute.

Though total primary energy supply is only weakly related to GDP, the relation between electricity consumption and GDP is much stronger. In many countries, electricity use and GDP grow more or less at the same rate. Although the reasons have not been fully investigated, there are some clear factors: (i) electricity use is spread over a wide range of energy functions, whereas fuel is to some extent concentrated in energy functions that reflect limited growth (space heating, basic material industries); (ii) as fuel represents a larger part of total energy use, most efforts to improve energy efficiency have been directed towards improving fuel efficiency rather than increasing electricity efficiency.

The fact that energy use generally grows with economic activity, does not mean that energy use cannot decline. For instance, the energy use for domestic heating has declined in many industrialized countries since 1980, despite a moderate growth in the number of homes and the available floor space per capita. This is mainly the result of intensive programmes focused on retrofit insulation of homes and improved boiler efficiencies.

The energy sector also makes an important contribution to GDP. The energy supply sector, consisting of energy production, conversion, transport and distribution, by itself contributes

5 – 15% of GDP. In addition, the total energy sector is much bigger, including producers of all kinds of energy related equipment, insulation manufacturers, and installers. However, since these are spread across different economic sectors, they are difficult to quantify. The contribution of the energy sector differs significantly from country to country and depends primarily on the resources position. In the group of oil producing and exporting countries (OPEC) dependence on the energy sector is even higher.

In terms of turnover, the biggest players are the oil companies, of which ExxonMobil, Royal Dutch Shell, and BP are the largest. With annual turnover of around 300 billion (300 · 10^9) US$, they are among the largest companies in the world. One order of magnitude smaller are electricity and gas companies, such as Suez and Electricité de France of France, E.On and RWE of Germany, and TEPCO of Japan. These companies are still partly state owned, though they also operate in partly liberalised markets. It is expected that further consolidation will take place. Manufacturers of electrical and electronic equipment (e.g., General Electric, Siemens), car manufacturers, and other manufacturers are also important players. Compared to these large companies, the renewable energy industry is still relatively small, but there are already several companies with a turnover larger than 1 billion US$, and growth rates of 50% per year and more are not uncommon.

The fact that energy and economy are closely related makes the economy particularly vulnerable to supply disruptions. Disruptions can take place on various scales and have different causes. Probably the most important disruption threat to date was the oil boycott in 1973/74 by OPEC. But smaller scale disruptions can also take place, especially in the electricity supply, caused by such things as lack of production capacity or severe weather conditions. Sometimes even though there is no real disruption, scarcity leads to price increases. One of the most important price increases, in 1979/80, had important economic effects: it led to a worldwide recession that lasted for several years.

6.2   Social aspects of energy use

Energy consumption patterns vary worldwide. At the end of the 20th century, world average energy use was about 65 GJ per capita. Figure 6.1 shows the differences in energy use per capita, with the industrialized countries at levels of around 150 GJ per capita, with some countries, notably the USA and Canada, at levels above 300 GJ per capita. Most developing countries are below the world average, but there are also substantial differences here. A group of countries, including China and Brazil have a per capita energy use of about 30 – 40 GJ. A number of countries, notably India and many countries in Africa, are far below this level, typically around 10 GJ per capita.

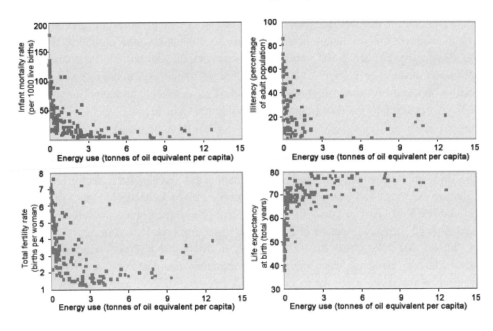

Figure 6.2. Commercial energy use (horizontal axis) and infant mortality, illiteracy, life expectancy, and fertility (1 tonne of oil equivalent is approx. 40 GJ). Source: World Energy Assessment, 2000.

When we compare countries, we find a relation between per capita energy use and important development indicators like child mortality, life expectancy and illiteracy (see Figure 6.2). Countries with a per capita energy use below 30 GJ are also the countries where child mortality is the highest, life expectancy is lowest, and illiteracy is highest. Though there is not always a causal relation between low energy use and lack of well-being, there are some important connections between energy availability on the one hand and poverty and disease on the other hand. Energy is needed for a sufficient food supply and the preparation of healthy food, for heating and lighting, and energy is needed for other important preconditions for development: water supply, health care and education. Much of the world's population lacks adequate energy resources to serve their basic needs. It is estimated that worldwide about 2 billion ($2 \cdot 10^9$) people do not have access to clean and safe cooking fuels and 1.7 billion are without electricity. Bringing energy to these populations is considered as an important target of international development policy.

As can be seen from Figure 6.1, the countries with the lowest per capita energy consumption still use around 10 GJ per capita. This minimal level can be explained by the consumption of wood and other biomass resources, mainly for cooking. This wood is often not produced in a sustainable way, and with increasing population densities, firewood is becoming scarcer. In areas where forests and plantations are not managed in a sustainable way, land degrades, which further reinforces the scarcity. For many people in developing countries, and especially women, taking care of the daily fuel supply has become a substantial burden, due to the increasing distances they must walk to collect firewood. The situation is worsened by the fact that the wood is often combusted in an incomplete and inefficient way, leading to unnecessarily high resource use, as well as an unhealthy indoor air quality.

Although most of the people suffering from a lack of access to sufficient energy live in developing countries, 'fuel poverty' also occurs in the industrialised world. Fuel poverty differs from country to country but it is often the people with the lowest income that do not have the possibility, due to lack of knowledge or financial resources, or for institutional reasons, to insulate their homes adequately. This can lead to high energy costs, to discomfort, running up debts, and ultimately to natural gas and electricity shut-offs.

6.3   Environmental and resource aspects of energy use

The production and use of energy depletes non-renewable resources and has a range of environmental impacts, which can occur on various levels.

Air pollution. Probably the most important impact on the local and regional level is air pollution. The combustion of fossil fuels leads to a number of emissions that affect human health:

* sulphur dioxide (SO_2)
* carbon monoxide (CO)
* fine particles (especially particles of soot with sizes smaller than 10 μm)
* ozone, an air pollutant produced indirectly, which forms from nitrogen oxides and hydrocarbons in a photochemical reaction
* lead

Of the different fossil fuels, coal makes the highest contribution to emissions (in relation to the consumption of fuel), mainly due to the inherent properties of coal, namely its high sulphur and ash content. Of the different end-use sectors, transportation accounts for the highest relative contribution to emissions.

Emission control measures have strongly reduced emissions in many industrialized countries. Nevertheless, substantial problems remain, the most important ones currently being fine particles and ozone. Fine particles can be deposited deep in the lungs and can cause damage there, especially if harmful substances like carcinogenic hydrocarbons are deposited. In Europe, thousands of cases of early mortality are attributed to this per year. Ozone also influences the lung functions, and is especially harmful for people already suffering from bronchial diseases, like asthma.

The biggest air pollution problems occur in large cities in developing countries. There are a number of causes for this: pollution control technology has been adopted less; cars and equipment are often older and less well maintained; and, the small-scale use of coal and other solid fuels is still common.

Other local and regional impacts are:
- accidents with oil transport, leading to oil spills at sea
- local depletion of wood resources
- regional impacts of hydropower
- waste from the fossil fuel cycle, including slag and fly ash from coal combustion
- accidents caused by unsafe nuclear power plants and possible discharges of radioactive waste from the nuclear fuel cycle
- disturbance and pollution caused by mining of coal and uranium

Acid deposition. Other environmental impacts occur on a continental scale, especially associated with the emission of sulphur dioxide and nitrogen oxides. Many fossil fuels contain sulphur: the sulphur content of coal can be 1 – 5%, and crude oil also typically contains several percent of sulphur. When the fuel is combusted, sulphur dioxide (SO_2) is formed. Nitrogen oxides are also formed out of nitrogen compounds present in the fuel (mainly in coal). However, more important is so-called thermal NO_x formation. At temperatures higher than 1400 °C oxygen in the air begins to dissociate, leading to the following reactions:

$$N_2 + O \rightleftharpoons NO + N$$
$$N + O_2 \rightleftharpoons NO + O$$

The net effect is the formation of NO out of air. The NO oxidizes further to NO_2, partly during combustion, but mainly in the atmosphere. Together, NO and NO_2 are referred to as nitrogen oxides (NO_x).

SO_2 and NO_2 are often emitted from high chimneys and can be transported over long distances, so this is a problem with a *continental* character. Via a number of chemical reactions, either in the open atmosphere or in water, SO_2 and NO_2 are converted to the acids H_2SO_4 and HNO_3. In an aqueous environment, the H^+ ions are separated off, leading to the well-known acidification of lakes and soil. The degree of acidification depends on the buffer capacity, especially of the soil. The impacts of acidification are various:
- loss of nutrients in soils
- release of harmful substances (like aluminium, cadmium, lead, copper and zinc)
- reduction of ecosystem variability
- direct impacts on plant vitality through stoma damage

Emission of sulphur dioxide can be prevented through the use of low-sulphur coal, fuel desulphurisation (applied in refineries) and flue gas desulphurisation (often applied in power plants). The formation of NO can be prevented by controlling combustion conditions and avoiding the presence of 'hot spots', which is relatively easy in boilers and furnaces, but more complicated in combustion engines. Further emission reduction can be achieved by selective catalytic reduction with NH_3. For gasoline engines, exhaust gas catalysts are used that reduce the emissions of several substances in one go.

Climate change. Probably the most important environmental problem associated with energy production and use is the problem of climate change. The combustion of all fossil fuels leads to the formation and emission of carbon dioxide (CO_2). About half of the CO_2 is absorbed by the oceans and the biosphere, but the remainder leads to an increased concentration of CO_2 in the atmosphere: from 280 parts per million (ppm) by volume in the pre-industrial period to over 370 ppm at present.

The presence of CO_2 changes the radiation balance of the Earth in the following way: The sun sends radiation energy to the Earth, mainly in the form of visible light. The light is partly reflected (by the Earth's surface and clouds), but it is to a large extent absorbed by the Earth's surface. The Earth also radiates energy, but due to the relatively low temperature at the Earth's surface, this is mainly in the form of infrared radiation[1]. The temperature at the Earth's surface is such that incoming and outgoing radiation are in equilibrium. Carbon dioxide molecules in the atmosphere absorb infrared radiation, and after absorbing it, emit the energy again in all directions, including the Earth's surface. With a higher amount of incoming radiation at the Earth's surface, a new equilibrium is formed, but with a higher amount of outgoing radiation, this can only be achieved through a higher surface temperature.

Gases that show absorption in the infrared spectrum and cause the mechanisms described here are called greenhouse gases. Carbon dioxide is not the only greenhouse gas. In fact, water vapour is the most important natural greenhouse gas, and without it in the atmosphere, the temperature on Earth would be substantially lower. Ozone, methane and nitrous oxides are other natural greenhouse gases, but the concentrations of these gases are also increasing as a result of human activities. Furthermore, there is a host of fluorinated compounds that act as greenhouse gases.

The climate system is very complicated, which makes it difficult to make precise estimations of the impact of increased greenhouse gas emissions in the atmosphere. There are many positive and negative feedbacks. An important positive feedback is through water vapour: an increased temperature of the atmosphere leads to an increased presence of water vapour in the atmosphere, which in turn increases the radiative forcing and thus the temperature.

---

[1] The important laws of physics are:
The Stefan-Boltzmann Law states that the radiation of a surface is proportional to the fourth power of the temperature of the surface: $Q = \varepsilon \cdot \sigma \cdot T^4$, in which Q is the radiation flux from the surface, ε is the emissivity, σ is the Stefan-Boltzmann constant (5.67×10^{-8} $W/m^2 \cdot K^4$) and T is the absolute temperature of the surface. The emissivity indicates how much the surface deviates from a black body. For a black body $\varepsilon = 1$.
Wien's Displacement Law says that the wavelength at which the maximum amount of energy is emitted is inversely proportional to the temperature of the surface. This explains why the Sun mainly radiates visible light (wavelength 400 – 800 nm) and the Earth mainly infrared (wavelength longer than 800 nm).

Since 1860, the average temperature on Earth has increased by 0.6 +/- 0.2 °C. It is expected that without measures to limit and reduce emissions, the average temperature will increase by another 1.4 – 5.8 °C. This wide range is caused both by uncertainty in the climate system simulations and by the variety of emission scenarios that underlie the estimates. The impacts of climate change are:

- Droughts and water shortages, especially in regions that are already vulnerable;
- Regional decreases in food production;
- Deterioration of ecosystems that cannot adapt rapidly enough to the changing climate;
- Spread of diseases, like malaria, to areas where they did not occur before;
- Sea level rise, due to expansion of sea water and melting of icepack and glaciers; and
- An increase of extreme weather events, such as hurricanes.

Emissions of CO_2 can be reduced by improving energy efficiency, by using more renewable and nuclear energy, and by capturing and storing CO_2, for example in underground reservoirs. A range of emission reduction options is available for all the other greenhouse gases, as well.

Resource depletion. From the figures presented in Section 4.1, it can be concluded that fossil fuel resources are still large and will probably last for many centuries. These resources are so large that complete use would go beyond any safe emission level with respect to climate change.

Nevertheless, shortages of specific resources will already occur in this century, particularly for conventional oil reserves, but also possibly for conventional reserves of natural gas and uranium. Although there are several substitution opportunities, shortages will still have an effect, if only in the form of increased energy prices and the associated negative economic impacts.

6.4   Sustainable development

Sustainable development is a concept that has attracted broad interest since the publication of the report *Our Common Future* by the World Commission on Environment and Development in 1987. According to one of the briefest definitions given in this report, sustainable development is *development that meets the needs of the present generations without compromising the ability of future generations to meet their own needs.* Sustainable development takes into account all three aspects that have been treated in this chapter: economic, social and ecological aspects.

It is widely acknowledged that current energy systems are not sustainable. If we consider the definition of sustainable development, we first see that many in the present generation still lack access to sufficient and clean energy. Possible supply disruptions and unreliability can also be seen as a lack of sustainability. Finally, resource depletion and the possibility of climate change and other environmental impacts may seriously affect the possibility of future generations to meet their own needs.

It is important to note that the two targets set out in the definition may be conflicting: development for the present generation may require more energy, which can lead to higher environmental impacts and a reduction of the quality of life for future generations. A possible way out of this potential conflict is the intensive use of efficient, clean, and renewable energy technologies.

According to the World Energy Assessment (2000), the main aims of sustainable energy policies should be:
- Delivering adequate and affordable energy supplies – including liquid and gaseous fuels for cooking and electricity for domestic and commercial use – to unserved areas;
- Encouraging energy efficiency;
- Accelerating the use of new renewables; and
- Widening the diffusion and use of other advanced energy technologies.

According to this assessment, the following strategies are key elements to reaching a sustainable energy system:
- Making markets work better by reducing price distortions, encouraging competition, and removing barriers to energy efficiency;
- Complementing energy sector restructuring with regulations that encourage sustainable energy;
- Mobilising additional investments in sustainable energy;
- Accelerating technological innovation at every stage of the energy innovation chain;
- Supporting technological leadership by transferring technology and building human and institutional capacity in developing countries; and
- Encouraging greater international cooperation.

Further reading

J. Goldemberg, T.B. Johansson, A.K.N. Reddy, R.H. Williams: Energy for a Sustainable World, John Wiley & Sons, New York, 1988.

J.A. Fay, D.S. Golomb: Energy and the Environment, Oxford University Press, New York, 2002.

J.T. Houghton, Y. Dings, D.J. Griggs, M. Noguer, P.J. van der Linden, X. Dai, K. Maskell, C.A. Johnson: Climate Change 2001 – The Scientific Basis, Cambridge University Press, Cambridge, UK, 2001.

International Energy Agency: Indicators of Energy Use and Efficiency – Understanding the
  Link Between Energy and Human Activity, OECD/IEA, Paris, 1997.
Our Common Future, The World Commission on Environment and Development, Oxford
  University Press, 1987.
V. Smil: Energy in World History, Westview Press, Boulder, CO, USA, 1994.
World Energy Assessment (WEA), UNDP/UNDESA/WEC, UNDP, New York, 2000. See:
  http://www.undp.org/energy/activities/wea/drafts-frame.html

Final achievement levels

After having studied Chapter 6 and the exercises, you should:
-   be able to discuss the relations between economic activity on the one hand and
    primary energy use and electricity use on the other hand;
-   have a basic understanding of other relations between energy use and economic
    activity;
-   be able to describe the main social challenges in relation to the energy system;
-   be able to describe the main mechanisms from source to effect of local air pollution,
    acid deposition, and climatic change; and
-   know how sustainable development is defined and be able to discuss the
    sustainability aspects of the current energy system.

Exercises Chapter 6

6.1. Energy intensity of GDP
The energy intensity of GDP for a country is defined as the total primary energy supply of
the country divided by the GDP of that country.
a.   Make an estimate of the world average energy intensity (see Figure 6.1).
b.   What is the energy intensity of countries with the highest energy intensity and
     countries with the lowest energy intensities? Can you think of explanations why these
     countries show such extreme values?

6.2. Exponential growth of energy use
In the period 1995 – 2005 world oil consumption increased by 1.7% per year. Assume now
that world oil consumption keeps on growing at the same rate.
a.   How long will it take before world oil consumption is doubled compared to 2005?
b.   What is the impact on the lifetime of world oil reserves and resources if we take this
     growth into account (you can either calculate it precisely or make a rough estimate)?
c.   Over the past 15 years the proven oil reserves/production ratio has remained relatively
     constant, despite the increase in consumption. How can this be explained?
d.   Think of reasons why the growth of oil consumption will not remain at the same rate.

6.3. Emission factors
An emission factor is the amount of emission per unit of activity. For fuels, emission
factors are given per unit of energy content (often in g/GJ or kg/GJ).
a.   Calculate the SO_2 emission factor for coal with 1% sulphur content;
b.   Calculate the CO_2 emission factors for oil products and natural gas, assuming an
     approximate composition of CH_2 and CH_4 for these fuels. For CH_4, use a LHV of 52.5
     MJ/kg.

6.4. The three-way catalyst

In an exhaust gas catalyst of a gasoline car (Otto engine) the active material is platinum or rhodium. The following reactions take place:

$$2\ CO + O_2 \rightleftharpoons 2\ CO_2$$

$$C_xH_y + (x + y/4)\ O_2 \rightleftharpoons x\ CO_2 + (y/2)\ H_2O$$

$$2\ CO + 2\ NO \rightleftharpoons 2\ CO_2 + N_2$$

$$C_xH_y + (2x + y/2)\ NO \rightleftharpoons x\ CO_2 + (y/2)\ H_2O + (x+y/4)\ N_2$$

a.   Examine these reactions. Two groups of two reactants can be considered. What is their role?

b.   Why is the exhaust gas catalyst also called a three-way catalyst?

c.   Explain why the exhaust gas catalyst works best when combined with a so-called lambda-sensor that measures the oxygen content of the exhaust gas, whereupon the fuel/air ratio is adjusted to achieve a preset oxygen content.

d.   A Diesel engine works with excess air. Why does this type of catalyst not work very well on a Diesel engine? Which substances are easiest to remove from Diesel engine exhaust gas?

6.5. Radiation balance of the Earth

The solar radiation density at the Earth's distance of the sun is 1370 W/m^2. Of this incoming radiation, 30% is reflected directly, the rest is absorbed.

a.   What is the average absorbed irradiation on the Earth's surface?

b.   Calculate what the average temperature on Earth would be if there were no atmosphere and the Earth's surface could be considered as a black body.

c.   Why is the temperature on Earth higher than the figure calculated in b?

d.   Assume now that the average temperature on Earth is 15 °C. It is estimated that a doubling of the CO_2 concentration in the atmosphere leads to a radiative forcing of 4.2 W/m^2, i.e. the radiation flux to the Earth's surface is increased by this value. Can you make a simple estimate of the temperature impact?

7

Energy analysis and energy management

A basic element in energy analysis is to determine what applications energy is used for and how much energy is needed for each application. The methodology is straightforward and set out in Section 7.1. A specific tool for buildings, the degree-day method, will be described in Section 7.2. For more complex facilities, additional tools, like exergy analysis (7.3) and pinch analysis (7.4) are needed. Section 7.5 will move from analysis to management of energy use, and Section 7.6 will broaden this concept.

7.1 Energy analysis of energy users

The aim of an energy analysis is to get a good understanding of the size, characteristics and main determinants of the energy use of an entity, whether that is a household, office building, industrial production site, or power plant. An energy analysis generally forms the basis for further action to improve energy efficiency, reduce energy costs, reduce emissions, etc.

An energy analysis generally combines top-down and bottom-up information. Top-down information is information about the entity as a whole (e.g., total energy purchase), whereas bottom-up information is information about individual equipment.

The following is a generic procedure for an energy analysis:
1. *Determine total energy use.* Total energy use is determined for all relevant energy carriers, using energy bills and meter readings. Such sources not only provide totals per year or per month, but also additional information such as day/night ratios of electricity use and peak demand.
2. *Registration of equipment.* An overview is made of all the energy-using equipment and all the energy conversion equipment (e.g., boilers). The nominal capacity is determined for all the equipment; this is often indicated on the equipment, or information is available from the manufacturer. The operation time, or the equivalent operation time, is also determined for all equipment. The product of the nominal capacity and operation time provides the annual amount of energy use of the equipment.
3. *Registration of building characteristics.* An overview is made of the characteristics of the buildings: i) area of the various components of the building envelope (walls, roofs, windows); ii) degree of insulation of the various components; iii) volume of the various part of the building; iv) ventilation rate of the building. This information

is necessary to determine the energy use for space heating and cooling (see Section 7.2).

4. *Additional measurements.* When the information provided in the two previous steps is not complete or not accurate enough, additional measurements of the uncertain energy flows are necessary.

5. *Closing the energy balance.* Finally, the energy balance is drawn up. The total energy inputs to the facility (step 1) are compared with the amounts converted and used (steps 2 – 4). In case these figures do not agree, additional investigations and measurements are necessary to bridge the gap. Note that this is actually a simple application of the first law of thermodynamics.

The energy balance resulting from an energy analysis is an indispensable basis for further action, such as an energy conservation plan or an energy management system.

It is obvious that the character of the energy balance depends on the character of the organization. For a facility like an office building with no other energy conversion equipment than a boiler (a simple facility in energy terms), a simple energy balance with annual aggregate figures for the various energy-using equipment will be a good starting point. For a more complex facility, like a chemical plant, an energy balance needs to be much more extended. In this case, the energy balance will consist of very detailed process flow sheets with material throughputs of the various components and associated energy inputs and outputs, possibly done for various modes of operation. For complex processes, especially those including chemical conversions and a variety of heat exchange processes, more complex tools should also be used, like exergy analysis or pinch analysis (Sections 7.3 and 7.4).

The standard follow-up of the energy analysis is an analysis of the options for improving the energy situation, for example through using energy more efficiently. Such analysis requires a systematic analysis of all the processes in the facility, and an analysis of the options for improving energy efficiency and for reducing costs and environmental impacts. Such options can include:

- improvement in the operation of individual processes;
- retrofit investments to make these processes more efficient;
- complete replacement of process equipment with more efficient equipment;
- more efficient combinations of processes, for example through heat recovery;
- adaptations in buildings (insulation, more efficient HVAC systems, more efficient lighting);
- adaptation in energy supply and conversion equipment (e.g., use of CHP); and
- application of new energy sources, such as waste streams, renewable energy sources, and cleaner fuels.

For each of the relevant options, an inventory is made of the energy and costs saved, the investments required, operation and maintenance costs, the effect on production, etc.

A special variant of energy analysis is the energy audit. An *energy audit* is a quick energy analysis which gives an indication of improvement options, as well as recommendations for easy adaptations and further investigation. Energy audits are often carried out as part of government programmes.

7.2 Degree-days

As we saw in Section 3.2, the heat loss through transmission and the heat loss through ventilation both depend on the heat difference between the inside of a building and the environment. Since this temperature difference is not constant, the heat loss needs to be determined through integration over a year. Instead of doing this, the temperature difference can be integrated separately, generally using the concept of *degree-days*. For each day that the average temperature is lower than a reference temperature (18 °C is often used), the difference between the reference and the average temperature is determined. All these differences are counted together and result in the number of degree-days per year:

$$D = \sum_{i=1}^{365} \max(T_{ref} - T_i, 0) \qquad [7.1]$$

where:
D   = the number of degree-days per year
T_{ref} = a reference temperature
T_i = the average temperature for day i

Of course, the number of degree-days per year depends on the climate zone; it may range from 1000 – 5000 per year. For any given location, the number varies from year-to-year (typically about 10%).

The total heat loss of a building over a year can now be calculated as:

$$Q_a = \underline{k} \cdot A \cdot D \cdot (24 \cdot 3600 \text{ s/day}) + c_p \cdot N \cdot V \cdot \rho \cdot D \cdot (24 \text{ h/day}) \qquad [7.2]$$

where:
Q_a = the annual heat loss of the building (J)
$\underline{k}$ = the average heat transfer coefficient of the building envelope (W/m²·K)
A = the surface area of the building envelope (m²)
c_p = the specific heat of air (c_p = 1.0 kJ/kg·K at 20 °C)
N = the ventilation rate (h⁻¹)
V = the air volume inside the building (m³)
ρ = the specific mass of air (1.20 kg/m³ at 20 °C)
D = the number of degree-days (°C-days)

As noted, 18 °C is of course used as a reference temperature. Why not use the average room temperature (20 °C in many cases)? The reason for this is that there are not only heat losses, but there are also internal heat sources. Internal heat sources are humans that live in the building (approx. 100 W per person), light sources, and other electric equipment. These heat sources need to be subtracted from the energy loss of the building to determine the remaining energy loss that needs to be made up using heating equipment, such as local space heaters or central heating systems. Of course, the 2 °C discount is only an approximation, and does not always represent the actual situation. For an example of the determination of degree-days, see Box 7.1.

Using the degree-day approach, an estimate can be made of a building's future energy use (when the design, including the degree of insulation and the ventilation rate, is known). The method can also be used to calculate a reference energy use, which can be compared to the actual energy use of a building. If the actual energy use is substantially higher than the reference energy use, one needs to look for the cause – e.g., an unidentified loss factor or wasteful behaviour on the part of the building's users.

7.3   Exergy analysis

An energy balance may be satisfactory for simple facilities, but for more complex facilities it does not give a good indication of where actual improvements need to be made. As an example, take the condenser of a power plant where low-pressure steam is condensed. The heat is transferred to cooling water at approx. 30 °C. Although the cooling water represents the majority of the power plant's energy loss, this heat is hardly usable anymore. This is reflected by the fact that the exergy loss associated with this cooling water flow is small. An exergy analysis provides a more fundamental understanding of the energy state of a facility.

An exergy analysis of a facility starts from a complete energy and material balance of all components of the facility. The physical characteristics of each material flow (temperature, pressure) also need to be known. Subsequently, the exergy content of all input and output flows for each component can be determined. Each component has exergy inputs and exergy outputs. The outputs can be divided into useful ones and waste. Useful outputs of a component are either saleable products or flows that are used elsewhere in the facility for further processing. Waste outputs include warm waste water flows, flue gases that leave through a chimney, radiation heat losses, or combustible residuals that are vented to the atmosphere.

Box 7.1. Calculating degree-days.

How many degree-days are there in the following week?
Take as a reference temperature 18 °C.

Day	Average daily temperature
Mon	17 °C
Tue	15 °C
Wed	20 °C
Thu	23 °C
Fri	18 °C
Sat	12 °C
Sun	10 °C

According to equation [7.1] on Monday we have 18 – 17 = 1 degree-days, this means a ΔT of 1°C during 1 day. On Tuesday we have 3 degree-days. On Wednesday and Thursday no degree-days are added as the outside temperature is higher then the cut-off level; no heating is needed. On Friday, the outside temperature equals the cut-off level, so again no heating is needed. Saturday and Sunday have 6 and 8 degree-days. In total there are thus 1 + 3 + 6 + 8 = 18 degree-days. This outcome is represented by the grey surface in the graph below:

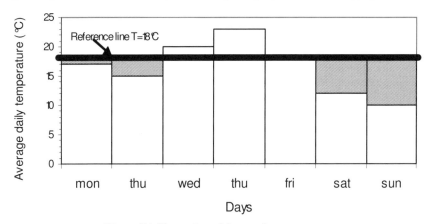

Figure 7.1 Illustration of degree-days concept.

What is the transmission heat loss from a house during this week, if the inside temperature is kept at room temperature? Assume a surface of 250 m² with an average heat transfer coefficient of 2 W/m²·K.

With a heat transmission coefficient of 2 W/m²·K, the wall loses 2 watt per square meter, if there is a ΔT of 1°C (see equation [3.2]). For the whole house this is thus 250 · 2 = 500 W/K. The total heat lost is thus 500 W/K · 18 degree-days · 86400 s/day = 778 MJ.

The exergy loss of a component is the difference between the total exergy inputs and the total *useful* exergy outputs. This exergy loss gives the theoretical maximum improvement that can be attained in the component. It is useful to distinguish between internal exergy losses and external exergy losses:

- The external exergy loss of a component is the total amount of exergy that leaves the component in the form of waste outputs.
- The internal exergy loss is the difference between the exergy of all the input flows and the exergy of *all* output flows (including the waste outputs). Possible causes of internal exergy loss are a temperature drop in a heat exchanger, mixing of media with different temperatures or pressures, or a chemical reaction which generates heat.

As an example, the results of an exergy analysis of the steel plant depicted in Figure 3.4 are given in Table 7.1. The total exergy input to the facility is about 18.2 GJ per tonne of rolled steel (this is about equal to the energy input). The useful exergy output of the total facility is 6.6 GJ/tonne rolled steel (the exergy content of steel). What happened to the rest?

As we see in Table 7.1, the external and internal exergy losses in this plant are about the same size. The external losses are broken down into four categories:

- losses through radiation and convection;
- heat flows that leave the plant (combustion air, hot water flows, cooling air, cooling water);
- waste flows that have a chemical energy content; and
- material losses.

In the steel plant, the losses through radiation and convection are the largest. This is not surprising, as iron and steel manufacturing includes processes with temperatures up to 1500 °C.

Internal exergy losses are caused by:

- combustion reactions;
- other chemical reactions;
- heat transfer; and
- compression and expansion of gases.

Most of the internal exergy losses of the steel plant occur during the combustion and partial combustion that occurs in the coke ovens, the sinter plant, the blast stoves, the reheating furnace, and the power plant.

After the exergy losses have been determined for all components, it is possible to select the components with the highest exergy losses. These are the components that need the most attention when looking for opportunities for improving energy efficiency.

It is important to note that not only can individual components be improved, but components can also be combined or replaced by completely different components. For instance, it is not easy to recover the heat from the steel that leaves the basic oxygen furnace; however, by feeding the hot steel directly into the caster (continuous casting), one cooling/heating sequence is avoided.

Table 7.1. Internal and external exergy losses of the steel production plant depicted in Figure 3.4 (all exergy quantities in GJ/ton rolled steel). Note that this is a simplified overview. In practice an iron and steel plant has hundreds of components.

Component	External exergy losses				Total internal exergy losses	Total exergy losses
	Radiation and convection losses	Chemical and physical exergy of waste streams	Material losses	Total external exergy losses		
Coke production	0.28	0.47	0.24	0.99	0.87	1.86
Sinter production	0.29	0.39		0.68	0.98	1.66
Hot blast stoves	0.25	0.11		0.36	0.41	0.77
Blast furnaces	0.44	0.18	0.04	0.66	1.35	2.01
Basic oxygen furnace	0.12	0.06		0.18	0.34	0.52
Continuous casting	1.05			1.05	0.06	1.11
Reheating furnaces	0.04	0.2		0.24	0.50	0.74
Hot strip mill	0.62			0.62	0.12	0.74
Power plant	0.20	0.21		0.41	1.51	1.92
Other	0.28			0.28	0.03	0.31
Total	**3.57**	**1.62**	**0.28**	**5.47**	**6.15**	**11.62**

7.4   Pinch analysis

In many facilities, exergy losses occur through the production, transfer and utilisation of heat. These can include both internal and external exergy losses:
- An example of internal exergy loss is the exergy loss caused by heat transfer over a heat exchanger (see Figure 3.3). The energy loss caused by a heat exchanger is generally very small. However, the exergy loss can be very substantial: the higher the temperature drop across the heat exchanger, the higher the exergy loss. Note that some temperature drop is always necessary as the temperature difference is the driving force for the heat exchange.
- External exergy losses are caused by all kinds of waste heat streams.

Energy can be saved by limiting these exergy losses, by avoiding big temperature drops across heat exchangers and by re-using waste heat streams as much as possible. However, how do we find the optimum configuration for complicated facilities?

Introduced by Linnhoff around 1980, pinch analysis is a tool for the optimisation of heat exchange activities within a facility. It can thus help to reduce external exergy losses and internal exergy losses that are associated with heat transfer. The basic idea, derived directly from the exergy approach, is that heat transfer across large temperature intervals should be avoided. Pinch analysis is an algorithm to systematically limit such heat transfer exergy losses. To clarify the principles, a simple approach will be described here.

Pinch analysis starts by mapping all streams that need to be heated ('cold streams') and all streams that need to be cooled ('hot streams'). The initial and final temperature and the specific heat need to be determined for each of these streams. Consider a hypothetical process in which four streams can be distinguished, two of which have to be heated and two to be cooled. We assume that the process is perfect, and no energy is lost. The data for these streams are given in Table 7.2. The cold streams are externally heated with 5000 kW and again by the hot streams. In this example, heat with a temperature below 25 °C is considered as useless. As we are dealing with flows, the heat capacities are given in kW/°C, instead of J/°C (which is used when dealing with reservoirs).

Table 7.2. Streams that have to be cooled and heated in the hypothetical process.

Stream	Initial temperature (°C)	Final temperature (°C)	Specific heat (kW/°C)
Hot streams			
1	275	85	40.0
2	165	25	23.3
Cold streams			
3	25	155	20.1
4	110	275	50.0

The first step is the construction of a so-called composite curve of the hot streams. The heat available from all hot streams is counted together (per temperature interval) and plotted against temperature. For temperatures below 85 °C, only hot stream 2 needs to be taken into account. At 25 °C the energy content of this stream is zero. At 85 °C, stream 2 has an energy content of (85 °C – 25 °C) x 23.3 kW/°C = 1398 kW. Between 85 °C and 165 °C the total specific heat of both streams 1 and 2 need to be taken into account, so in that range the specific heat is 63.3 kW/°C. The composite curve continues above 165 °C with stream 1 only. The results are summarised in Table 7.3, and graphically presented in Figure 7.2. This diagram provides information about the heat available at various temperature levels. For example, it shows that 3000 kW is available at a temperature of 200 °C or higher.

Table 7.3. Data for the composite curve of the hot streams.

Interval	Temperature range (°C)	Specific heat (kW/°C)	Enthalpy of interval (kW)	Cumulative enthalpy (kW)
1	25 – 85	23.3	1398	1398
2	85 – 165	63.3	5064	6462
3	165 – 275	40.0	4400	10862

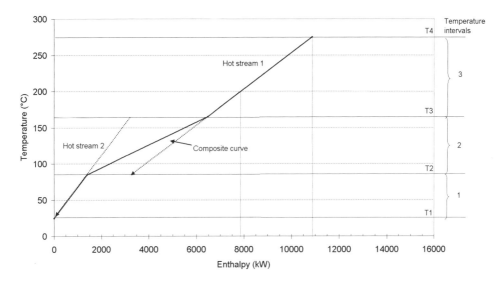

Figure 7.2. Example of a temperature-enthalpy diagram showing the composite curve of two hot streams.

The next step of the pinch analysis is to make a composite curve for the cold streams, as presented in Table 7.4.

Table 7.4. Data for the composite curve of the cold streams.

Interval	Temperature range (°C)	Specific heat (kW/°C)	Enthalpy of interval (kW)	Cumulative enthalpy (kW)
1	25 –110	20.1	1708	1708
2	110 – 155	70.1	3154	4862
3	155 – 275	50.0	6000	10862

Now the cold streams are added to the same graph as the hot streams. The cold stream is shifted to the right, with the external heat supply (5000 kW), determining the distance between the two curves (it can also be considered as one of the 'hot streams').

We will now calculate the starting point in the upper right corner of the cold stream. If no heat is recovered from the hot stream during the process, 10862 kW is needed to heat the cold streams. However, heat recovery from the hot streams reduces the external heat input to 5000 kW. This amount of heat determines the distance between both curves at the high end of the temperature range. Thus, the upper right point of the cold stream has an enthalpy of 10862 + 5000 kW = 15862 kW. The streams are presented in Figure 7.3.

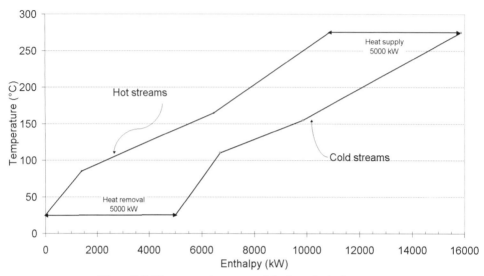

Figure 7.3. The composite curves of the hypothetical process.

The distance between the two curves at the lowest temperature level will also be 5000 kW, as we are dealing with an ideal process where no energy is lost.

To optimise the process we need to exchange as much heat as possible between the hot and cold streams and to limit the amount of heat that needs to be supplied externally or that needs to be cooled away. For heat exchange between flows, a temperature difference between the hot and cold flows is needed as a driving force. A practical value is 30 °C (though this value should be determined through economic optimisation). We will now move the cold streams curve horizontally until the minimum distance between the curves is 30 °C (see Figure 7.4). Point A determines the shortest vertical distance between the two curves, so this point is the limiting factor, called the pinch point.

Point A is now shifted horizontally until the temperature difference between A^* and the hot stream at point B is 30 °C. In this example, the temperature of A (and A^*) is 110 °C. Since the temperature difference of the two curves at the pinch point is 30 °C, the temperature of point B is 140 °C. We can now calculate how much the line has been shifted to the left, as the original enthalpy of A is 15862 kW (upper right) – 6000 – 3154 = 6708 kW. The cold stream has thus moved 6708 – 4879 =1829 kW leftwards. So, in theory we can save almost 1830 kW if we take a minimum ΔT of 30 °C for the heat exchangers.

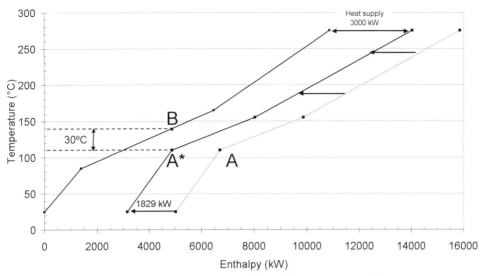

Figure 7.4. The composite curves, where the curve of the cold streams is moved for optimisation.

General guidelines for optimisation. The pinch point divides the system into two subsystems. Using this analysis, a system can be designed with a minimum external heat supply. The optimal configuration of the heat transfer system can be derived directly from Figure 7.4: the heat should be transferred from the hot streams to the cold streams vertically in the diagram. However, there may be all kinds of practical obstacles to achieving this in an actual industrial plant. Three principles need to be obeyed to achieve an optimum situation:

a.   Do not transfer heat from above the pinch point to below the pinch point.
b.   Do not supply external heat below the pinch point.
c.   Do not use external cooling above the pinch point.

By following these principles, an optimum heat exchanger network can be designed for the process.

7.5   Energy management

Energy management is the permanent and systematic management of the production, conversion, and use of energy within an organization.

In general, energy management will be a cyclical process (see Figure 7.5), consisting of:
- monitoring of energy production, conversion and use;
- reporting and analysis, including indicators of energy use and energy efficiency, and re-analysis of improvement options;

- preparation and planning of adaptations in the energy system (adaptations may include organisational changes, investments in energy conservation, adaptations to the production process, campaigns aimed at changing behaviour); and
- implementation of the adaptations.

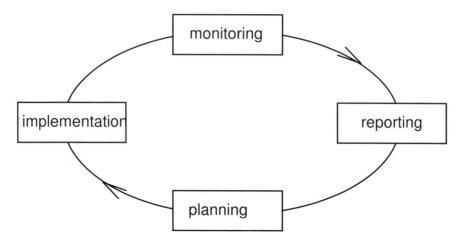

Figure 7.5. Schematic representation of the energy management cycle.

There may be a variety of reasons for implementing energy management in an organisation. Reducing energy costs will usually be predominant, but other reasons may include the wish to produce in a more environmentally friendly way, the desire to improve the corporate image, or obligations imposed by the government.

Energy management systems may take various forms, depending on the targets, the type of organisation, and the complexity of energy use in an organisation. Being properly embedded in the organisation is a key component of an energy management process. In general, it is important that the organisation's higher management levels are involved. They should determine the targets to be achieved by the introduction of energy management, and the results should be reported to the management level. Furthermore, the management will generally be involved in decisions about important investments. An energy coordinator should have the overall responsibility for the energy management system; working procedures and responsibilities of other personnel also need to be defined.

Energy management may be part of an environmental management system. Since the late 1980s, environmental management has received more and more attention. Several formalized codes of environmental management practice have been developed, such as ISO 14001 (the Eco-Management and Audit Scheme EMAS is an extension used in the European Union). Such a code requires that participants identify environmental impacts of their activities, develop an environmental policy, establish environmental objectives and targets, keep track of environmental regulatory requirements, train employees about their environmental responsibilities, implement measurement systems, and audit themselves periodically.

7.6   Beyond energy management

In its original form, energy management is mainly focused on the energy use within an organisation and its reduction. With the changing environment of energy-using companies and other organisations, the concept has widened. Some developments are energy contracting, energy chain management, carbon management, and climate neutrality.

Energy contracting. With the liberalisation of energy markets, customers are, in principle, free to choose how and where to purchase energy. They can 'shop around' for the cheapest energy, but other options have also become available. For instance, an organisation can purchase a combination of energy and services that is more suitable for its specific needs. For instance, an energy user who needs heat can buy natural gas, and produce heat in a boiler. But the user can also decide to buy the heat directly, and leave the generation of this heat to the energy supplier. Or the organisation may choose to purchase energy from specific sources (e.g., green electricity produced from renewable energy sources) to reduce environmental impact.

Energy chain management. Decisions by an organization not only affect energy use within its own facilities, but also upstream and downstream energy use. For instance, the choice of input materials or the efficiency with which these materials are used affects the amount of energy required by the supplying sectors. Downstream sectors may also be affected; for example, the production of higher quality materials may make it possible for a downstream company (e.g. a car manufacturer using steel) to use less material. Another example is the production of energy-efficient electrical equipment that helps reduce energy use on the part of the consumers.

Energy chain management needs to consider all the upstream and downstream effects of company decisions. Thus, energy chain management requires a much more extended analysis than the energy analysis discussed in this chapter (for methods see Chapter 9). The previously mentioned examples show that implementing energy chain management often requires cooperation in the production chain. Energy chain management can be important for several reasons, by reducing the company's vulnerability to energy price changes and new regulation, but also reducing overall environmental effects and creating long-term competitive advantages.

Carbon management. Carbon management is an extension of energy management and energy chain management, focused on one of the major environmental impacts of energy use: climate change. Carbon management has become more important now that various countries, including the entire European Union, have introduced CO_2 emission trading (see

Chapter 15). Participation in an emission trading scheme means that carbon emissions 'get a price' and that financial risks and liabilities can increase substantially. A scheme for implementing carbon management is given in Figure 7.6. As with energy chain management, the emphasis is on anchoring the process within the organisation.

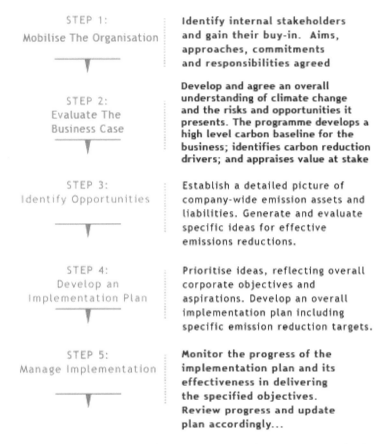

STEP 1:
Mobilise The Organisation

Identify internal stakeholders and gain their buy-in. Aims, approaches, commitments and responsibilities agreed

STEP 2:
Evaluate The Business Case

Develop and agree an overall understanding of climate change and the risks and opportunities it presents. The programme develops a high level carbon baseline for the business; identifies carbon reduction drivers; and appraises value at stake

STEP 3:
Identify Opportunities

Establish a detailed picture of company-wide emission assets and liabilities. Generate and evaluate specific ideas for effective emissions reductions.

STEP 4:
Develop an Implementation Plan

Prioritise ideas, reflecting overall corporate objectives and aspirations. Develop an overall implementation plan including specific emission reduction targets.

STEP 5:
Manage Implementation

Monitor the progress of the implementation plan and its effectiveness in delivering the specified objectives. Review progress and update plan accordingly...

Figure 7.6. Process for implementing carbon management within a company as developed by the UK Carbon Trust (www.carbontrust.co.uk/carbon).

Climate neutral entrepreneurship. When an activity is climate neutral, the total climate impact of the activity is intended to be zero. As it is often difficult to completely eliminate the emission of greenhouse gases in the short term, the pursuit of carbon neutrality is often a combination of reducing emissions and compensating for the remaining emissions. Compensation can be direct: for instance, a forestry project can be financed that sequesters the amount of CO_2 emitted by the original activity. But compensation can also be indirect, through alternative emission reduction projects, where the emission reduction is equal to remaining emissions of the original activity. A company or organization can pursue climate neutrality for all its activities or for part of them. In addition, climate-neutral products can be developed, where all the emissions over the product's whole life-cycle are compensated.

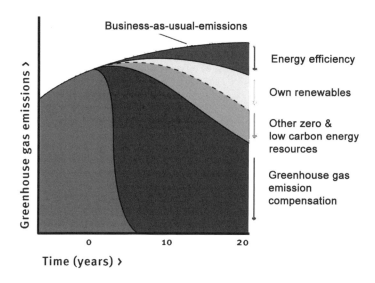

Figure 7.7. Schematic representation of emission reductions and compensation needed to reach climate neutrality for a given activity.

Further reading

K. Baumert, M. Selman: Data Note – Heating and Cooling Degree-Days, World Resources Institute, Washington D.C., 2003. Available at http://cait.wri.org/downloads/DN-HCDD.pdf (provides listings of heating degree-days per country).

J.G. de Beer: Potential for Industrial Energy Efficiency-Improvement in the Long Term, Kluwer Academic Publishers, Dordrecht, The Netherlands, 2000.

B. Linnhoff, D.W. Townsend, D. Boland, G.F. Hewitt: A User Guide on Process Integration for the Efficient Use of Energy, The Institute of Chemical Engineers, Rugby, UK, 1982. (on pinch analysis)

J.J. Romm: Cool Companies: How the Best Businesses Boost Profits and Productivity by Cutting Greenhouse Gas Emissions, Island Press, Washington D.C., 1999.

T.J. Kotas: The Exergy Method of Thermal Plant Analysis, Butterworths, London, 1985.

Final achievement levels

After having studied Chapter 7 and the exercises, you should:
- be able to design an energy analysis for a simple energy user (e.g., a household or simple office building);
- be able to work with the degree-day concept;

-   be able to carry out an exergy analysis of a simple system (e.g., a heat exchanger or a boiler);
-   be able to carry out a pinch analysis,
-   be familiar with the energy management cycle and be able to describe its components; and
-   be able to describe the various new developments that can be included in energy management.

Exercises Chapter 7

7.1. Energy analysis of electric appliances
For 5 – 10 electric appliances in your home, determine the nominal capacity, estimate the annual load factor and calculate the annual electricity consumption.
What share do these appliances have in the annual electricity use of your home?
Also, provide an indicative analysis of improvement options.

7.2. Derive equation [7.2] from the basics described in Section 3.2.

7.3. Degree-days in an apartment building
You live in a corner apartment with a surface of 10 m deep and 8 m wide. The outside walls are 8 m wide and 3 m high on each side. Twenty-five percent of the walls have single glazing (k-value 6 W/m²·K), the rest are uninsulated cavity walls (R-value of 0.5 m²·K/W). Your house is heated by a natural-gas fired boiler. Assume that the indoor temperature is always 20 °C. Your neighbours next to you and below and above you have the same temperature in their homes. The ventilation rate in your home is once per hour. Further assumptions: the specific heat of air is 1.0 kJ/kg·K; the specific gravity is 1.2 kg/m³; number of degree-days per year is 3000; boiler efficiency 90% LHV; natural gas with a LHV of 35 MJ/m³.
a.   Calculate the annual heat loss through transmission and ventilation.
b.   Calculate the annual natural gas demand for space heating.
c.   What would you save if you replaced the glazing with state-of-the-art double glazing (k-value 1.2 W/m²·K) and insulated the cavity walls (R-value increases to 2.5 m²·K/W)?

7.4. Degree-days of a refrigerator
Take the refrigerator from exercise 3.3.
a.   One can define the equivalent of the number of degree-days for this refrigerator. Calculate this number of degree-days.
b.   What does this tell you about the degree of insulation of this refrigerator?

7.5. Exergy analysis: mixing of thermal oil
Thermal oil is often used as a carrier for heat transport in the process industry.
a.   A chemical plant produces 1 tonne of hot oil (300 °C) and 1 tonne of medium hot oil (100 °C). Calculate the energy and exergy contents of the oil (the heat capacity of the oil is 2.0 kJ/kg·K).
b.   The two tonnes of oil are mixed in a vessel. Calculate the energy and exergy contents of the mixed oil.
c.   What do we learn from this result?

7.6. Exergy analysis: using waste heat

A factory produces 150 kg/s water at 175 °C under pressure. There are two options to use this waste heat:

Option 1: Heating a swimming pool. In this case 750 kg/s water is heated from 25 °C to 50 °C.

Option 2: Heating an industrial flow. In this case 150 kg/s water is heated from 25°C to 150 °C.

In both cases the final temperature of the water from the factory is 50 °C.

a.   Draw a scheme for both options and calculate the energy and exergy contents of the flows.
b.   Calculate the energy and exergy losses for both options. Which option do you prefer?
c.   What do we learn from this example?

7.7. Exergy analysis: combustion

Natural gas is burned stoichiometric with air. The combustion gases have a temperature of 2200 °C.

a.   Calculate the exergy efficiency of the combustion process.
b.   In practice, no materials can withstand 2200 °C, so the temperature in a gas turbine is reduced to 1400 °C. What is the exergy efficiency in this case?
c.   What do we learn from this? How can we reduce losses?

7.8. Going climate-neutral

A service sector company has an annual turnover of 250 million € and makes a profit of 10 million € per year. The annual energy use is 2 million m³ natural gas (32 MJ/m³, 6 €/GJ) and 10 million kWh of electricity (80 €/MWh) per year. CO_2 emissions are 56 kg/GJ for natural gas and 600 g/kWh for electricity. The company has several options to limit the climate-impacts of its activities. It can:

• save 20% of its natural gas use (cost-neutral)
• save 40% of its electricity use (net costs 100,000 € per year)
• generate 1 million kWh through photovoltaic energy systems (0.4 €/kWh)
• switch partly or completely to green electricity (100 €/MWh)
• buy partly or completely green gas, upgraded from biogas (10 €/GJ)
• off-set remaining emissions by buying carbon credits (8 €/tonne CO_2).

a.   What are the total CO_2 emissions associated with the company's direct energy use? What are the energy costs?
b.   Design an attractive package of measures that makes the company climate-neutral and calculate the costs. How does this relate to energy costs and turnover?
c.   Determine what is the cheapest way to make the company climate-neutral and how much it costs.

8

Analysis of energy chains

When I light a lamp, the fuel input into a power plant somewhere has to be increased. In general when energy is used somewhere (direct energy use), it induces energy use somewhere else (indirect energy use). The total demand for primary energy can therefore be much higher than the direct energy use, because several prior processes are involved that have less than 100% conversion efficiency. To calculate primary energy use, we need to analyse the energy chain that contributes to a certain final energy use. This chapter deals with the problems one may encounter when trying to determine the primary energy use.

This chapter starts by presenting the general approach to energy chain analysis (8.1), and then discusses the accuracy levels (8.2). Next, two categories of energy conversion that require special attention are considered: the electricity sector in general (8.3) and combined generation of heat and power as an example of a multi-output process (8.4). The chapter concludes by discussing the concept of emission factors (8.5).

This chapter only analyses energy chains, chains that result in a certain final energy use. Other activities, such as the use of products or services, also require primary energy, but this will be treated in Chapter 9.

8.1   General approach to energy chain analysis

The general formulation of the problem treated in this chapter is: when one uses a given amount of a certain energy carrier, what energy use is induced elsewhere? This question is important in many cases. Some examples of relevant questions involving the energy chain:

- A household may choose to invest in a fuel switch option, such as the installation of a heat pump. This substitutes the use of 60 GJ of natural gas for 25 GJ of electricity. Is this an interesting option from an energy saving point of view?
- A household extracts heat from a district heating system. Is this heat 'free' from the point of view of demand on primary energy carriers, and if not, what primary energy demand should be allocated to it?
- Two products have a similar function. One requires the use of 1 GJ of coal for a certain performance; the other requires the use of 1 GJ of electricity for the same performance. Which should be preferred from the point of view of reducing primary energy demand?
- A company using natural gas, coal and electricity wants to know how much carbon dioxide it emits.

The basic approach to answering such questions is straightforward. One starts with the final energy use for which the indirect effects are to be determined, and one follows the chain of energy conversions "upstream" in the direction of primary energy use (see Figure 8.1). Starting with the final energy use, one goes through the various energy conversion processes, and taking into account energy conversion efficiencies, one calculates how much input is required to supply the output for each of the processes. One continues until one arrives at the primary energy input. This result is the total primary energy input needed to supply a certain amount of final energy, called the *primary energy requirement*[1]. For one unit of energy, this value is also indicated with the term *energy requirement for energy* (ERE).

In practice, calculating ERE is not so simple, and a number of problems are encountered, which will be addressed in Sections 8.3 and 8.4.

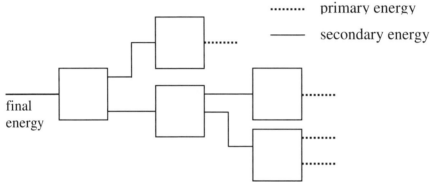

Figure 8.1. Schematic representation of the energy conversion processes required to supply a certain final energy use.

8.2 Accuracy

When carrying out energy chain analysis, one always has to decide to what level of detail the indirect energy use should be included. In fact, this is a question of system boundaries: to what extent should the energy chain be developed and analysed? In general, the wider the system boundaries are drawn, the more accurate the result of the analysis will be. In practice, this means that the system boundaries are extended until the required accuracy is achieved.

A number of orders of reporting can be distinguished with increasing accuracy:

---

[1] This procedure is complicated by the fact that the energy supply chain may be cyclical. For instance, an oil refinery consumes electricity from an electricity supply system which uses oil products as one of the inputs. This means that the procedure set out in this section cannot be carried out in a straightforward way. In practice, there are cyclical loops in every energy supply system, but in many cases the interdependencies will be small. In order to obtain a complete picture of all inputs in the case of cyclical energy supply systems, an input-output analysis of the energy supply system can be carried out. The principles of input-output analysis are described in Section 10.3.

- Zero order representation: only total final energy use is presented. While reporting this is useful, but for purposes of comparison, the accuracy is too small to be acceptable.
- First order representation: fuel inputs are counted together with electricity inputs, taking into account conversion losses in electricity generation for these inputs. This is the minimum level of accuracy required and may be useful for many purposes (error generally smaller than 10%).
- Second order representation: all losses in energy conversion are taken into account for conversion and transportation of energy carriers, including coal mining and transportation, oil transportation and refining, gas liquefaction and transport and nuclear fuel cycle losses (the error here is generally about 5 percent[2]). For the main fossil fuels, the second order representation is obtained by multiplying the first order value with factors like those given in Table 8.1. This approach only makes sense if allocation in the electricity sector is sensibly and accurately dealt with (see Section 8.3).
- Third order representation: all previous losses are taken into account, as well as the energy required for the capital stock of the energy conversion processes and operation and maintenance. This order may reduce the error to 1 or 2%, at least in terms of excluding errors made by failing to consider different energy inputs. However, other errors, such as those due to different approaches in electricity production or those caused by uncertainty in allocation in multi-output processes, may be much larger. Therefore, a third order representation does not often lead to significantly different results than a second order representation.

Table 8.1. *Second order values for the energy requirement for energy (ERE) for different delivered fuels.*

Fuel	Energy requirement for energy (MJ primary per MJ delivered)	Breakdown of indirect energy requirement	Remarks
Coal	1.04 – 1.10	1% extraction 0 – 7% transport 1 – 2% storage	Transport is low if coal is used directly at mine-mouth
Oil products	1.08 – 1.15	<1% extraction 3% transport 2% storage 5 – 10% refineries	Light products (e.g., gasoline) on average require more energy use in refining than heavy products (e.g., heavy fuel oil).
Natural gas	1.01 – 1.05	Mainly transport and distribution	Depends mainly on transportation distance. Figures not valid for liquefied natural gas (LNG)

---

[2] This is only true if not too many capital-intensive energy sources, like photovoltaic energy or nuclear energy, are involved.

8.3   Allocation in the electricity sector

If one kWh is taken from the electricity network, how much fuel is required to generate that one kWh of electricity? Since an electricity production system consists of many plants operating together, this question is difficult to answer.

There are two main approaches that can be taken: *average* and *marginal* approach. The 'average' approach is relatively simple and quite widely used. Average numbers are calculated for the whole electricity system (e.g., for a country). This can be the average *conversion efficiency,* the total electricity output E of power plants divided by the total fuel use F. Once the average conversion efficiency has been determined, the fuel use associated with the use of a given amount of electricity can easily be calculated.

The problem with the average approach is that it does not tell us how much fuel consumption is *caused* by one specific application. What happens when I switch on a light? Or what difference does it make if the number of dishwashers increases? How much does it help if we replace incandescent lamps with compact fluorescent lamps? In general such changes do not have an 'average' impact on the fuel consumption of the electricity system (see Figure 8.2).

In order to answer such questions, a marginal approach can help. In a marginal approach, we consider the amount of additional fuel that is needed to generate an additional amount of electricity (= dF_t/dE_t) for each moment of the year. This may be less than average (e.g., if the additional fuel is generated in efficient natural-gas fired power plants instead of the average production that is mainly based on coal), but it can also be more than average (e.g., if the additional electricity demand requires that older, less efficient capacity, be put into operation). The value of this marginal fuel use, integrated over the year, provides us with the *short-term marginal* fuel consumption for a specific application.

There are some problems with using marginal specific fuel use:
- The sum of the marginal fuel uses for all demand categories does not necessarily add up to the total fuel use.
- It cannot be derived from statistics.

In general, one needs simulation models of the electricity system to approximate the marginal fuel use. As the name suggests, a simulation model simulates the behaviour of an electricity supply system throughout a year, for example on an hour-by-hour basis. The model determines the operational dispatch of all the production units in the electricity supply system, and calculates the electricity output, fuel use, emissions, etc. of each plant.

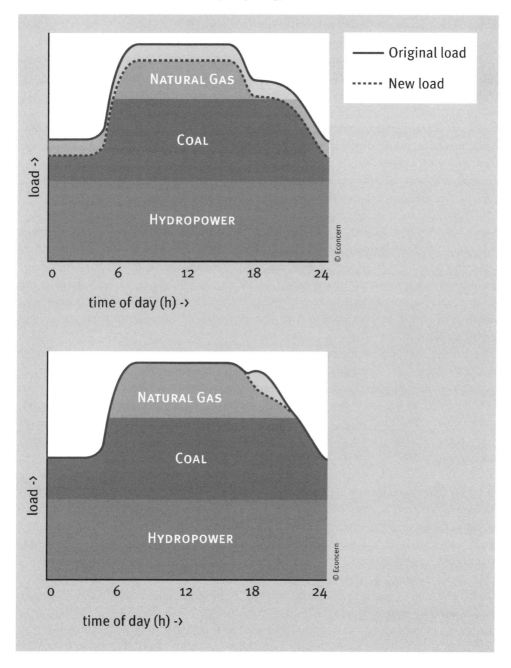

Figure 8.2. Illustration of the impact of an electricity conservation measure on the fuel use of the power system. The reduction of a constant demand (e.g., base load industrial demand, refrigerators) saves natural gas and coal. The reduction of a demand that peaks in the evening (e.g. lighting, TV) mainly saves natural gas. The use of hydropower is unaffected.

A simulation model generally takes into account start-up and stop procedures, limits to partial load operation, and the safety margins needed to guarantee a sufficient supply. In general, one needs to run such a simulation model twice: once with and once without a specific change in energy demand. This gives the *incremental* or *differential* fuel use ($\Delta F/\Delta E$ = change in fuel use divided by the change in electricity requirement).

If no sophisticated simulation model is available, the following approach may be useful. Since fossil-fuel power plants have higher variable costs than other plants (i.e., nuclear and most renewables) (see Section 5.4), these plants will be taken out of operation first when demand decreases. So, the marginal fuel use may be approximated by taking the average specific fuel use for fossil fuel-fired power production.

Short-term marginal approaches versus long-term marginal approaches. If an investment in equipment that improves the efficiency of electricity use is done *now*, this will limit electricity use *in the future* by a certain amount. In this case, it is not very sensible to use the present average specific or marginal fuel use to calculate the saved fuels. Instead, one needs to integrate over the period in the future for which the savings are valid. As various development paths may be conceivable, one may need to calculate fuel use for various different scenarios.

This can be very laborious, especially if one applies a marginal approach (for which simulations of the electricity system may be necessary). In some cases, simple approximations are possible. For instance, in many regions of the world the dominant technology for new electric power generation plants is the natural-gas fired combined-cycle power plant. Hence, in such cases, one can simplify the analysis by using the energy conversion efficiency of a natural-gas fired combined-cycle plant to calculate primary energy use.

What are the boundaries of the power system? The electricity supply system varies from country to country, and we could use each of the previous approaches for an individual country. However, hardly any country has an autonomous power grid anymore, and power grids connect most countries. In the past, the international connections were mainly used to warrant the reliability of the national grids and for limited (contracted) deliveries from one country to another, but now that we are moving towards open international electricity markets, it makes more sense to analyse energy chains on an international basis rather than on a country-by-country basis.

Recommendations. There is no straightforward answer to the question posed at the beginning of this section. Though the approach should be carefully considered for each study, some general recommendations can be made:
- In case of life-cycle (energy) assessment to compare products, one may use the actual average specific fuel use to calculate primary energy consumption, in accordance with existing practices in that field.

- When one wants to determine the effect of a change in a specific year, one may use marginal or differential approaches to determine the additional or saved fuel requirement.
- To calculate marginal fuel use, one needs to use a simulation model of the electricity production system. As an alternative, one can often make a reasonable estimate using the average specific fuel use of fossil-fired power generation.
- To determine the effect of an investment in new production equipment, one can calculate the impacts over the lifetime of the equipment by using a scenario approach.

8.4 Allocation in multi-output processes

In processes with more than one product, the input needs to be allocated to the different products. For example, what percentage of the fodder of a cow contributes to the milk, the leather, and the meat? Examples of energy conversion processes with more than one product are refineries (which produce a wide range of products) and plants for combined generation of heat and power (CHP). The general question is, how can the input fuel be divided among the products?

In this section, various allocation rules will be discussed and applied to a CHP plant. A CHP plant produces an amount of electricity E and an amount of heat H, while using an amount of fuel F as input. Here the question is, how can we allocate this total fuel use F to the products electricity (E) and heat (H)? A certain part of the fuel use needs to be allocated to the electricity production and a certain part to the heat production, but which do we allocate to each? The only requirement is that, in the end, all the fuel input needs to be allocated.

Various allocation methods are possible; some are better than others, but their usefulness always depends on the aim of the analysis for which they are used.

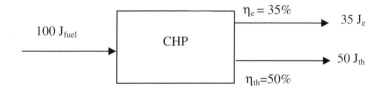

Figure 8.3. Energy flows for an industrial CHP plant.

Method 1. Allocation on the basis of the energy content of the products.

In this method, the fuel demand is allocated to the products on the basis of their energy content. Consider an industrial CHP plant (see Figure 8.3) that has an electrical efficiency of 35% and a heat efficiency of 50% (LHV). The total output from an input of 100 J_{fuel} is 35 J_e + 50 J_{th} = 85 J of energy. Electricity makes up 35/85 = 41% of the energy output, so 41% of the input fuel is allocated to the production of electricity. As the input is in this case 100 J_{fuel}, we say that 41 J_{fuel} was needed for the production of the 35 J of electricity and the remaining 59 J_{fuel} was needed for the production of 50 J_{th} (the whole input being 41 J + 59 J = 100 J). This method can be written in the following equations:

$$F_E = \left[\frac{E}{E+H} \right] \cdot F \qquad\qquad F_H = \left[\frac{H}{E+H} \right] \cdot F \qquad\qquad [8.1]$$

where:
E = net electricity production of the CHP plant
H = net heat production of the CHP plant
F = fuel input for the CHP plant
F_H = the amount of fuel that is allocated to heat production
F_E = the amount of fuel that is allocated to electricity production.

A problem with this approach is that the energy content does not properly reflect the quality and usefulness of the energy carriers (see Section 1.4), which makes this approach less suitable. Nevertheless, this allocation method is still widely in use, for example by the International Energy Agency.

Method 2. Allocation on the basis of the exergy content of the products.

A better approach is to allocate the fuel demand to the products on the basis of their exergy value. The exergy/energy ratio can be called the quality factor β. For electricity, this ratio is 1, and this ratio is close to one for most fuels. For heat flows, though, the value is much lower: typically 0.1 for hot water and 0.35 for steam. The fuel demand is allocated to the outputs as follows:

$$F_E = \left[\frac{E}{E+\beta \cdot H} \right] \cdot F \qquad\qquad F_H = \left[\frac{\beta \cdot H}{E+\beta \cdot H} \right] \cdot F \qquad\qquad [8.2]$$

where:
β = the ratio between the exergy and the energy content of the heat produced.

The exergy production with an input of 100 J_{fuel} of the industrial CHP plant in Figure 8.3 consists of two parts: electricity production (35 J_e) and heat production (50 J_{th}). The exergy content of the produced electricity is equal to the energy content. To calculate the exergy content of the heat, we use the rule of thumb for steam, exergy/energy = 0.35. Thus the exergy content is 50 $J_{th} \cdot 0.35 = 17.5$ J. Hence, the total exergy output is 52.5 J. This is summarised in Figure 8.4.

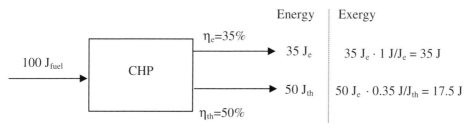

Figure 8.4. Exergy flows in a CHP plant.

The total exergy output from an input of 100 J is 52.5 J. The allocation to electricity is thus 35 J/52.5 J = 67 %. In other words 67% of the input is allocated to the electricity, and the remaining 33% is allocated to the heat.

Method 3: Allocating all the savings to one product:
Method 3a. Allocating all the savings to the electricity production
Method 3b. Allocating all the savings to the heat production.

In many cases CHP is studied from the perspective of one of the sub-systems, either the electricity supply system or the heat supply system. In these cases the savings induced by the application of CHP may be allocated to one of these two subsystems. When the savings are allocated to electricity, we act as if the heat were produced in a boiler, and the fuel demand is allocated to this energy carrier accordingly. The remainder of the fuel is allocated to the electricity production:

$$F_H = \frac{H}{\eta_b} \qquad\qquad F_E = F - \frac{H}{\eta_b} \qquad\qquad [8.3]$$

where:
η_b = efficiency of the boiler that would have been used in the case of separate production of heat and electricity ('reference boiler').

When the savings are allocated to heat, we act as if the electricity were produced in a conventional power plant, and the fuel demand is allocated to this energy carrier accordingly. The remainder of the fuel is allocated to the heat production:

$$F_E = \frac{E}{\eta_{pp}} \qquad\qquad F_H = F - \frac{E}{\eta_{pp}} \qquad\qquad [8.4]$$

where:
η_{pp} = efficiency of the power plant that would have been used in the case of separate production of heat and electricity ('reference power plant').

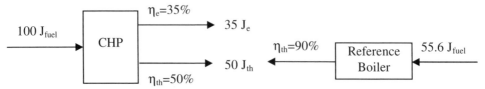

Figure 8.5. Example of allocation of a CHP plant with a reference boiler.

Let us apply this method to the example of the CHP plant in Figure 8.3 to calculate the energy needed for 1 kWh of electricity. In the CHP plant, 50 J_{th} is produced. If this were done in a separate boiler, 50 J_{th}/90%=55.6 J_{fuel} would be needed, assuming a reference conversion efficiency of 90%. As the total input is 100 J_{fuel}, (100 – 55.6) J_{fuel} = 44.4 J_{fuel} is allocated to the production of 35 J of electricity. Hence, the amount of fuel allocated to one kWh (3.6 MJ) is 4.6 MJ$_{fuel}$.

A disadvantage of these two methods is that reference values for the alternative energy technologies are needed, and choosing these is not unambiguous.

Method 4. Allocation on the basis of the economic value of the products

In this case, fuel demand is allocated to the products on the basis of their market value:

$$F_E = \left[\frac{c_e E}{c_e E + c_h H}\right] F \qquad\qquad F_H = \left[\frac{c_h H}{c_e E + c_h H}\right] F \qquad\qquad [8.5]$$

where:
c_e = market value of electricity produced (per unit of energy content);
c_h = market value of heat produced (per unit of energy content);

This approach is often taken in modern life-cycle assessment. Generally, an economic activity is undertaken because of the products that add most to the income of the activity. This approach allocates inputs to products according to the value of the product in the market.

For CHP allocation, a main problem is that the value of one of the products is often artificial or not known, for example when the operator of the CHP plant also uses the heat and no explicit payment takes place. An additional problem of this approach is that prices may change rapidly, leading to results that are not necessarily relevant.

Method 5. Allocation on the basis of the mass of the products

Traditionally, energy analysis has allocated on the basis of the mass of the products, but this method is meaningless for CHP. Nevertheless, the approach can be considered for other applications (e.g., refineries or naphtha crackers). However, this approach is considered less acceptable when the value per unit mass differs significantly between the various products, for example where a process produces a very valuable product (e.g., ethylene), as well as a less valuable by-product (e.g., fuel gas). In this case, allocation on a mass basis would clearly allocate too much of the input to the by-product.

8.5   Emission factors

When fuels are burned, this generally leads to emissions to the atmosphere, as well as to soil and water. Important emissions are those of carbon dioxide (CO_2), nitrogen oxides (NO_x, which includes both NO and NO_2), sulphur dioxide (SO_2) and particles. Emission factors represent the amount of emission that is generated per unit of fuel combusted. They are expressed as g/GJ or kg/GJ. Emissions of CO_2 (see Table 8.2) are sometimes expressed in units of carbon instead of units of CO_2. Emissions of NO_x are always expressed in units of NO_2–equivalents.

Table 8.2. Overview of CO_2 emission factors for various fuels. Source: IPCC, 1995.

Fuel	Emission factor ($kg\ CO_2/GJ_{LHV}$)
Bituminous coal	95
Lignite (brown coal)	101
Peat	106
Motor gasoline	69
Jet fuel	72
Diesel fuel	74
Heavy fuel oil	77
LPG	63
Natural gas	56

Emission factors can be influenced by taking measures to mitigate emissions. Emission of CO_2, SO_2 and particles mainly depend on the composition of the fuels and the degree of flue gas treatment; emissions of NO_x depend on the combustion conditions and the degree of flue gas treatment.

By applying the same methods as presented in the previous sections, total emissions can be determined for a certain amount of final energy use.

Further reading

Some literature on the simulation of electricity systems:

K.R. Voorspoels, W.D. D'haeseleer: An Evaluation Method for Calculating the Emission Responsibility of Specific Electricity Applications, Energy Policy, 28 (2000) 967-980.

A.J.M. van Wijk, W.C. Turkenburg: Costs Avoided by the Use of Wind Energy in the Netherlands, Electric Power Systems Research, 23 (1992) 201-216.

IPCC Guidelines for National Greenhouse Gas Inventories, I: Greenhouse Gas Inventory Reporting Instructions, II: Greenhouse Gas Inventory Workbook, III: Greenhouse Gas Inventory Reference Manual, Intergovernmental Panel on Climate Change, UNEP/OECD/IEA/IPCC, 1995 (part III is the source of the emission factors).

Final achievement levels

After having studied Chapter 8 and the exercises, you should:
-   be able to explain why it is important to calculate primary energy and describe the general procedure to calculate this;
-   be able to describe the various accuracy levels, and the cases in which they are needed;
-   be able to explain the differences between the average and marginal/differential approach for allocation in electricity production and present the advantages and disadvantages of both approaches;
-   be able to use the various allocation approaches in multi-output processes; and
-   know what emission factors are and be able to use them.

Exercises Chapter 8

8.1. Heating a house
There are two options for heating a house: a modern condensing boiler with a thermal efficiency of 95% HHV and a heat pump with a COP of 4.
Which option is the best regarding primary energy consumption?

8.2. Orders of accuracy
In your household, you use 1500 m^3 of natural gas (35 MJ/m^3) and 3500 kWh of electricity per year. Furthermore, you drive 15,000 km per year in a car that has a specific fuel use of 6 litres per 100 km. Assume that the electricity that you use comes half from coal-fired power plants (40% conversion efficiency LHV) and half from natural-gas fired power plants (55% conversion efficiency).
Calculate the zero, first, and second order representation of primary energy use.

8.3. The electricity supply system in Centimillia

The electricity production system of the country Centimillia consists of 1000 MW nuclear energy capacity, 2000 MW coal fired electricity and 3000 MW natural-gas capacity (with increasing variable costs in this order). The conversion efficiency is 40% for the coal-fired power plants and 55% for the natural gas-fired power plants.

All year round, the electricity demand is 4500 MW during daytime (7.00 – 23.00) and 2500 MW during night time (23.00 – 7.00).

a. Sketch the way the power plants are dispatched to achieve the lowest possible costs.
b. 1000 MW of wind energy is added to the electricity production system. The annual load factor is 20%. The wind power production fluctuates, but on average is evenly spread over the day. Sketch how the power plants are dispatched after the addition of wind energy.
c. Calculate the fuel savings achieved through the application of the wind energy.
d. Do the same if 1000 MW solar photovoltaic energy were applied instead of wind energy (load factor 15%).

8.4. Average and marginal approaches

The electricity demand in Lusitania is 4000 MW at night time and 8000 MW during the day (constant over the year). Power is supplied by hydropower (1000 MW), nuclear energy (1000 MW), coal-fired power stations (3000 MW) and natural-gas fired power stations (5000 MW). All plants have an availability of 90%.

a. An overall saving of electricity is achieved of 5%. Calculate the actual fuel savings achieved and also the reduction in CO_2 emissions.
b. Calculate the fuel savings achieved if the analysis had been based on an average approach.

8.5. Allocation in CHP plants

Apply the various allocation methods presented in Section 8.4 to two of the CHP plants listed in Table 4.4: the 10 – 50 MW gas turbine and the gas engine. Express your results in terms of fuel requirement per unit of electricity produced and per unit of heat produced. Discuss your outcomes.

Assume that a gas engine plant produces heat with a temperature of 120 °C and that the gas turbine produces steam with an exergy/energy ratio of 0.35.

8.6. Co-production of methanol and electricity

Methanol can be produced out of biomass. Biomass is gasified, which results in a mixture of carbon monoxide and hydrogen. Methanol can be formed from this so-called synthesis gas. The synthesis gas does not convert fully; the remainder is fed to a power plant where it is converted to electricity. A co-production plant converts 80 tonnes oven dry wood per hour into 14.8 m^3 methanol and 110 MWh electricity. The energy content of methanol is 22.7 MJ/kg, the density is 0.79 kg/litre. The market-price of methanol is 10 €/GJ, and of electricity 0.03 €/kWh.

a. Make a flow-chart of the process and convert the flows to comparable energy units.
b. How much wood is needed for the production of 1 GJ methanol and for the production of 1 GJ of electricity if you allocate according to economic value, energy content, and exergy content, respectively?

8.7. Climate neutrality

Consider your household again (exercise 8.2).

a. What is the emission factor for the electricity that you use?
b. Calculate the CO_2 emissions for each of the three components of your energy use.
c. How much would it cost you to become completely climate neutral (see Section 7.6) if the price of CO_2 compensation certificates were 10 €/tonne CO_2?

9

Life-cycle energy analysis

Developed in the 1970s, life-cycle energy analysis was one of the first forms of energy analysis. Life-cycle energy analysis is concerned with the question how much *primary energy* is required to deliver a certain function, like the production of a certain material, or the delivery of a specific product or service.

In fact this question is an extension of the question posed in the previous chapter. There, we discussed how much primary energy is needed for final energy use. Here, we go a step further and talk about how much primary energy is needed to deliver specific products and services.

At present, life-cycle energy analysis can be considered as a part of the broader discipline of environmental life-cycle assessment (LCA). As LCA has become a dominant tool for determining the environmental impact of products and services, we discuss this approach first in Section 9.1. The subsequent sections treat three different approaches in life-cycle energy analysis: one based on process analysis (9.2), one based on economic input-output analysis (9.3), and one that combines both (9.4).

9.1   The systematic approach in environmental life-cycle assessment

Life-cycle assessment or life-cycle analysis (LCA) has developed since 1990 as a methodology for the comparative environmental assessment of products and services. The methodologies are standardized, and several countries have national guidelines for performing life-cycle assessment in addition to ISO standards.

LCA is usually divided into four phases (see Figure 9.1):
1. goal and scope definition;
2. inventory analysis;
3. impact assessment; and
4. interpretation.

1. *Goal and scope definition.* The goal definition phase describes the reasons, the intended application, and the audience of the LCA. The most common application is comparison from an environmental point-of-view, for example comparing two or more products that are functionally equivalent (e.g., two types of floor covering). In addition, different processes that are available to produce a specific product can be compared.

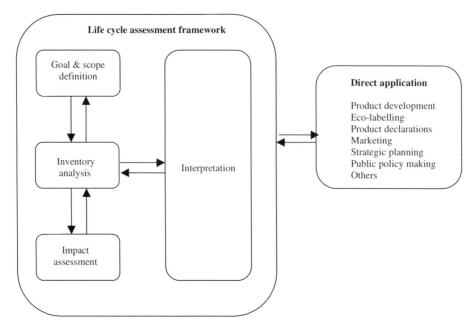

Figure 9.1. The phases of an environmental life-cycle assessment. Source: ISO 14040.

The scope definition specifies the main characteristics of an LCA, whether it be temporal, geographic or technological. A particular product can provide different services and a given service can be provided by different products. Since the object studied in an LCA is actually a product service, rather than a product itself, it is important to select the *functional unit*, a measure for the service performance of a product. Proper selection of the functional unit ensures that comparison of products is made on a common basis[1]. For example, if one wants to carry out a life-cycle assessment of floor coverings, one may choose one square meter of floor covering as the functional unit, comparing one square meter of vinyl floor covering with one square meter of linoleum floor covering. However, linoleum has a longer lifetime than vinyl, so a better definition of the functional unit would be the floor covering required per square meter of floor area for a period of ten years.

Another important activity within this phase is the definition of the system boundaries: which of the activities needed for the production, use and disposal of the product are included in the assessment. This is determined by such things as the goal of the assessment and the required accuracy.

2. *Inventory analysis.* The life-cycle of a product usually consists of four stages:
- Resource extraction and processing of raw materials;

---

[1] Note that this concept has some relation to 'energy function' (Chapter 3). However, the concept 'energy function' is not only used for final product services, but also for intermediate services (e.g. heating), which are often considered merely as input for the final services in environmental life-cycle assessment.

146

- Product manufacture;
- Distribution and use of the product; and
- Processing of the disposed product.

In each of these stages, natural resources may be consumed, and harmful substances may be released to the environment. These are referred to as environmental interventions.

Each stage may consist of a number of processes, which can provide output to one or more subsequent processes. Each input can be followed upstream to its origins and each output downstream to its final end. The sum of the connected processes is called the product system, process tree, or life cycle. The system boundaries determine which processes are included in the LCA.

In the inventory analysis, the environmental interventions (resource extractions, harmful emissions) are determined for each of the processes included in the analysis.

3. *Impact assessment.* The third part of a life-cycle assessment is the *impact assessment.* Environmental interventions may have different effects, and several categories of environmental effects can be distinguished, like climate change, resource depletion, acid deposition, and human toxicity. These are called impact categories.

In this phase, the contributions of environmental interventions to the various environmental impact categories are determined. For example, emissions of sulphur dioxide and nitrogen oxides are summed together in order to determine their total impact on soil acidification. This is not a simple summation of the mass of material emitted, as a tonne of SO_2 causes the release of a different amount of H^+ than a tonne of NO_x. The place of deposition also affects the impact. There are various approaches, ranging from simple to sophisticated, to weigh the various contributions to an impact category. For energy use, climate change is an important environmental effect, and so-called global-warming-potentials are used as a weight factor (see Table 9.1).

4. *Interpretation.* The final phase of a life-cycle assessment is the *interpretation.* The often huge amount of quantitative material is combined to draw conclusions, for example which product is preferable from an environmental point-of-view. The next step can be a life-cycle improvement analysis that systematically goes through the life cycle of the product in order to identify opportunities to reduce the environmental impacts.

Energy use, including primary energy use, is generally not considered as a separate environmental impact category. However, resource depletion is often considered as an impact category, but using different weighing factors: the primary energy used can not simply be summed together on the basis of the energy content[2]. Nevertheless, primary

---

[2] The most common approach in environmental life-cycle assessment is to use the inverse of the ultimate resources as a weighing factor. For instance, the ultimate resources of coal are much larger than those of crude oil. Hence,

energy use is a clear quantity for characterizing the life-cycle of a product and is an important indicator for a range of environmental problems. Life-cycle energy analysis remains an important tool, whether employed by itself, or as part of an environmental life-cycle assessment.

Table 9.1. Global warming potentials (GWPs) for a number of gases. The global warming potentials are a measure of the radiative forcing caused by the emission of one unit mass of the substance relative to the radiative forcing caused by the emission of one unit mass of carbon dioxide. In this table, global warming potentials are listed for a time horizon of 100 years – i.e., the radiative forcing is integrated over a period of a hundred years. The values include both direct and indirect effects, such as the formation of other substances (like ozone) that also cause radiative forcing. The 1996 figures are relevant, as they were included in the Kyoto Protocol in 1997. The 2001 figures represent the state-of-the-art of scientific understanding. Source: Houghton et al., 2001.

Substance		GWP	
		1996	2001
Carbon dioxide	CO_2	1	1
Methane	CH_4	21	23
Nitrous oxide	N_2O	310	296
Hydrofluorocarbons (HFCs)		140 – 11,700	120 – 12,000
Perfluorocarbons (PFCs)	CF_4	6,500	5,700
	C_2F_6	9,200	11,900
Sulphur hexafluoride	SF_6	23,900	22,200

9.2   Process energy analysis

Before discussing process energy analysis, some definitions are in order. Some older definitions are sometimes used:

- Process Energy Requirement (PER): the sum of the direct and indirect amounts of energy that is required to keep the process operational. Hence, this includes the direct energy use plus the energy conversion losses that occur in the energy supply system (power plants, refineries, etc.).
- Gross Energy Requirement (GER) is defined as the total energy (or enthalpy) that is released from naturally occurring energy sources and consumed in the system in order to maintain the system in production. In other words, the GER of a product or service is the PER of the process that delivers the product plus the PER values of all the upstream processes that provide input to the process. In this case, both the direct energy use and the energy conversion losses that occur in the energy supply system (power plants, refineries, etc.) are included.

---

for the same amount of primary energy, the use of oil products weighs heavier in the impact category 'resource depletion' than the use of coal products.

Cumulative energy demand (CED) is the term currently used most often. The term is used in two different ways:

- First, a cradle-to-factory-gate approach. In this case, the definition is the same as that of the GER.
- Second, a cradle-to-grave approach. In this case the full life-cycle is taken into account, including the energy consumed during utilization and eventual disposal.

In many cases it is not necessary to take the full life-cycle into account, for example when comparing two products that have the same energy use in the utilization and disposal phases. Nevertheless, it is always wise to check how the term cumulative energy demand is being used.

Process energy analysis examines the energy use of a process in detail. The production is broken down into different stages, and complex processes are broken down into a series of more simple ones. An energy and material balance is composed for each process, and the energy use is determined as closely as possible, based on the physical or chemical processes that occur during production or use. All inputs into the processes are taken into account:

- direct energy inputs;
- feedstock materials and other consumables; and
- capital goods.

In addition, the energy use associated with labour might also be included. However, it is argued that in industrialised societies the contribution of energy use associated with labour inputs is so small that it can be neglected.

To illustrate process energy analysis, let us consider the production of aluminium. Generally, the analysis is done in such a way that the output of the process delivers exactly one standard unit of product, in this case one tonne of aluminium. How much energy is required to produce 1 tonne of aluminium?

The first step is to map all the relevant upstream production chains for aluminium. The production of aluminium starts with the mining of bauxite. Bauxite is converted to alumina (Al_2O_3) using the so-called Bayer process, after which the alumina is converted to aluminium using an electrochemical reduction process. Process analysis asks how much energy is used in each step of the complete production process. In addition, other feedstocks are used. In the Bayer process, these are NaOH (caustic soda) and steam, and in the electrochemical process, cryolite and carbon electrodes are used, in addition to alumina. Clearly, the production of all these inputs requires energy.

The analysis follows the production chains back, and stops when a primary feedstock is reached that is extracted from the Earth.

The next step is to determine the process energy requirement (PER) for each of the processes. The direct energy use of the various processes can be derived in various ways:

- it can be derived from data provided by companies;
- it can be calculated on the basis of the equipment used in the process and the energy consumption data for this equipment;
- it may be possible to measure it directly; or
- it can be derived from statistical data, if they are sufficiently detailed (in general this method will be less reliable, but it may be acceptable for small contributions).

The energy use for remaining issues, such as capital goods and overhead costs, can be determined by using energy intensity coefficients derived from input-output analysis (see Section 9.3).

The data gathered in a process energy analysis can subsequently be visualised using symbols (see Figure 9.2). In Figure 9.3, these symbols are used to map the results of the process energy analysis for aluminium production. From this figure, we can read that the following are needed to produce 1 tonne of aluminium:

- tonnes bauxite
- 0.23 tonne NaOH
- 6.60 tonnes steam
- 0.04 tonne cryolite
- 1 tonne carbon electrodes

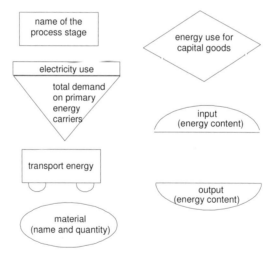

Figure 9.2. The symbols used for process energy analysis as recommended by the International Federation of Institutes of Advanced Study (IFIAS). The energy use figures present the primary energy requirements associated with the various energy carriers, both for electricity and fuels.

In Figure 9.3 we can see that the electricity input to the electrolysis process is one of the main primary energy requirements in aluminium production (54 GJ of electricity, which is responsible for most of the 216 GJ primary energy per tonne of aluminium). The energy use for capital goods is estimated on the basis of input/output-analysis (see next section). The contribution of capital goods to the CED is neglected, with the exception of the capital goods needed for electrolysis. The energy requirement for the production of caustic soda and cryolite is also neglected. The cumulative energy demand for the production of aluminium is thus the sum of all the individual contributions: 352 GJ (modern processes are more efficient, see Table 9.2).

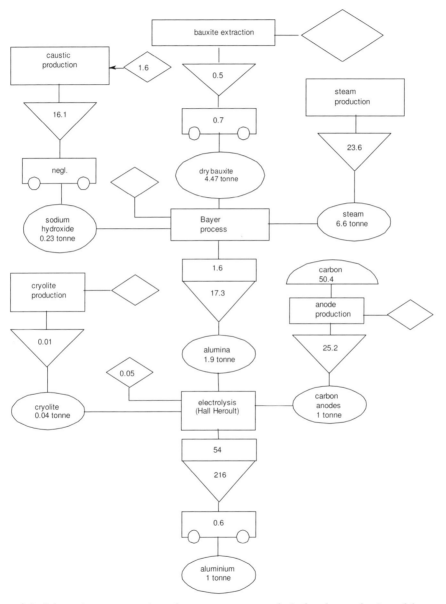

Figure 9.3. Schematic representation of process energy analysis for the production of 1 tonne of aluminium (in GJ). Electricity use is reported in GJ primary energy.

Process energy analysis has been widely used to estimate the cumulative energy demand of different materials (see for example Table 9.2). Since the values of the cumulative energy demand develop over time, it is always important to check whether more recent figures are available or should be derived for a specific purpose.

Table 9.2. Figures for the cumulative energy demand (CED) of a number of important materials. The figures are typically valid for Western Europe. For materials that use wood as a feedstock, one may or may not consider wood as an energy carrier (see discussion in Section 2.3). For those materials, this table gives both the values excluding and including the energy content of the wood feedstocks. Source: Worrell et al., 1994.

Material	CED (GJ/tonne)	Material	CED (GJ/tonne)
Steel – slabs	19.9	Portland clinker	4.0
Steel – hot rolled	22.7	Portland cement	3.9
Steel – cold rolled	25.2	Fly-ash cement	3.6
Aluminium	187.1	Blast furnace cement	2.5
Copper	82.8	Bricks	3.0
Ethylene	60.6	Container glass	8.1
Propylene	60.6	Limestone bricks	0.7
Butadiene	66.6	Sand and gravel	0.1
Benzene	63.0	Broken gravel	0.3
Polyethylene	67.8	European softwood	2.7 / 32.6
Polypropylene	63.2	European hardwood	5.4 / 35.3
Polyvinyl chloride	52.4	Tropical hardwood	6.4 / 36.3
Polystyrene	82.7	Chipboard	10.2 / 19.5
Polyethylene terephtalate (PET)	78.2	Plywood	13.9 / 37.4
Acrylonitrile butadiene styrene (ABS)	79.9	Ammonia	34.0
Styrene butadiene rubber (SBR)	77.5	Urea	22.4
Printing paper	12.9 / 39.0	Nitric acid	7.1
Packaging paper	12.2 / 20.4	Ammonium nitrate	11.7
Newsprint paper	18.9 / 25.2	Calcium ammonium nitrate (CAN)	10.3
Sanitary paper	12.7 / 19.3	Phosphoric acid	6.7
Corrugated board[3]	13.2 / 13.2	Potash fertilizer	0.9
Folding board	14.1 / 19.7	NPK compound fertilizer	11.2

---

[3] Both values are the same, as it is assumed that the feedstock is 100% secondary paper.

9.3   Input-output energy analysis

Process energy analysis follows the flows of mate   uch
primary energy is required to deliver a certain prod   ssed
in physical terms, like tonnes of material. Input-ou   but
now the flows are expressed in monetary terms. Or   ctor
produces something, how much primary energ   eam
activities?

The result is generally expressed as the energy intensity (or cumulative energy intensity) of
the output of this sector: the primary energy requirement per unit of monetary output.
Input-output analysis is widely used by economists to analyse policy issues, such as the
effect changing government investments might have on employment and gross domestic
product.

What are input-output statistics?

One way to describe an economy is to map all the deliveries between each producer, trader
and consumer. To do this would require an enormous amount of data and would be hardly
manageable. A useful summary of all these deliveries can be made in the form of a so-
called input-output table. Here, the economy is broken down into a number of sectors (say,
60) and all the deliveries between these sectors are mapped.

What deliveries occur in an economy? First of all, there are the final deliveries: products
are delivered to the final consumers. These deliveries can be to households, companies, and
the government, but they also include investments, exports and stockpiling. Second, there
are the intermediate deliveries: companies deliver goods and services to each other. These
are deliveries that are needed in order to produce other products: e.g., feedstock materials,
parts of products, production equipment, office supplies, maintenance services and security.
Finally, there are imports: some of the products originate from abroad. Both companies and
final consumers import products. Of course, other expenditures of companies also need to
be described: depreciation on investments, salaries, taxes and profits.

An input-output table for an economy is organized by sector. If an input-output table is
broken down into n sectors (typically n = 60), the core of the input-output table is an n by n
matrix, in which each cell describes the deliveries between two particular sectors. On the
lines (the rows) one finds the supplying sectors, in the columns the receiving sectors (both
make up the same sets of sectors). So, at the intersection of row i and column j, one would
find the monetary value of the goods and services that are delivered from companies in
sector i to companies in sector j. Additional rows and columns of size n are used to describe
final deliveries, imports and exports and the other cost components of companies.

Input-output analysis

To get accustomed to the input-output approach, here is a fictitious economy, consisting of three sectors and only households as final consumer. The three sectors are basic metal production, electrotechnical industry and the machinery industry. The I/O table could look as follows:

Table 9.3. I/O-table of a simplified economy (in million Euros).

		1	2	3	4	5
		Basic metal industry	Electrotech-nical industry	Machinery industry	Households	Total
1	Basic metal industry	784	217	135	2	1138
2	Electrotechnical industry	32	737	234	1066	2069
3	Machinery industry	300	89	160	4271	4820
4	Added value	22	1026	4291	0	5339
5	Total	1138	2069	4820	5339	13366

In this example, the basic metal industry delivers products worth 217 million Euros to the electrotechnical industry and the machinery industry delivers products worth 4271 million Euros to the households. The intermediate deliveries (columns 1 to 3 and rows 1 to 3) form the core matrix of intermediate deliveries that we will call **D** in the following. Table 9.3 can be written in a more general way:

Table 9.4. General representation of an I/O table.

		1	2	3		
		Basic metal industry	Electrotech-nical industry	Machinery industry	Final deliveries	Total
1	Basic metal industry	d_{11}	d_{12}	d_{13}	f_1	x_1
2	Electrotechnical industry	d_{21}	d_{22}	d_{23}	f_2	x_2
3	Machinery industry	d_{31}	d_{32}	d_{33}	f_3	x_3
	Added value	w_1	w_2	w_3		
	Total	x_1	x_2	x_3		

Legend:
d_{ij} = the deliveries from sector i to j
f_i = the final deliveries from sector i to the end users (including export)
w_i = the added value from sector i (added value is the total of sales minus the total of purchases; added value can be used to pay salaries and dividends, etc.)
x_i = the total deliveries from sector i

Note that x_i is not only the total deliveries from sector i, but also the total input (including added value) of sector i. Thus:

$$x_i = \sum_{j=1}^{n} d_{ij} + f_i = \sum_{k=1}^{n} d_{ki} + w_i \qquad [9.1]$$

In our example, the total deliveries of the basic metal industry, $x_1 = 784 + 217 + 135 + 2 = 1138$ M€. To produce these deliveries, an equal input of 1138 M€, including the added value, was needed ($x_1 = 784 + 32 + 300 + 22 = 1138$).

Ultimately, we are interested in the energy that is used to deliver the products. To this end, we need to know what activities are generated when something is delivered. Let us consider a concrete purchase in more detail. Assume that a household purchases a product of the electrotechnical industry that costs 1 Euro – e.g., a light bulb. First of all, this generates a delivery (and associated activity) by the electrotechnical industry itself, which we call the zero-order delivery: if the consumer spends one Euro, the electrotechnical industry has to deliver one Euro[4].

The electrotechnical industry cannot produce the light bulb out of thin air; it has to purchase materials, machinery or services from other sectors. To determine these indirect deliveries, we use the input-output table, and derive a so-called technology matrix, **A**. The technology matrix does not represent the total deliveries between the sectors, but the deliveries that are needed per unit of total output (i.e., per Euro of output). Hence, each value in the core matrix **D** is divided by the total delivery (row 5 in Table 9.3). In our simplified case, the technology matrix is a 3 x 3 matrix:

$$\mathbf{A} = \begin{bmatrix} 0.689 & 0.105 & 0.028 \\ 0.028 & 0.356 & 0.049 \\ 0.264 & 0.043 & 0.033 \end{bmatrix} \qquad [9.2]$$

In the formal way this is written as:

$$a_{ij} = \frac{d_{ij}}{x_j} \qquad [9.3]$$

E.g. $a_{13} = d_{13}/x_3 = 135/4820 = 0.028$.

In each column we can see the purchases producers in that sector need to make to deliver a product with a value of one Euro. Column two represents the purchases by the electrotechnical industry: if we buy a light bulb of one Euro, this sector needs to spend 0.105 Euro in the basic metal industry, 0.356 Euro in the electrotechnical industry, and 0.043 Euro in the machinery industry. These are called the first order deliveries.

---

[4] Note that this example is very simplified; among other things, the retail sector has been omitted.

In fact this outcome can be considered as the result of the multiplication of the matrix **A** with the vector $\begin{pmatrix} 0 \\ 1 \\ 0 \end{pmatrix}$, where the latter vector represents the purchase of 1 Euro from the electrotechnical industry. This vector is called the extra final deliveries and is represented by **ΔF**.

This is not the end of the story. If the electrotechnical industry purchases 0.105 Euro from the basic metal industry, this sector in turn needs to purchase 0.105 x 0.689 Euro from the basic metal industry, 0.105 x 0.028 Euro from the electrotechnical industry, and 0.105 x 0.264 Euro from the machinery industry. These are called the second order deliveries. They can be represented as: **A·A·** $\begin{pmatrix} 0 \\ 1 \\ 0 \end{pmatrix}$ or more generally as **A·A·ΔF**.

To make a long story short: for our simple light bulb purchase, there are also third order deliveries, fourth order deliveries, and so on. The total deliveries by the sectors such that one Euro is delivered by the electrotechnical industry is:

$$[\,\mathbf{I} + \mathbf{A} + \mathbf{A}^2 + \mathbf{A}^3 + \mathbf{A}^4 + \mathbf{A}^5 + \dots\,] \cdot \begin{pmatrix} 0 \\ 1 \\ 0 \end{pmatrix} \qquad [9.4]$$

Note that the unit matrix **I** (with 1 on the main diagonal from upper left to lower right and 0 in all the other places) represents the zero-order deliveries.

The sum of the series of matrices $\mathbf{I} + \mathbf{A} + \mathbf{A}^2 + \dots$ is called **P**. From matrix algebra, we know that the sum of the series of matrices can – under certain conditions – be replaced by a simple expression:

$$\mathbf{P} = \mathbf{I} + \mathbf{A} + \mathbf{A}^2 + \mathbf{A}^3 + \mathbf{A}^4 + \mathbf{A}^5 + \dots = (\mathbf{I} - \mathbf{A})^{-1} \qquad [9.5]$$

For our simplified case, the matrix **P** gets the following form[5]:

$$\mathbf{P} = \begin{bmatrix} 3.37 & 0.56 & 0.13 \\ 0.22 & 1.59 & 0.09 \\ 0.93 & 0.22 & 1.07 \end{bmatrix} \qquad [9.6]$$

---

[5] Spreadsheet computer programmes, like Excel, contain functions for matrix operations.

The matrix **P** is called the Leontief inverse, after the economist W. Leontief who played a key role in developing input-output analysis.

It should be clear that the figures in matrix **P** represent the total direct and indirect activities that are needed to provide a certain delivery. More precisely, the figures in a column represent how much each sector should deliver in order to provide one unit of final output for the sector associated with that column. For the case of our simple input-output table this means that if the electrotechnical industry wants to deliver 1 Euro of final product, the total of direct and indirect production needed for this delivery is 0.56 Euro by the basic metal industry, 1.59 Euro by the electrotechnical industry, and 0.22 Euro by the machinery industry. The extra (cumulative) deliveries are called **ΔX**.

This is an important result: we are now able to describe how much activity is required to supply something to a final consumer. The above calculation can be written formally as:

$$\mathbf{\Delta X} = (\mathbf{I} - \mathbf{A})^{-1} \cdot \mathbf{\Delta F} = \mathbf{P} \cdot \mathbf{\Delta F} \qquad [9.7]$$

where:
$\mathbf{\Delta X}$ = the cumulative (direct and indirect) deliveries
$\mathbf{P}$ = Leontief matrix
$\mathbf{\Delta F}$ = extra final deliveries

In the case of the light bulb:

$$\mathbf{\Delta X}_{lightbulb} = \begin{bmatrix} 3.37 & 0.56 & 0.13 \\ 0.22 & 1.59 & 0.09 \\ 0.93 & 0.22 & 1.07 \end{bmatrix} \begin{bmatrix} 0 \\ 1\,Euro \\ 0 \end{bmatrix} = \begin{bmatrix} 0.56 \\ 1.59 \\ 0.22 \end{bmatrix} \qquad [9.8]$$

Note that **P** · **F** is equal to the total deliveries **X**, as all the intermediate deliveries are allocated to the final consumers[6]: $x_1 = 3.3716 \cdot 2 + 0.5577 \cdot 1066 + 0.1257 \cdot 4271 = 1138$ M€. In matrix form we get:

$$\mathbf{X} = \begin{bmatrix} 3.3716 & 0.5577 & 0.1257 \\ 0.2173 & 1.5945 & 0.0864 \\ 0.9290 & 0.2230 & 1.0724 \end{bmatrix} \begin{bmatrix} 2 \\ 1066 \\ 4271 \end{bmatrix} = \begin{bmatrix} 1138 \\ 2069 \\ 4820 \end{bmatrix} \qquad [9.9]$$

---

[6] We have to write **P** with more decimals to avoid rounding errors.

Input-output energy analysis

We will use these findings to determine how much energy is required to deliver one unit of product. To go back to our simple economy, we know that if we purchase 1 Euro from the electrotechnical industry, this induces the production of 0.56 Euro in the basic metal industry. We now need to know how much direct energy is needed in the basic metal industry to produce this 0.56 Euro. Here, a simple last step is required: we need to add information on the total amount of energy that is needed for each of the sectors. To this end, we assume the following figures:

Table 9.5. Primary energy use figures for our simple economy.

Sector	Energy use (TJ)
Basic metal industry	25
Electrotechnical industry	4
Machinery industry	6

From this table, for each sector i we can derive the so-called direct energy intensity $\varepsilon_{dir,i}$. This is the energy use of the sector divided by its total output (found in the last column in Table 9.3). For instance, for the basic metal industry $\varepsilon_{dir,1}$ = 25 TJ / 1.138 G€ = 22 kJ/€, which means that the basic metal industry needs 22 kJ of energy to deliver 1 € of product. For the other two sectors, the figures are 1.9 kJ/€ and 1.2 kJ/€ (rounded figures). The last step in our light bulb problem is now to multiply these energy intensities with the extra activity in each sector that was generated by the light bulb purchase: 22 kJ/€ · 0.56 € + 1.9 kJ/€ · 1.59 € + 1.2 kJ/€ · 0.22 € − 15.6 kJ.

In matrix notation, this gets the following form. Note that the first vector denotes the three ratios of energy input divided by output for each sector.

$$E_{lightbulb} = \begin{bmatrix} 25TJ/1.138G€ & 4/2.069 & 6/4.820 \end{bmatrix} \begin{bmatrix} 3.37 & 0.56 & 0.13 \\ 0.22 & 1.59 & 0.09 \\ 0.93 & 0.22 & 1.07 \end{bmatrix} \begin{bmatrix} 0 \\ 1\,Euro \\ 0 \end{bmatrix}$$

$$[9.10]$$

$$E_{lightbulb} = \begin{bmatrix} 21.97kJ/€ & 1.933 & 1.24 \end{bmatrix} \begin{bmatrix} 3.37 & 0.56 & 0.13 \\ 0.22 & 1.59 & 0.09 \\ 0.93 & 0.22 & 1.07 \end{bmatrix} \begin{bmatrix} 0 \\ 1\,Euro \\ 0 \end{bmatrix}$$

Check that again $E_{lightbulb}$ = 15.6 kJ.

We can generalise our findings in the following way. Assume that we carry out a set of purchases denoted by the vector **ΔF**, where each row denotes the purchase from the sector associated with that row. We further define the vector ε_{dir} as the vector describing the direct (normalised) energy intensities of the various sectors. $\varepsilon_{dir,i}$ is the ratio E_i/X_i, where:

158

E_i = the primary energy requirement associated with the direct energy use of sector i (see Table 9.5)

X_i = the total deliveries of sector i (the total of the rows in the input-output table – e.g., column 5 in Table 9.3).

We can now describe the total extra energy ΔE required for the delivery of ΔF as:

$$\Delta E = \boldsymbol{\varepsilon}_{dir}^{t}\,(\mathbf{I} - \mathbf{A})^{-1}\,\Delta \mathbf{F} = \boldsymbol{\varepsilon}_{dir}^{t} \cdot \mathbf{P} \cdot \Delta \mathbf{F} \qquad [9.11]$$

Note that the index t for vector $\boldsymbol{\varepsilon}_{\mathbf{dir}}$ is only to denote that the vector is transposed (the vertical vector is written horizontally).

In general we are not interested in the total energy requirement, but in the specific value: the amount of energy needed per unit of purchase. This is what is called the cumulative energy intensity of production. Cumulative means that all the direct and indirect energy requirements are included in this calculation. The cumulative energy intensities can be described as a vector $\boldsymbol{\varepsilon}$, where ε_i is the cumulative energy intensities of sector i:

$$\boldsymbol{\varepsilon}_{cum}^{t} = \boldsymbol{\varepsilon}_{dir}^{t}\,(\mathbf{I} - \mathbf{A})^{-1} \qquad [9.12]$$

The cumulative energy intensities in our example are equal to:

$$\boldsymbol{\varepsilon}_{cum}^{t} = \boldsymbol{\varepsilon}_{dir}^{t}(\mathbf{I} - \mathbf{A})^{-1} = \begin{bmatrix} 25/1.138 & 4/2.069 & 6/4.820 \end{bmatrix} \begin{bmatrix} 3.37 & 0.56 & 0.13 \\ 0.22 & 1.59 & 0.09 \\ 0.93 & 0.22 & 1.07 \end{bmatrix}$$

$$\boldsymbol{\varepsilon}_{cum}^{t} = \begin{bmatrix} 75.6 & 15.6 & 4.3 \end{bmatrix} kJ\,/\,Euro \qquad [9.13]$$

$$E = \boldsymbol{\varepsilon}_{cum}^{t} \cdot \Delta \mathbf{F} \qquad [9.14]$$

We can also use $\boldsymbol{\varepsilon}_{cum}^{t}$ to calculate the total cumulative energy needed for an extra purchase:

$$E = \begin{bmatrix} 75.6 & 15.6 & 4.3 \end{bmatrix} kJ/\text{€} \cdot \begin{bmatrix} 0 \\ 1 \\ 0 \end{bmatrix} \text{€} = 15.6\,kJ \qquad [9.15]$$

But E is NOT:

$$E \neq \boldsymbol{\varepsilon}_{cum}^{t} \cdot \mathbf{X} \qquad [9.16]$$

as in this case the intermediate deliveries would be counted twice; they are included in the cumulative energy intensity $\boldsymbol{\varepsilon}_{cum}^{t}$ and in the cumulative deliveries $\mathbf{X}$.

Note that we can calculate the total energy input by multiplying the cumulative energy vector with the final demand (see column 4 of Table 9.3). We then get $E_{tot} = 75.7 \cdot 2 + 15.7 \cdot 1066 + 4.4 \cdot 4271$ (kJ/€ · M€) = 35.7 TJ. Apart from a rounding error, this is equal to the total energy input of 35 TJ (see Table 9.5).

The energy sector in input-output tables

The simple input-output tables we have used (Tables 9.3 and 9.4) do not contain an energy sector. Of course, all real input-output tables include one or more energy sectors in the core matrix. There are two ways to treat deliveries by the energy sector in energy input-output analysis:

- The first is to treat the energy sector as a normal sector. A country's energy extraction plus its energy imports are delivered to the energy sector. Through the regular I/O formalism, this energy is re-allocated to the other sectors. In practice, this means that the energy vector ε contains values representing extraction and imports. However, this approach has trouble dealing with the differences in energy prices (e.g., households often pay twice as much per kWh as large consumers of electricity). If the distribution of energy inputs were done on the basis of monetary flows, this would lead to a wrong allocation (too much primary energy use would be allocated to the households).

- The second approach takes figures from energy statistics that are directly allocated to all the sectors in the I/O table and distributes them manually. This is the approach described above. To avoid double counting, the energy deliveries to the energy sector need to be set to zero. This approach requires some extra work, but it is more accurate. Whether this accuracy gain is important, will depend on the aim of the analysis.

The accuracy of input-output energy analysis

The most important drawback of input-output analysis is its implicit assumption that all deliveries between sectors are homogeneous, which is not always the case. For example, we have seen that the energy sector prices volumes of electricity differently. Another example is where the chemical industry is considered as one sector in an input-output table. This sector produces both feedstocks for plastic (like polyethylene) and pharmaceuticals. The first requires very energy-intensive feedstocks from refineries, whereas the second uses high-value low energy-intensity materials. Aggregating the various outputs of the chemical industry as one group of deliveries may lead to senseless results.

This problem makes input-output energy analysis less suitable for detailed analysis (e.g., of individual products), than for getting an overall picture. Furthermore, input-output analysis may be useful in combination with process energy analysis (see the next section).

Another complication is that the input-output tables are based on the average technology mix in use in an economy. Deliveries for new technologies or new products can differ significantly from average purchases or investments.

9.4 Hybrid methods of process and input-output analysis

Both process energy analysis and input-output energy analysis have their strong and weak points. Process energy analysis is very accurate, but it is difficult to include the whole product cycle. Input-output energy analysis covers all indirect deliveries, but is less precise. Sometimes it is useful to combine both.

A hybrid method will be described in this section. The basic idea behind this method is that the big chunks of the energy requirement are estimated using process energy analysis and that the remaining, less important parts are estimated with input-output energy analysis. Experience teaches us that the production of basic intermediate materials often makes up an important part of a product's total energy requirement. This leads to the design of the hybrid method, which method consists of two parts. First, a flow chart of the production network has to be made. For this, both a mass balance and a financial balance of the product have to be determined (process energy analysis and energy input-output analysis each need only one of these balances). Second, the energy requirements of the various activities in the production network are determined, sometimes using process energy analysis data, in other cases using the input-output approach. The various contributions made by the activities to the energy requirement are added together.

Mass and monetary balances

The first step is to make a flow chart of the production chain and to select the functional unit. The functional unit is the (physical) unit of the product being studied. The flow chart should include all the activities that are expected to make an important contribution to the energy requirement. This flow chart will usually include four activities: production, trade and transport, consumption, and waste disposal (see Figure 9.4). When using the hybrid method, it is important to select the so-called *basic materials*: materials that are expected to play an important role in the energy requirement over the complete life cycle of the product. One can achieve greater accuracy by making a more detailed flow chart and by selecting more basic materials, but this also increases the amount of work involved.

The next step is to compile a mass balance for each of the basic materials selected in the first step. In many cases, a fairly accurate estimate of the total amount of basic materials can be made on the basis of the product's composition. Of course, if there is a considerable loss of material during production, this loss needs to be taken into account. Special attention should be paid to packaging materials.

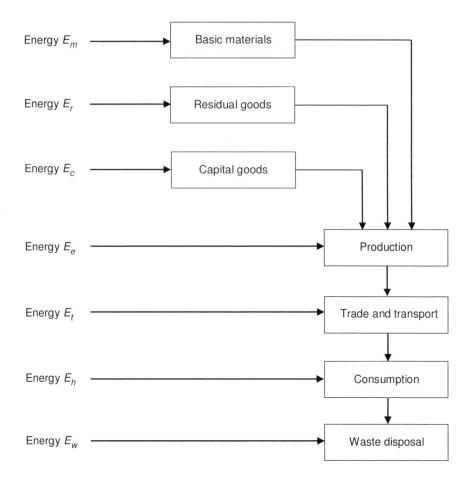

Figure 9.4. The life-cycle of a product according to the hybrid method. Source: K. Vringer: Analysis of the Energy Requirement for Household Consumption, PhD thesis, Utrecht University, 2005.

The third step is to determine the financial balance for the product. The retail price of the product must be broken down into the following components:

- the trade margin (including taxes);
- the costs of the basic materials that are purchased by the manufacturer;
- the costs of the direct energy required to manufacture the product;
- the depreciation incurred by the manufacturer;
- the added value (excluding depreciation) realised by the manufacturer; and
- the purchase of residual goods by the manufacturer.

These figures can be obtained from the manufacturer or from the trade sector involved in producing and selling the product. Otherwise, an approximation can be obtained in the following way. First of all, one determines an average product price, using information provided by retailers, retailers' associations, or consumer's groups. The cost of basic materials is determined on the basis of the mass balance, combined with the specific costs for the various materials, expressed as costs per kg. From national statistical data (e.g., production statistics and input-output tables), one can obtain sector-averaged values for the trade margin, depreciation, and the added value. The remaining costs are attributed to the final entry, so-called *residual goods.*

Determining energy requirement

If the mass and monetary balances are known, the determination of the total energy requirement is relatively straightforward.

Process inputs. The cumulative energy required for producing the input materials for the production process is determined as follows, where the primary energy demand is determined for basic materials (E_m), for capital goods (E_c), and for residual goods (E_r):

$$E_m = \sum_{i=1}^{n} M_i \cdot CED_i \qquad [9.17a]$$

$$E_r = C_r \cdot \varepsilon_{r,k} \qquad [9.17b]$$

$$E_c = C_c \cdot \varepsilon_c \qquad [9.17c]$$

where:

M_i = the total net use (in the whole production network) of basic material i (in kg)

CED_i = the cumulative energy demand of material i (in MJ/kg)

n = the number of basic materials selected in step one

C_r = the costs of residual goods (including services) purchased by the manufacturing sector (in €)

$\varepsilon_{r,k}$ = the energy intensity of the residual goods as purchased by sector k (the sector under study) – i.e., the energy requirement per financial unit purchased (in MJ/€)

C_c = the depreciation incurred by the manufacturing sector in question (in €)

ε_c = the energy intensity of the capital goods supplied to all the sectors – i.e., the cumulative energy requirement per unit of investment (in MJ/€)

M_i, C_r and C_c are all expressed per functional unit.

The energy intensity of residual goods $\varepsilon_{r,k}$ requires some explanation. It is determined by applying input-output analysis. However, this approach has to be modified, since the energy requirements of the basic materials have already been taken into account, and have to be omitted from the analysis. The sectors that produce the selected basic materials are 'neglected', by setting the direct energy requirement of these sectors to zero. Subsequently, an energy I/O analysis can be carried out as described in section 9.3. Capital goods need to be treated separately from the other inputs, following the convention in input-output tables published by national bureaus of statistics, where all capital goods for the entire economy are lumped together and treated separately.

The production process. The energy needed for the production process E_e is determined:

$$E_e = \sum_{i=1}^{n} E_i \cdot ERE_i \qquad [9.17d]$$

where:

E_i = the total demand for energy carrier i to produce one functional unit (in MJ) (preferably determined by process energy analysis);

ERE_i = Energy Requirement for Energy: the demand made on primary energy carriers associated with the delivery of one unit of energy carrier i (in MJ/MJ);

n = the number of energy carriers involved in manufacturing the product.

Transport and trade. The primary energy demand that wholesale and retail trade (E_{trade}) and the various forms of freight transport ($E_{transport}$) require is calculated by:

$$E_{transport} = \sum_{i=1}^{n} M_i \cdot d_i \cdot SEC_i \cdot ERE_i \qquad [9.17e]$$

$$E_{trade} = \sum_{i=1}^{m} T_i \cdot \varepsilon_i \qquad [9.17f]$$

where:

M_i = the total mass to be transported by mode of transport i (in kg) in order to supply one functional unit

d_i = the distance covered by transportation mode i (in km)

SEC_i = the specific energy requirement of transport mode i (in MJ/kg-km)

ERE_i = the demand made on primary energy carriers for the delivery of the direct energy carrier used by transport mode i (in MJ/MJ)

n = the number of transport modes used

T_i = the trade margin of trade sector i associated with one functional unit (in €)

ε_i = the energy intensity of trade sector i – i.e., the demand made on primary energy carriers per unit of value added (in MJ/€)

m = the number of trade sectors involved in delivering the product

Energy in the use phase. Some products, such as cars, refrigerators and cookers, require an energy E_h when used:

$$n$$
$$E_h = \sum_{i=1} E_i \cdot ERE_i \qquad\qquad [9.17g]$$

where:

E_i = the total demand made on energy carriers i *during the whole lifetime* of one functional unit (in MJ)

ERE_i = the demand made on primary energy carriers for the delivery of energy carrier i (in MJ/MJ)

n = the number of energy carriers involved in the use of the product

Waste disposal. Waste disposal can consume energy, for instance in connection with collection and transport. But disposal can also yield energy if the materials are recycled or incinerated. The energy requirement (E_w) associated with waste disposal is calculated as follows:

$$n$$
$$E_w = M_{tot} \cdot E_{ctt} + M_d \cdot E_d - \sum_{i=1} M_i \cdot \Delta CED_i \qquad\qquad [9.17h]$$

where:

M_{tot} = the total mass to be transported to the disposal/recycling unit (in kg) per functional unit

E_{ctt} = the demand made on primary energy carriers associated with the collection, transhipment and transport of waste (in MJ/kg)

M_d = the mass to be disposed of (in kg) per functional unit

E_d = the demand made on primary energy carriers associated with the disposal of the waste per unit of disposal (in MJ/kg): this value can be negative if useful energy is produced, such as in the case of refuse incineration

M_i = the mass of material i that is recycled (in kg per functional unit)

ΔCED_i = the primary energy saved due to the recycling of the waste per unit of recycled waste of material i (in MJ/kg)

n = the number of materials that are recycled

Finally, the amounts of primary energy demand calculated through equations [17a-h] is summed together and provides the total energy use. As can be seen from the description, a lot of data are required to determine a product's cumulative energy. However, much of this data is the same for all products, and can to a large extent be standardized. For a specific product, all we need to determine is the material balance, some cost data, and some specific data on energy use in production and use. An example of the application of the hybrid method is given in Box 9.1.

Box 9.1. Example of the application of the hybrid method.

The financial and material balance for one refrigerator turns out to be as follows:

Cost component	Cost (€)
Basic materials: 0.9 kg steel, 1.4 kg aluminium, 0.7 kg polyethylene, 3.6 kg polyurethane, 1.6 kg copper, 0.9 kg cardboard, 1 kg polystyrene, 0.4 kg wood	43
Energy for manufacturing	1
Depreciation in manufacturing	8
Value added	67
Retail margin	130
Residual goods (= rest)	57

Input-output analysis indicates that the energy intensity of residual goods is 5.7 MJ/€. This is the energy intensity of the electrotechnical industry, when the energy input of the sectors that produce the primary materials is neglected.

With some additional assumptions about energy intensity of materials, capital goods, the retail sector and transport, the following energy requirement is determined:

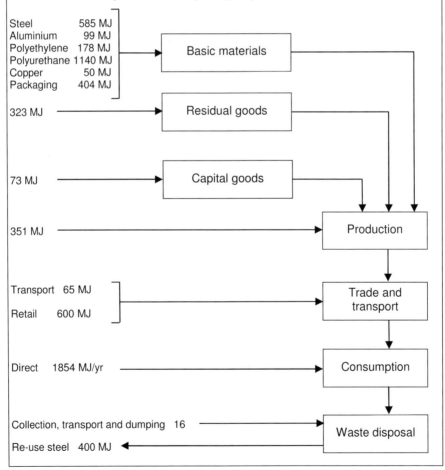

Further reading

I. Boustead and G.F. Hancock, Handbook of Industrial Energy Analysis, Ellis Horwood, Chichester, UK, 1979.

C.W. Bullard, R.A. Herendeen: The Energy Costs of Goods and Services, Energy Policy, 3 (1975) pp. 268-278.

C.W. Bullard, P.S. Penner, D.A. Pilati: Net Energy Analysis – Handbook for Combining Process and Input-Output Analysis, Resources and Energy, 1 (1978) pp. 267-313.

B.C.W. van Engelenburg, T.F.M. van Rossum, K. Blok, K. Vringer: Calculating the Energy Requirements of Household Purchases - a Practical Step by Step Method, Energy Policy, 22 (1994) pp. 648-656.

J.B. Guinée (ed.): Handbook on Life-Cycle Assessment - Operational Guide to the ISO Standards, Springer, Berlin, 2002. Available for inspection at: http://www.leidenuniv.nl/cml/ssp/projects/lca2/lca2.html

J.T. Houghton, Y. Ding, D.J. Griggs, M. Noguer, P.J. van der Linden, X. Dai, K. Maskell, C.A. Johnson: Climate Change 2001: The Scientific Basis, Cambridge University Press, Cambridge, UK, 2001. (Section 6.12 is on Global Warming Potentials)

M.A.J. Huijbregts, L.J.A. Rombouts, S. Hellweg, R. Frischknecht, A.J. Hendriks, D. van de Meent, A.M.J. Ragas, L. Reijnders, J. Struijs: Is Cumulative Energy Demand a Useful Indicator for the Environmental Performance of Products?, Environmental Science and Technology 40 (2006) pp. 641-648.

IFIAS (International Federation of Institutes for Advanced Studies), Report of the workshop on Energy Analysis, Guldsmedshyttan, Sweden, 1974. Also published in: Energy and Resources, 1 (1978) 151-204.

ISO 14040: Environmental Management - Life Cycle Assessment - Principles and Framework, International Organization for Standardization (ISO), 1997. Other relevant standards are ISO 14041 - 14043.

E. Worrell, R.J.J. van Heijningen, J.F.M. de Castro, J.H.O. Hazewinkel, J.G. de Beer, A.P.C. Faaij, K. Vringer: New Gross Energy-Requirement Figures for Materials Production, Energy, the International Journal, 19 (1994) pp. 627-640.

A database with figures for environmental impact assessment is available from the German Ministry of Environment and the Öko-Institut at:
www.probas.umweltbundesamt.de (in German)

Final achievement levels

After having studied Chapter 9 and the exercises, you should:
- be able to describe the general procedure in life-cycle assessment;
- be able to formulate a goal, functional unit and system boundaries for a life-cycle assessment;
- know the concept of cumulative energy demand (CED) and be able to design the procedure for determining the CED for a given product;
- be able to explain the elements of an input-output table;

- understand how input-output analysis for life-cycle energy analysis works and be able to carry out such an analysis for a simple system; and
- be able to explain the advantages of combining process energy analysis and input-output energy analysis.

Exercises Chapter 9

9.1. Definition of functional units
In a certain LCA, two products/services are compared. For each of the following pairs, define a functional unit:
a. milk in a plastic bottle or in a cardboard container
b. a wooden and a metal bookshelf;
c. a traditional light bulb and a compact fluorescent lamp (CFL); and
d. travelling by car and by public transport.

9.2 Life-cycle assessment
Assume that you have to make an environmental life-cycle assessment of tables (for use at home).
a. Give a possible goal definition.
b. Give a (possible) definition of the functional unit.
c. Provide a possible scope description.
d. Sketch the life-cycle for one or two types of tables.

9.3. Cumulative energy demand of glass bottles
The raw materials needed to produce glass are 60% sand (SiO_2), 20% soda (Na_2CO_3) and 20% limestone ($CaCO_3$). Small amounts of other additives are neglected. The energy requirements for the production of these raw materials are:
- sand: 83 MJ/tonne, mainly for extraction; neglect transport distance.
- soda: energy use is 1.5 GJ/tonne for the extraction of salt and the fabrication of soda (the electricity use for this process is 0.5 GJ/tonne and natural gas use is 1.0 GJ/tonne); the soda is transported per truck over a distance of 100 km;
- limestone: 17.8 MJ diesel oil/tonne for the extraction, 1.25 MJ explosives/tonne, 1.75 kWh/ton for the breaking of the limestone into small pieces, the limestone is transported by ship over a distance of 150 km.

Out of 1.2 kg of these raw materials, 1.0 kg of glass is produced. But glass can also be produced from recycled material. These glass pieces are called "cullet"; 1 tonne cullet results in 1 tonne glass. We assume furnaces that have an average load of 85% cullet and 15% raw materials. In the melting furnace the mixture of raw materials is heated and converted into molten glass. The molten glass is led to a forming machine, where the glass gets its final shape (e.g. bottles) and then annealed (controlled cooling down of the products). The energy use of the furnace is 4.57 GJ/ton melted glass, of which 9% is electricity. Per tonne glass products that are produced, 0.04 tonne is rejected, because of deficiencies.

Assume an electricity production efficiency of 40% and an energy requirement for freight transportation by truck and by ship of 4 and 0.4 MJ/ton·km, respectively. Use first order values for energy carriers.
a. Depict the flow diagram for producing glass bottles and the associated energy inputs
b. Calculate the cumulative energy demand for producing glass

9.4. Plastic and aluminium in cars

Assume that a standard car has a total weight of 1200 kg, of which 200 kg is plastic (assume 100% polypropylene) and the rest is steel (assume that 50% is hot rolled and 50% is cold rolled). The average specific fuel consumption is 7 litres per 100 km, and the car is driven 15,000 km per year. Manufacturing one car out of the basic materials costs 10 GJ.

a.   Calculate the energy use of the car during the life-cycle of 12 years during which it runs 15,000 km per year. Assume that the car is completely landfilled.

b.   The standard car is redesigned and 400 kg of the steel is replaced by 100 kg of aluminium and 100 kg of polypropylene. What is the effect on the energy use for producing the car? What is the effect on life-cycle energy use? Use the rule-of-thumb in section 3.4.

c.   How much energy would be saved over the lifecycle of the redesigned car if it were fully recycled (i.e., if new cars were made out of it). Take into account the following energy use for recycling: steel: 8 MJ/kg; polypropylene: 10 MJ/kg; aluminium: 10 MJ/kg.

d.   If the choice were to recycle the polypropylene or use it for electricity production, what would be preferable (assume that conversion efficiency in this case is 30% and that it replaces coal-fired power plants). Assume that the energy content of polypropylene is 45 MJ/kg.

9.5. Input-output energy analysis

Consider the simple economy presented in Table 9.3.

a.   How much energy is needed to produce a metal strip of 10 € by the basic metal industry?

b.   How much energy is needed for a router-table of 3000 € produced by the machinery industry?

c.   Calculate the energy requirement for the fictitious light bulb from section 9.3 if you halve the energy consumption of the sectors separately (halve the energy consumption of each sector, while keeping the other two constant).

9.6. Orders in input-output analysis

a.   How much energy is needed to produce the light bulb in our simple economy, if you take only the direct energy into account (0-order)?

b.   Calculate also the amount of energy needed according to the 1st-order.

c.   The matrix of the 5th order $(\mathbf{I+A+}...\mathbf{+A}^5)$ and the 10th order $(\mathbf{I+A+}...\mathbf{+A}^{10})$ are as follows:

$$\begin{bmatrix} 2.937 & 0.429 & 0.099 \\ 0.160 & 1.575 & 0.083 \\ 0.758 & 0.172 & 1.061 \end{bmatrix} \qquad \begin{bmatrix} 3.292 & 0.534 & 0.126 \\ 0.207 & 1.590 & 0.088 \\ 0.898 & 0.214 & 1.073 \end{bmatrix}$$

   5th   10th

Calculate the energy requirement for the light bulb for these orders as well. What do we learn for this?

9.7. Hybrid energy analysis

For a bottle of beer, calculate the cumulative energy demand using the hybrid method. Determine as many characteristics as possible (e.g. mass, prices) and make reasonable estimates for the remaining elements of the product's life cycle (e.g., transportation distances). Data can be taken from Tables 3.3 and 9.2. All other information can be taken from the tables below.

Basic goods and packaging	Price (€/kg)	CED
Barley	0.30	4.24 MJ/kg
Water	1.95 €/m^3	5.74 MJ/m^3
Reused glass	0.04	

Manufacturing	Energy price €/GJ	Energy use per Euro turnover MJ/€
Brewery	10.28	0.96

Trade	Ratio of purchase price : selling price	Energy use per Euro turnover MJ/€
Grocery	0.777 : 1	2.29

Waste	Energy use MJ/kg
Collection and transport	0.11

Energy intensity	MJ/€
Residual goods	4.73
Capital goods	3.51

10

Measuring energy efficiency and energy intensity

The concept 'energy efficiency' was already introduced in Chapter 3. This concept is not as straightforward as it seems, and there are various complications to measuring energy efficiency, which will be treated in this chapter. First, this chapter will discuss the meaning of energy efficiency further (10.1), and provide a taxonomy of energy efficiency measures (10.2). Then, the physical energy efficiency indicators (10.3 and 10.4) and monetary indicators (10.5) are considered.

10.1 What is energy efficiency?

Striving for efficiency is trying to obtain a certain result with a minimum of input. As energy is used to fulfil human needs, one may define the energy efficiency of an activity as the degree to which given human needs can be fulfilled with a minimum amount of energy.

More practically, one may consider the efficiency of a piece of equipment. This equipment produces some uniform, measurable output P, and uses an amount of energy E. Then, energy efficiency η of the equipment can be defined as:

$$\eta = P / E \qquad\qquad [10.1]$$

For the inverse of energy efficiency, the term *specific energy consumption* (or specific energy use or unit energy consumption) is used.

$$SEC = E / P \qquad\qquad [10.2]$$

For many energy conversion processes, energy is the useful output, and the energy efficiency is the usual measure, becoming a dimensionless quantity.
For end-use applications, the specific energy consumption is usually used to indicate how 'efficient' the equipment is. The denominator depends on the type of energy function involved, so the units of specific energy consumption may be MJ/ton of product output, MJ/vehicle-km, etc.

The energy efficiency of a specific piece of equipment depends on its design and its operation. As far as it depends on the design, energy efficiency is also called the technical energy efficiency. This can be measured under uniform operation conditions, which have been specified in test protocols for many types of equipment (e.g., cars, electric appliances, power plants, electric motors, etc.). Efficiency also depends on the operation: the conditions under which the equipment is used, such as temperature and altitude, and also the behaviour of the user.

As long as the output of several pieces of equipment is the same, they can be compared with each other, and we can determine which is more or less efficient. In many cases, however, the different pieces of equipment do not have a uniform output, or we do not know whether the output is uniform. For instance, we want to determine whether the energy efficiency of steel production in a certain country has improved over time, but the mix of steel products has also changed; or we want to compare the specific fuel consumption of passenger cars in two countries, but we do not know whether cars are used comparably in the two countries.

We thus enter the area of *energy efficiency indicators*. Energy efficiency indicators are meant as approximations that give as clear a picture as possible of the aggregate energy efficiency of equipment that is operated on a number of sites, under different conditions, with non-uniform outputs. We will discuss this in the section 10.3, but first we will address the various ways energy efficiency can be improved.

10.2 Options for improving energy efficiency

Improving the energy efficiency of equipment can be achieved by an increase in the energy conversion efficiency or a decrease in the specific energy consumption. The terms *energy saving* and *energy conservation* are often used as synonyms for the term *energy efficiency improvement*. Note that improving energy efficiency does not necessarily have to lead to an absolute decrease of energy use (though the terms energy saving and energy conservation sometimes have this connotation). There is a range of technological and other options that may lead to energy efficiency improvement, including the following:

a. *Good housekeeping* improves energy efficiency through better operation of energy conversion or end-use equipment. An important category is avoiding unnecessary energy use, for example by switching off lighting in a room where nobody is present, or turning off a machine that is not producing. Good housekeeping is mainly a matter of changed behaviour, but can be supported by simple equipment (for example, fuel consumption indicators in cars, or timers that switch off the lighting in complete office floors at night and during weekends).

b. *Energy management systems* are related to the previous category, but the improved operation is automated, and hence requires some upfront investment. In general, more sophisticated control (not just on/off) is possible. Examples are building management systems and process control systems. For large industrial sites, energy management systems may provide real-time optimisation of all energy conversion and utilisation processes on the site.

c. Reduction of heat losses through surfaces is one of the most important forms of energy efficiency improvement. The insulation of walls (including windows), roofs and floors of buildings is the most well known technique. Table 10.1 provides some characteristic values of the heat transmission coefficients of various types of building envelope (see Section 3.2) and shows the progress that can be achieved by applying more and more efficient technology. Reduction of heat losses is also important in many other cases, such as in high-temperature industrial process equipment, steam pipes, district heating pipes, ovens, refrigerators, and freezers.

Table 10.1. Overview of heat transmission coefficients of various types of walls and windows.

Wall or window type	Heat transmission value (W/m^{2}K)
Single glazing	6
Double glazing	3
Argon-filled, low emissivity double glazing	1.2
Superwindows	< 1
External wall double blade, not insulated	~2.0
External wall, 6 cm insulation (mineral wool or polystyrene foam)	0.5
External wall, 15 cm insulation (mineral wool or polystyrene foam)	0.25
External wall, 15 cm vacuum insulation	~0.1

d. Heat recovery can be applied whenever a hot stream leaves a process and a cold stream enters the same process or another process simultaneously. Heat recovery requires the use of heat exchangers, and is already widely applied for continuously operating industrial processes, especially where liquids are involved. Another important application is the recovery of heat from building ventilation air. Heat recovery is more expensive for gases than liquids (due to the generally higher heat exchanger surface required per unit of heat transfer; see Section 3.3). Heat recovery is difficult in certain cases: i) extremely high temperatures, ii) from solids, and iii) media containing dirt or aggressive compounds.

e. Process integration is basically the same as heat recovery but refers to the way that all incoming and outgoing heat flows are considered in a comprehensive way, for example in power plants and complex industrial facilities. The total heat exchange system is optimised for minimum energy use, of course taking economic constraints into account. Pinch analysis is an analytical method to design such optimum networks (see Section 7.4).

f. Fuel recovery. Other energy forms than heat can also be recovered. In industrial processes, combustible gases are sometimes released; these can be captured and used as an energy source. There are important examples in the iron and steel industry, where coke oven gas, blast furnace gas and basic-oxygen-furnace gas can be recovered (and in many cases already are).

g. Power recovery can be applied where pressurized fluid media are expanded to atmospheric pressure. Expanding gases, for instance, can be used to drive a turbine.

h. Reduction of friction losses in motion can often be achieved. Probably the most important reduction of friction is the improved aerodynamic shape of cars and other vehicles (see Section 3.4). Another example is the reduction of losses in pipes that are used for the transportation of fluid media, through better design ("avoiding bottlenecks"), and the application of wider pipe diameters.

i. More efficient conversion of electric power to motion can be achieved through a range of technologies. First of all, more efficient electric motors can be applied. Although the difference in energy conversion efficiency between 'normal' and high-efficiency motors frequently does not exceed 5 – 10%, the wide use of motors still makes this a relevant option. In addition, motors often do not run at their full capacity, and the use of too large motors for a given task (over-dimensioning) should be avoided, as part-load efficiency is generally worse than full-load efficiency. Furthermore, many motors run at variable loads, for example to drive pumps, compressors, and fans. Partial load is often achieved by throttling (which increases friction) or introducing recycling loops, both of which are very energy-inefficient. Power-speed control is more efficient, with a variable frequency converter applied to the motor, allowing the motor to run at different speeds. This makes it possible to run the motor and the connected equipment at the appropriate speed for the task at hand.

j. More efficient lighting is a special category, with many options. One important option is changing the light source, especially replacing incandescent bulbs with fluorescent ones (see Table 10.2). Fixtures and lampshades that provide a better light utilisation are also important. Finally, switching off light depending on daylight and occupancy should be mentioned (though in fact this is a variation of good housekeeping or energy management).

Table 10.2. Efficiency of various light sources. The lumen is the unit of light flow.

Light source	Efficiency (lumen/W)
Fluorescent tube	65 – 100
Compact fluorescent lamp	40 – 80
Incandescent light	6 – 18
Halogen lamp	8 – 20

k. New process technologies can also improve the energy-efficiency of end-use. In many cases, there are already processes that are completely different from standard processes, with a step-change difference in energy-efficiency. In most cases, they offer substantial improvements in other performance characteristics as well (e.g., lower capital costs, higher product quality). The range of new process technologies is broad. For example, in the home and office place, cathode ray tubes in televisions and computer screens are being replaced by LCD screens. In the steel industry casting and rolling can be replaced by so-called strip casting. Traditionally, steel is first cast in thick slabs (15 – 20 cm thick) and then rolled to obtain thin strips or plates (0.1 – 2.5 cm thick). The new technology, strip casting, made possible by advanced process control systems allows the steel to be directly cast into the required thickness. This saves the energy needed for rolling and sometimes also the energy for reheating.

In addition to the options for improving end-use energy efficiency, there are also options for *conversion efficiency improvement*.

l. More efficient boilers and furnaces are important because these belong to the most important energy conversion equipment in many sectors. Boilers and furnaces are already fairly efficient. Large-scale industrial boilers (for steam raising) and furnaces (for process heat) typically have conversion efficiencies of about 90%. Nevertheless, small improvements, through better operation and maintenance, are often possible. Small-scale household boilers for space heating and hot water production typically have conversion efficiencies of about 75 – 85% (HHV). A substantial improvement can be achieved by applying condensing boilers, in which the flue gases are cooled to such a low temperature that the water vapour condenses, thus contributing to the useful heat production. Condensing boilers can achieve conversion efficiencies of 95% and more (HHV).

m. Heat pumps. As was already described in Chapter 1, the theoretical energy required to produce low-temperature heat is low, corresponding to the low exergy content (relative to the energy content) of low-temperature heat. This opportunity can be addressed by the heat pump, which extracts heat from a low temperature heat source (e.g., the environment) and delivers it at a higher temperature level. Heat pumps can also be used in industry to upgrade waste heat to a useful temperature level.

n. Combined generation of heat and power (CHP) was already described in Section 4.5.

o. More efficient conversion of fuel to power is important, both on a large scale and on a small scale. On a large scale, the improvement of the conversion efficiency of power plants is an important option, among other things through the application of gas turbines (see Chapter 4). On a small-scale, the car engine should be mentioned; as substantial improvements are still possible. New processes can also play a role here, with the hybrid car (combining a conventional engine and an electric one) and the fuel-cell car.

10.3 Energy efficiency indicators

For homogeneous activities that provide only one well-specified energy function or service, the specific energy consumption can easily be defined by measuring the energy per unit of service provided (see equation [10.2] in Section 10.1). But for activities that supply more than one energy function, we need to construct *aggregate* indicators of energy efficiency. Even to measure the specific energy use of simple household equipment like a refrigerator/freezer combination, we already need aggregation. For a simple refrigerator, one can define the specific energy use as the amount of electricity that is needed per litre volume. However, how can we compare the electricity use of a refrigerator with a small freezing compartment to that of a combination whose freezer compartment is equal in size to the refrigerator? We can still divide the electricity use by volume, but this time we need to give different weights to the compartments with the different functions. (For an elaboration, see Box 10.1.)

Box 10. 1. An energy efficiency indicator for refrigerator/freezer combinations.

We want to construct an energy efficiency indicator for a refrigerator/freezer combination. Technical analysis has shown that freezer compartments typically require 2.1 times as much electricity per unit of volume as refrigerator compartments, because of the lower temperatures in the freezer. The following energy-efficiency index provides a suitable form for the aggregate specific energy use:

$$\sigma = \frac{E}{V_r + 2.1 \cdot V_f} \qquad [10.3]$$

where:
σ = aggregate specific energy consumption (e.g., kWh/litre)
E = annual electricity consumption (under test conditions)
V_r = volume of the refrigeration compartment
V_f = volume of the freezer compartment

In practice, in addition to refrigerator and freezer volume, we also need to distinguish different temperature classes for the freezer compartment and different sizes of the equipment.

To construct energy efficiency indicators, we generally need to determine the ratio of energy over physical activity (E/P), where both E and P can be aggregate quantities. Aggregation of different energy carriers to primary energy use is not trivial, but relatively easy (see Chapter 8).

Aggregation of different forms of activity expressed in physical terms is less straightforward. In the case of industrial activity, for instance, it does not make sense to add tons of steel and tons of copper together. Nevertheless, in one or the other way, a weighted aggregate should be constructed:

$$PPI = \sum_{x=1}^{n} w_x \cdot P_x \qquad [10.4]$$

where:
PPI = the physical production index (or activity index)
P_x = the amount of production of product x
w_x = the weighting factor for product x
n = the number of products

The aggregate specific energy consumption, generally indicated by the term energy-efficiency index (EEI) or physical energy intensity, then gets the form:

$$EEI = \frac{E}{PPI} \qquad [10.5]$$

where E is the energy use and PPI the physical production index for a specific sector in a specific year (in a specific country).

An appropriate candidate value for the weighting factor w_x is the average specific energy use for the product x in a certain reference year ($SEC_{x,t0}$). (See Box 10.2.)

If we aggregate using specific energy consumption figures as weighting factors, the energy efficiency index becomes a dimensionless index. For a sector producing a range of products indicated with subscript x:

$$EEI = \frac{\sum_x SEC_x \cdot P_x}{\sum_x SEC_{ref,x} \cdot P_x} = \frac{E_{sector}}{\sum_x SEC_{ref,x} \cdot P_x} \qquad [10.7]$$

where:
P_x = the production volume for product x in a specific year/country
SEC_x = the specific energy use for product x in a specific year/country
$SEC_{ref,x}$ = the reference specific energy use for product x (e.g., $SEC_{x,t0}$)
E_{sector} = the total energy consumption of a sector in a specific year/country

The denominator term $\sum_x SEC_{ref,x} \cdot P_x$ can be considered as the energy that would have been used if the production quantities had changed, but the levels of specific energy consumption for each product had remained the same. We call this the *reference energy use* (also known as the frozen-efficiency energy use). The energy efficiency index now can be written in the following simple form, as the ratio of the actual energy use and the reference energy use:

$$EEI = E_{actual}/E_{ref} \qquad [10.8]$$

Box 10.2. Justification for the use of average specific energy consumption in a reference year as weighting factor for the energy-efficiency index.

The choice of $w_x = SEC_{x,t0}$ can be justified if we consider what happens if no energy efficiency change occurs from year t_0 until the next year t_0+1 for any of the products. For simplicity we assume that $EEI_{t0} = 1$. Because there is no change in energy efficiency, $EEI_{t0+1} = 1$. We then get:

$$EEI_{t0} = \frac{E_t}{PPI_t} = 1$$

$$EEI_{t0+1} = \frac{E_{t0+1}}{PPI_{t0+1}} = \frac{\sum_x SEC_{x,t0+1} \cdot P_{x,t0+1}}{\sum_x w_x \cdot P_{x,t0+1}} = \frac{\sum_x SEC_{x,t0+1} \cdot P_{x,t0+1}}{\sum_x SEC_{x,t0} \cdot P_{x,t0+1}} \qquad [10.6]$$

where:
EEI_t = the aggregate specific energy use in year t
$SEC_{x,t}$ = the specific energy use for product x in year t

Other weighting factors than $SEC_{x,t0}$ do not necessarily lead to the result that $EEI_{t0+1}=1$. This can easily be seen if one considers that EEI_{t0+1} should be one for every situation where only one of the P_x is not zero and all the others are zero. Hence, choosing specific energy use in a reference year as the weighting factor satisfies the logical requirement that the aggregate specific energy use remains constant when all the SEC-figures of all the underlying products remain constant.

Though the specific energy use in a reference year $SEC_{x,t0}$ is a good choice for $SEC_{ref,x}$, these values are not always known, because energy use is not always known on product-by-product basis. Furthermore, we not only want to compare the development of energy efficiency over time, but also across countries, or across companies. In such cases we can use alternative sets of SEC values. A set of best-practice SECs (SEC_{BP}) is often used, as these represent the specific energy consumption of the production plant with the lowest specific energy consumption that is already in full operation. (For an example, see Box 10.3.)

Note that, to calculate EEI, it *is* necessary to know the amount of production for each specific product, but it *is not* necessary to know the energy use for each product separately (only the reference SECs need to be determined). This is convenient, as production statistics are generally more detailed than energy statistics.

Although we used the terms 'production' and 'production processes' in this section, similar approaches can be used to aggregate activities in other sectors, for example analysing the energy efficiency of various household appliances or various transportation modes.

The aggregation method described here can be used to monitor the development of the energy efficiency of a sector within a country over time. They can also be used for international comparison of energy efficiency.

Box 10.3. An energy efficiency index for the iron and steel industry.

We want to compare the energy-efficiency of the iron and steel industry in different countries. We know the production of different products of the iron and steel industry and also the total energy use for each of the countries.

To determine the reference energy use, we take the best-practice specific energy use as the reference. The following set of values is available:
- iron making: 15.5 GJ/tonne
- oxygen steel making: -0.3 GJ/tonne (i.e., the best practice process produces more energy than it consumes)
- electric steel making: 3.7 GJ/tonne
- hot rolling: 2.4 GJ/tonne
- cold rolling: 2.4 GJ/tonne

We can then calculate the reference energy use:

$$E_{reference} = 15.5 \cdot P_{BF} - 0.3 \cdot P_{BOF} + 3.7 \cdot P_{EAF} + 2.4 \cdot P_{hot} + 2.4 \cdot P_{cold} \qquad [10.9]$$

and subsequently the energy efficiency index (scaled to 100):

$$EEI = 100 \cdot E_{actual}/E_{reference} \qquad [10.10]$$

where:
EEI = energy efficiency index
E_{actual} = actual energy use
$E_{reference}$ = reference energy use
P_{BF} = iron production (in blast furnaces)
P_{BOF} = oxygen steel production (in basic oxygen furnaces)
P_{EAF} = electric steel production (in electric arc furnaces)
P_{hot} = amount of hot rolled steel
P_{cold} = amount of cold rolled steel

If the country operated all its processes at the best-practice level, the EEI would be exactly 100. In practice the EEI is higher, ranging from 110 to 200.

Finally, it is important to note that *all energy efficiency indicators remain approximations*. Every energy efficiency indicator contains structural components, and limited data availability nearly always prevents us from excluding all differences in type of human activity from the energy efficiency indicator.

10.4 Examples of energy efficiency indicators

We will now discuss the practical use of some energy efficiency indicators.

Space heating. Space heating is an important part of household energy use. An energy efficiency indicator for this energy function is the energy used per m^2 total heated area. It seems logical to correct for differences in climate from year to year and from country to country (using degree-day correction, see Section 7.2). The number of degree-days in a certain location, averaged over long periods, may range from 1000 – 5000 per year. The variation from year-to-year within a country is typically about 10%. Energy efficiency indicators for space heating are given in Figure 10.1.

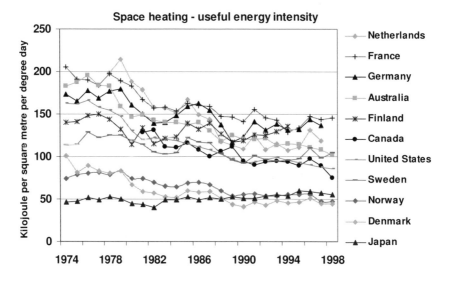

Figure 10.1. Energy use for space heating per m^2 total residential area and per degree-day. The amount of energy is useful heat (i.e., corrected for conversion losses in heat production equipment). The low value for Japan is (partly) caused by the fact that the Japanese heat a smaller part of their home than the inhabitants of other countries.
Source of data: IEA, 2004.

Electrical appliances. In general no energy use data are available for individual electrical appliances. Two approaches are available:
- Constructing energy use data for individual appliances on the basis of the characteristics of the sold appliances (see Table 10.3)
- Constructing an aggregate indicator for all appliances together, using total electricity and penetration data for individual appliances (see Figure 10.2).

Table 10.3. *Average energy efficiency index (see Box 10.1) for new refrigerators and freezers in different European Union member states. Figures are sales-weighted. European Union average in 1992 was set to 100. Source: Waide, 2001.*

Country	1992	1994	1995	1996	1997	1998
France	104	105	102	98	95	90
Germany	97	85	81	78	78	72
Italy	105	102	99	97	95	91
Spain	101	100	101	98	95	96
United Kingdom	109	103	103	102	101	97

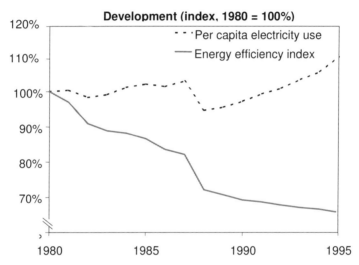

Figure 10.2. *Aggregate energy efficiency index for electrical household appliances in the Netherlands. The physical production index (PPI) is constructed on the basis of the penetration of the following equipment: number of refrigerators (429), freezers (380), coffee-makers (68), kitchen hoods (60), clothes washer (236), clothes dryer (530), dish washer (360), vacuum cleaners (63), central heating system pumps (290), central ventilation (219), water beds (1548), colour TV (149), VCR (116) and lighting (480, assuming the penetration of light per dwelling is constant). For the various types of appliances, the specific energy use in the year 1994 serves as weighting factor and is given in parenthesis (in kWh per year). Source: Farla and Blok, 2000.*

Passenger transport. The logical energy efficiency indicator for passenger cars is the fuel consumption per vehicle-kilometre (see Figure 10.3). Of course, other indicators, like the fuel consumption per passenger-kilometre, can be useful for different purposes.

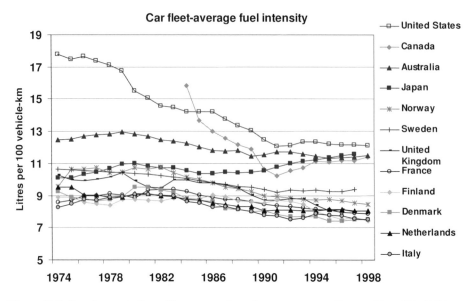

Figure 10.3. Development of specific consumption of passenger cars. Source: Data IEA, 2004.

Manufacturing industry. In manufacturing, the energy efficiency indicator is generally given in energy use per tonne of product. Energy efficiency indicators for three industrial products are given in Figure 10.4. A more complicated example of actual energy efficiency in manufacturing is given for pulp and paper production (Figures 10.5a and 10.5b). In Figure 10.5a, the ratio of energy use and PPI is presented, where PPI is the aggregate production, weighed by reference values for the specific energy use (see equation [10.7]).

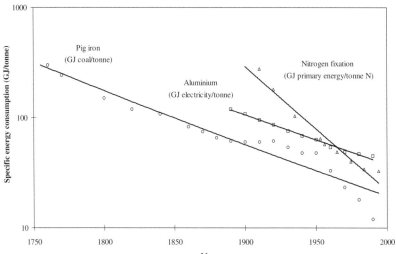

Figure 10.4. Historical development of the specific energy use for some industrial bulk products. For recent years, the data represent best-practice new installations. Before 1950, the data are not well defined. Note that the vertical axis has a logarithmic scale. Source: De Beer, 2000 (referenced in Chapter 7).

As we can see from these examples, specific energy consumption has generally declined. There is a *rule of thumb* that specific energy consumption decreases autonomously at a rate of 1% per year. Although this often holds for long periods and broad energy use categories, it is important to recognize that there are a lot of exceptions to this rule. For example, in the period 1975 – 1985 the rate of energy efficiency improvement was higher (because of high energy prices and strong energy policies). Some periods show very low rates of improvement, or even deterioration, while others show more rapid improvement (for example, iron production in the period 1950 – 1990, Figure 10.4).

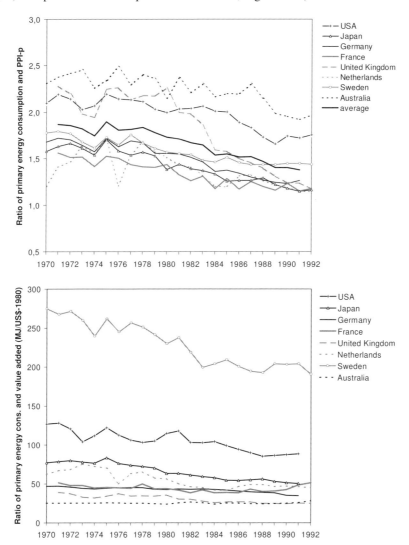

Figure 10.5. Several energy efficiency indicators for the pulp and paper manufacturing industry. Source: Farla et al., 1997.
a: (top) Energy efficiency index, taking into account differences in product mix. As weight factors, specific energy use values for a "typical" modern plant are used.
b: (bottom) Monetary energy intensities (MJ/US$).

10.5 Monetary energy intensity

Let us now go back to equation [10.2] where the specific energy consumption was defined as energy use divided by output (E/P). Section 10.3 discussed a methodology that makes it possible to measure output for a variety of human activities.

However, a much simpler indicator of output is already available for most sectors in the economy: value added. Value added is defined as the difference between the revenues and the costs of inputs. The costs of labour and capital are not included in the costs of inputs, only the costs of goods and services. This means that the value added is available for the two production factors: labour (through salaries) and capital (e.g., by paying dividends). Value added is considered as the most important indicator of the economic importance of a company or a sector within an economy. As a result, value added is widely reported in national and international statistics.

A possible energy-efficiency indicator based on value added is the monetary energy intensity ε:

$$\varepsilon = E \, / \, VA \qquad\qquad [10.11]$$

where:
E   = energy use (of the sector, the company)
VA = value added (of the sector, the company)

Actually, this expression is a variant of equation [10.4], where w_x is replaced by value added per tonne. Monetary energy intensity is widely used as an energy efficiency indicator, especially for manufacturing industry. An advantage of using this indicator is that value-added figures are readily available from statistics. Furthermore, the value added of different products can easily be combined – so, there is no aggregation problem. A disadvantage is that the resulting indicator is influenced by all kinds of factors that have nothing to do with energy efficiency, such as the sector structure. Every sector has activities with a high energy intensity (high energy use per unit of value added) and those with a low energy intensity (low energy use per unit of value added). A change in the mix of activities will lead to a change in sector energy intensity, and changes in prices of products or feedstock can also affect value added.

As we emphasised in Section 10.3, every energy-efficiency indicator is an approximation. In that sense, energy intensity can also be considered an energy-efficiency indicator, but it is a relatively poor indicator; where physical energy-efficiency indicators are available, these are preferred.

So far, we have talked about the energy intensity of a company or a sector. Energy intensity can also be defined at a national level: the total primary energy consumption per unit of GDP (GDP is roughly equal to the sum of value added of all the sectors in a country).

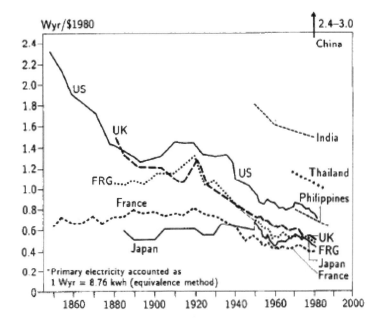

Figure 10.6. Primary energy intensity: primary energy use (incl. wood) per unit of constant GDP for eight countries (Wyr/1980 US$). Source: N. Nakicenovic, A. John: CO₂ Reduction and Removal: Measures for the Next Century, Energy, 16 (1991) p.p. 1347-1377.

In nearly all countries, energy intensities have decreased over time (see Figure 10.6). Energy intensity has decreased in the USA at an average of about 1%/yr since the middle of the 19th century, although this decrease was not continuous. France and Japan have always had lower energy intensity than the USA, the UK or Germany. The current energy intensity of Thailand resembles the USA situation in the late 1940s. The energy intensity of India and its present rates of improvement are similar to those of the USA about a century ago.

GDP is a measure of economic activity, but as a measure of standard of living it has limitations. The informal economy, which is not included in GDP, varies over countries and time. In turn, parts of the services obtained using non-commercial energy are not accounted for in the GDP. Another problem that arises when making GDP-based comparisons is that many goods and services are less expensive in developing countries[1]. GDP estimates in dollars based on market exchange rates will result in large understatements for GDP of low-income countries relative to real income. To address this, GDP data can be converted to constant dollars using purchasing power parity (PPP) rather than the regular market exchange rates. The PPP method weighs the GDP against a basket of goods and services and may therefore provide better figures for cross-country comparisons.

---

[1] The purchasing power of low-income countries may be two or three times as large as the market exchange rate indicates.

Further reading

J.C.M. Farla, K. Blok: The Use of Physical Indicators for the Monitoring of Energy Intensity Developments in the Netherlands, 1980-1995, Energy – the International Journal, 25 (2000) pp. 609-638.

J.C.M. Farla, K. Blok, L.J. Schipper: Energy efficiency Developments in the Pulp and Paper Industry – A Cross-Country Comparison using Physical Production Data, Energy Policy, 25 (1997) 745-758.

L.D.D. Harvey: A Handbook on Low-Energy Buildings and District Energy Systems: Fundamentals, Techniques, and Examples, Earthscan, London, 2006.

International Energy Agency: Indicators of Energy Use and Efficiency, OECD/IEA, Paris, 1997.

International Energy Agency: Oil Crises & Climate Challenges – 30 Years of Energy Use in IEA Countries, IEA/OECD, Paris, 2004.

N. Martin, E. Worrell, M. Ruth and L. Price: Emerging Energy-Efficient Industrial Technologies, Lawrence Berkeley National Laboratory, Berkeley, CA, USA, 2000. More on industrial energy efficiency: http://ies.lbl.gov/ieua/ieua.html

L.J. Schipper, S. Meyer: Energy Efficiency and Human Activity, Cambridge University Press, Cambridge, UK, 1995.

G.J.M. Phylipsen, K. Blok, E. Worrell: Handbook on International Comparisons of Energy Efficiency in the Manufacturing Industry, Dept. of Science, Technology and Society, Utrecht University, 1998.

P. Waide: Monitoring of Energy Efficiency Trends for Refrigerators, Freezers, Washing Machines, Washer-Dryers and Household Lamps Sold in the EU, PW Consulting, Manchester, UK, 2001.

Final achievement levels

After having studied Chapter 10 and the exercises, you should:
- know the definition of energy efficiency and specific energy consumption and be able to use these concepts;
- understand the various ways of improving energy efficiency;
- be able to explain the difference between energy efficiency and energy efficiency indicators;
- know how energy efficiency indicators are used in the various sectors and what the problems are;
- be able to use the energy-efficiency index concept in practice; and
- be able to discuss advantages and disadvantages of physical and monetary energy-efficiency indicators.

Exercises Chapter 10

10.1. Energy labels for refrigerators and freezers
In many countries in the world a labelling system for electrical appliances is in place. Such a system could work as follows. The energy efficiency index $EEI = C/C_{ref}$, where C is the annual electricity consumption (under test conditions) and C_{ref} (in kW/litre) is the reference annual energy consumption. The latter is calculated as follows (see Box 10.1):

$$C_{ref} = \alpha \cdot (V_r + 2.1 \cdot V_f) + \beta; \quad \alpha = 0.6; \quad \beta = 200$$

where V_r = refrigerator volume (in litres); V_f is freezer volume (in litres); α and β are constants. The term β is introduced to compensate for the fact that smaller equipment has a relatively larger energy use than larger equipment. The EEI is converted to a label, according to the following classification.

A	B	C	D	E	F	G
< 0.55	0.55–0.75	0.75–0.90	0.90–1.00	1.00–1.10	1.10–1.25	> 1.25

Note that this exercise is based on existing labelling systems, but numbers are fictitious and the system description is highly simplified.

Below is a list of refrigerators, freezers and combinations with measurements of energy use. Classify this equipment in the classes A to G.

Make	Refrigeration volume (litre)	Freezer volume (litre)	Annual electricity consumption under test conditions (kWh)
Almo	120	-	200
Bato	120	20	300
Caldone	180	20	300
Dolca	140	140	400

10.2. Standard and actual energy use
To determine the specific energy consumption of refrigerators, their electricity consumption is measured under the following standard conditions: ambient temperature 25 °C; door always closed; empty.
a.   In practice, there are three sources of heat that need to be cooled away. What are these?
b.   Which options can you think of to improve the efficiency? In what categories of section 10.2 can these be included?
c.   How do the different options for energy efficiency improvement affect the electricity consumption under the standard test procedure and under practical conditions? Are there options of which the effect is overstated or understated under the standard test procedure?
d.   What adaptations to the standard test procedure would you propose?

10.3. Comparing energy efficiencies
The dairy industry in country X produces butter, cheese and milk powder. Production quantities and energy consumption in 1998 and 2003 are given in the following table. An analysis carried out in the year 1990 showed the following best-practice values for the specific energy consumption for each of these: butter: 3 GJ/tonne; cheese: 5 GJ/tonne; milk powder: 10 GJ/tonne.

Year	Production of butter (million tonnes)	Production of cheese (million tonnes)	Production of milk powder (million tonnes)	Primary energy consumption (PJ)
1998	2.0	2.0	1.0	36
2003	1.0	3.0	1.0	28

a. Determine how much more efficient the dairy industry in country X has become, taking into account the change in product mix (express in percent per year).
b. Is it a problem that best-practice values are only known for 1990?

10.4. Energy efficiency in the fruit and vegetables industry
In the industry that processes fruit and vegetables, the following products can be distinguished (in parenthesis the typical value for the specific energy consumption in 2000 is given for each of the product groups):
  • canned fruit and vegetables (2 MJ/kg)
  • frozen fruit and vegetables (8 MJ/kg)
  • dried fruit and vegetables (15 MJ/kg)
In the following fictitious table some information is given about the fruit and vegetables processing industry in three countries in the year 2005.

	Canned fruit and vegetables production (ktonnes)	Frozen fruit and vegetables production (ktonnes)	Dried fruit and vegetables production (ktonnes)	Primary energy use for fruit and vegetables production (TJ)
Germany	800	300	0	4,400
Netherlands	600	250	0	3,700
France	300	300	100	6,300

a. Give an expression to calculate the energy-efficiency index
b. Which of the three countries quoted in the table is most energy-efficient, based on the information that you have? Provide the calculation.
c. Give two reasons why the conclusion drawn in (b) might be wrong.

10.5. Energy efficiency of household appliances
Examine Figure 10.2.
a. Write out the expression for the energy-efficiency index that is used to construct this picture.
b. What criticism can you formulate with respect to this index?
c. What does it mean that the two lines in the diagram show a different development? If the electricity use per household had also been depicted, where would this line go?
d. Consider the development from 1987 to 1988. Is this likely? What could explain it?

188

10.6. Does the rule of thumb apply?

Check to what extent the rule-of-thumb on the average reduction of specific energy consumption mentioned at the end of Section 10.4 applies to the examples given in Section 10.5.

10.7. Energy intensity of ammonia manufacturing

In Figure 10.7 below, the value added, the ammonia production and the primary energy consumption of the Netherlands' ammonia production is given for the period 1980 – 2002.

a. What happened to the specific energy consumption in this period (trend and volatility)?
b. Estimate the average rate of reduction of the specific energy consumption.
c. What happened to the monetary energy intensity (trend and volatility)?
d. Can you think of causes for the development of the monetary energy intensity in the period 1988 to 1994?

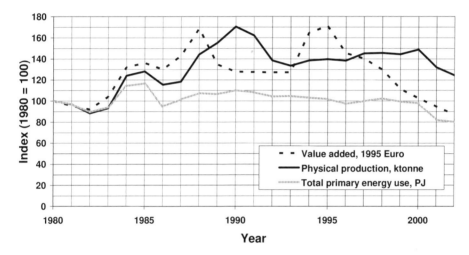

Figure 10.7. Development of value added, ammonia production and primary energy consumption of the Netherlands' ammonia manufacturers

11

Methods for the analysis of energy technologies

Several types of equipment, processes or combination of processes are possible for a certain energy function or energy conversion process. The question becomes: Which of these alternatives is best? What can the alternatives contribute in terms of cost savings or emission reduction?

This chapter discusses the general approach to the analysis of energy technologies (11.1), as well as some approaches to obtaining the necessary basic data (11.2). Subsequently, cost-benefit analysis will be introduced (11.3) and treated from different perspectives (11.4 and 11.5). Finally, some specific tools are covered: scale laws and learning curves (11.6).

11.1 General approach to the analysis of energy technologies

Before analysing an energy technology, one needs to take some important preparatory steps:
- Determine the aim of the analysis;
- Determine the functionality;
- Analyse existing or reference processes; and
- Identify technology.

Aim of the analysis. First of all it is important to determine what the technology characterisation will be used for. It is instructive to use the following questions:
- Why is the analysis being carried out (e.g., R&D planning, development of a market strategy, policy support), and what consequences does this have for the scope of the analysis?
- For whom is the analysis being carried out (e.g., government, a company, an international body), and what specific requirements does this pose for the analysis?
- What types of targets is the analysis supposed to serve (e.g., cost reduction, energy conservation, emission reduction)?
- What is the time frame for the analysis (e.g., when do specific policy targets have to be met)?
- What level of accuracy and detail is required in the analysis?

Functionality. A second issue that needs to be considered before the actual analysis is the functionality of the energy end-use and conversions that we want to consider. The functionality describes the requirements for the equipment to be studied, as much as possible in quantitative terms. A good formulation of the functionality is necessary for a fair comparison of alternatives, and it determines the range of alternatives that are considered in the analysis.

For instance, it makes a difference whether we want to consider equipment that produces low temperature heat in general or only equipment that just produces low temperature heat out of fuel. In the latter case, only boilers will be considered, whereas in the former CHP equipment and heat pumps will be included. Another function that may be specified is output. For instance, in the previous example it makes a difference whether heat of 40 °C or heat of 80 °C is required. Other aspects may also be specified, like load factor.

Reference technology. Third, the reference technology needs to be determined and analysed. A reference technology is the technology that will be partly or fully replaced by the new technologies being studied. It forms a common basis for comparison of various alternative technologies. A reference technology is often the one that is most commonly in use at present. Depending on the aim of the analysis, one could also select the most commonly sold technology or the most modern commercial technology available. Once the boundary conditions have been determined with the two previous steps, it is useful to analyse the existing processes, e.g. through process energy analysis or exergy analysis.

Technology identification. Especially when a study examines long-term options for energy conversion and end-use, it is important to obtain an adequate inventory of relevant technologies. Long-term options, ones that may become commercial within 5 to 20 years also need to be considered.

Technology can be identified by:
- scanning scientific journals, professional journals and conference proceedings related to the sector being analysed;
- consulting experts world-wide (e.g., in sector-oriented research institutes), as well as equipment manufacturers; and
- screening technologies applied in other sectors to see whether they could be applied to improve the energy efficiency of the process being analysed.

A careful inventory should cover all the technologies that may become commercial in the next 20 years. For longer time frames, the inventory becomes incomplete, since identifying technology beyond 20 – 30 years is impossible: technologies that may become relevant may not even have been conceived.

11.2 Technology characterization

After the technologies have been selected, the next step is to determine their characteristics. The two most important characteristics of energy technologies are:

- technical performance; and
- costs.

Technical performance is often expressed in terms of energy conversion efficiency or specific energy consumption. However, other issues may also be important, like applicability (e.g., the output ranges for which the technology is available, the environment conditions that are tolerated) or partial load behaviour.

The costs can generally be expressed in terms of cost per unit of output. We can distinguish:

- Costs of investment (which are made initially); and
- Operation and maintenance costs (which return every year).

Costs of investment can include many things, but generally they include:

- The cost of equipment;
- Costs of buildings for housing the equipment;
- The costs of land;
- Engineering costs;
- Installation costs; and
- Other costs, like the costs of adapting existing equipment, lost production costs, and operator training costs.

The costs of collecting information about the alternatives and making the decision are not usually included in the costs of investment (these costs are often called transaction costs). In Sections 11.3 to 11.5 we will discuss how to perform a cost-benefit analysis on the basis of these primary quantities.

Technology characterization has to be carried out carefully. It is the real basis of energy technology analysis, it often takes much of the investigation time, and it is the source of many errors. Although good data acquisition needs to be learned in practice, some general rules can be given regarding the usefulness of various sources. There are many sources on which the characterization of technologies can be based, but the quality of the information varies widely, and in fact no source is without problems.

1. The first category is *published sources*, first of all scientific articles and books. Even if these publications have been peer-reviewed, the information should be handled with care. Sometimes figures are just used as an example (for instance, if the exact figure was not very relevant for the analysis concerned), and it is always important to check which method was used to obtain the figures. Technical journals may also be a useful source of data, since they are generally distributed among producers and users of equipment. Information is often provided – directly or indirectly – by producers, but the information they provide may be biased in some direction (see producer information below). Though they will get in trouble sooner or later for providing incorrect information, it is still important to double check the information.

Other published materials, such as newspapers, should never be used directly, but only as a lead to other sources.

2. A second category is information from *producers of equipment*. It is important for producers to provide correct figures on the cost and performance of their product, but these figures should be used with care. The costs that are presented might just be the cost of the equipment itself, excluding auxiliary equipment that is required, or excluding installation costs. Furthermore the stated performance may be for 'stripped' equipment, excluding losses associated with auxiliary equipment, or it may only be the performance under certain standard conditions. For products that are not yet on the market, equipment manufacturers may choose to present optimistic figures to focus attention on the future product or to obtain government funding for the development. On the other hand, they may choose caution, avoiding too optimistic figures, which might disturb their present markets.

3. A third category of information about technology includes *existing studies* that were especially dedicated to providing such information. There are various sources for such studies, in particular engineering companies (or engineers/contractors). Though these companies generally rely on well-established models and methods to determine the performance parameters, the way cost data are determined is often less transparent. Sometimes, cost estimates are on the high side, especially where new technology is concerned. The stated costs may be valid for a first plant (with all the risk involved), but not for a mature technology. Other studies – e.g., from universities and research institutes involved in the development of the technology – may be too optimistic about the rate of acceptance of a new technology, and may discount the need for auxiliary equipment and costs associated with this.

4. A fourth category is *project information*, from field experiments, demonstration projects, and other – generally government sponsored – projects. Technology databases typically include this kind of information, and it may be very useful. Nevertheless, one should keep in mind that performance and costs of demonstration projects do not always reflect those of mature technology: technological learning often occurs, leading to better performance and lower costs.

From this list, we can see that data collection is not a straightforward process. In every situation, the data should be carefully considered and the way it was obtained (as well as the purpose of the research) should be taken into account. For example, the information provided by manufacturers may be quite useful, but it becomes more relevant when input from users is also considered. Gathering information is often an iterative process, involving cross-checking of information from various sources.

11.3 Principles of cost-benefit analysis: net present value

Most activities lead to costs and benefits. From an economic perspective, it is assumed that an activity is only undertaken if the total benefits exceed the costs. We call such activity a 'project'. When is a project attractive in economic terms?

Cost-benefit analysis is complicated by the *time preference*. Most people and organizations would rather receive a certain sum of money now instead of next year. Time preference makes it impossible to simply add and subtract the money inflows and outflows associated with a project, when they occur at different points in time.

We solve this problem as follows. If someone does not care whether they receive $100 now or $108 a year from now, it is said that they have a time preference that can be expressed by a discount rate of 8%. More generally, if someone has a time preference that can be expressed by a discount rate r, they are indifferent about receiving an amount of x now or an amount of $x \cdot (1+r)^n$ in n years from now. Using this indifference we can now convert all current and future expenditures and receivables to the present situation and count them together. We call this the net present value of the project:

$$NPV = \sum_{i=0}^{n} \frac{B_i - C_i}{(1+r)^i}$$
[11.1]

where:
NPV = net present value of the project in year 0
B_i = the benefits of the project in year i
C_i = the costs of the project in year i (at the beginning of the project this could
          include an initial investment)
r   = the discount rate
n   = the lifetime of the project

A project is considered to be attractive if the net present value is positive.

Many activities consist of an initial investment, followed by a constant annual net benefit. In that case, calculating the net present value as presented in equation [11.1] is highly simplified, but we have to introduce a capital recovery factor α that is a function of the discount rate and the lifetime of the project:

$$NPV = -I + \sum_{i=1}^{L} \frac{B-C}{(1+r)^i} = -I + \frac{B-C}{\alpha}$$
[11.2a]

$$\alpha = \frac{r}{1-(1+r)^{-L}}$$
[11.2b]

where:

I = initial investment

B = annual benefits

C = annual costs (excluding capital costs)

α = the capital recovery factor (sometimes also called the 'annuity factor')

r = the discount rate

L = the life time or depreciation period of the equipment

Table 11.1. The capital recovery factor (α) as a function of the discount rate and the depreciation period, cf. equation [11.2b].

Discount rate	4%	5%	10%	15%	20%	25%
Depreciation period (years)						
5	22.5%	23.1%	26.4%	29.8%	33.4%	37.2%
10	12.3%	13.0%	16.3%	19.9%	23.9%	28.0%
15	9.0%	9.6%	13.1%	17.1%	21.4%	25.9%
20	7.4%	8.0%	11.7%	16.0%	20.5%	25.3%
25	6.4%	7.1%	11.0%	15.5%	20.2%	25.1%
30	5.8%	6.5%	10.6%	15.2%	20.1%	25.0%
50	4.7%	5.5%	10.1%	15.0%	20.0%	25.0%

An overview of capital recovery factors is given in Table 11.1. Note that at high discount rates the length of the depreciation period is less relevant, and for long lifetimes α approaches the discount rate.

A series of constant future costs and benefits can be made present by dividing the annual values by the capital recovery factor α. In many cases, however, we are interested in the opposite problem. We want to know how an initial investment translates to annual costs during a series of years. In that case the initial investment can be converted to constant annual capital costs by multiplying it by α. The result represents the total expenditure needed for interest and depreciation.

A well-know application is the calculation of the costs-of-electricity for a power plant:

$$coe = \frac{\alpha \cdot I + OM + F}{E}$$

[11.3]

where:

coe = costs of electricity (e.g. per kWh or MWh)

α = capital recovery factor

I = initial investment

OM = annual costs for operation and maintenance

F = annual fuel costs

E = annual electricity production

196

It is important to do the whole calculation on the same basis, e.g. for 1 kW of capacity, or for a complete power plant.

A factor that complicates all cost-benefit analyses is that the value of money changes over time, generally decreasing through inflation. In a first order approach, we can correct for this by taking the real discount rate instead of the actual (market) discount rate:

$$r = R - i \qquad\qquad [11.4]$$

where:
r = real discount rate
R = actual discount rate
i = rate of inflation

Inflation rates in western countries typically lie in the range of 1 – 4% per year, but they can go up to 10% per year. In developing countries, higher inflation rates occur, sometimes above 100% per year.

11.4 Cost-benefit analysis: the private perspective

When considering an investment, a firm may do a cost-benefit analysis, for example by calculating the net present value of the investment (using a certain preset discount rate). The net present value, however, is an absolute figure, and does not necessarily give a good indication of the project's profitability in relation to the initial investment. In order to provide an indication of this profitability, two indicators are often used:
  • pay-back period (rule-of-thumb); and
  • internal rate of return (derived from the net present value approach).

The rule-of-thumb criterion that is widely used in firms is the simple pay-back period (PBP):

$$PBP = \frac{I}{B - C} \qquad\qquad [11.5]$$

where:
I = the initial investment
B = annual benefits
C = annual cost (excluding capital costs)

In order to evaluate projects, many firms have a pay-back period cut-off criterion, and will only consider projects with a shorter pay-back period. Most firms have fairly short pay-back period cut-offs. Table 11.2 gives an overview of the criteria that are used.

Table 11.2. Distribution of required pay-back periods by firms, based on surveys in Germany and the Netherlands. Most firms use the same pay-back period criterion for energy-related investments as for other investments. Sources: Gruber and Brand, 1991 and Gillissen et al., 1995.

	1–2 years	3 years	4 years	5 years	>5 years
Germany	8%	27%	13%	27%	15%
The Netherlands (industry)	12%	15%	31%	29%	12%
The Netherlands (services)	-	19%	4%	43%	34%

The simple pay-back period is an easily applicable criterion, but it does not consider benefits obtained later in the lifetime of equipment, and it does not consider interest. For the latter reason, the simple pay-back period becomes meaningless beyond 10 years: depending on the discount rate and depreciation period, there may be no pay-back at all.

An alternative criterion for cost-benefit analysis is a project's internal rate of return (IRR). In general, the net present value of a project with an initial investment will depend on the discount rate used. At very low discount rates, virtually every project will have a positive net present value. At very high discount rates, every project with an initial investment will have a negative net present value (check this with equation [11.2a]). Somewhere in between, a discount rate exists where the net present value of the project is zero. This discount rate is called the internal rate of return of the project. The internal rate of return is the discount rate at which the net present value is equal to zero. The calculated internal rate of return can be compared to a test discount rate r_t that a decision maker uses. In line with the definition of the IRR, for a given discount rate r_t the two following expressions are fully equivalent.

$$\text{NPV}(r_t) > 0 \quad \Leftrightarrow \quad \text{IRR} > r_t \qquad [11.6]$$

In recent years, there has been a tendency to use internal-rate-of-return criteria instead of simple pay-back period criteria. Typical cut-off values r_t for the internal rate of return may be 10% to 25%. As a rule of thumb, projects with a lifetime of more than 15 years have a slightly higher internal-rate-of-return than the inverse of the pay-back period.

Examining the cut-off values for the pay-back period and the IRR, one may observe that these are fairly strict. Pay-back period requirements are generally much shorter than the lifetime of the equipment, and IRR cut-off criteria are much higher than interest rates charged by banks. There are a number of reasons for this:
- First of all, an investment with just a zero net benefit is not enough to be profitable; the balance needs to be positive.
- Second, an investment is generally irreversible. There are always business risks (e.g., changes in market conditions), which could make the investment less profitable. By that time, withdrawing the investment is generally not possible. Furthermore, in the future, better equipment may become available, but investing now lowers the likelihood that the new equipment will be purchased later.

- Finally, some firms have limited access to capital and need to select the investments with the best revenues.

Households generally do not have explicit decision criteria like critical pay-back periods or internal rates of return. Nevertheless, one can derive *implicit* discount rates from actual consumer behaviour, which are equivalent to the IRR cut-offs for companies. Given a set of alternatives (e.g., different refrigerators of the same size) with different cost prices and different levels of annual energy use, one may investigate what percentage of consumers choose a certain type. Based on this, one can derive average discount rates, using econometric techniques; these implicit consumer discount rates are generally fairly high, from 10 – 30%, and in some cases even up to 100%. In general, high-income groups show a lower implicit discount rate than low-income groups.

11.5 Cost-benefit analysis: the social perspective

The main difference between cost-benefit analysis from a private perspective and cost-benefit from a social (or government) perspective is the time preference. The social perspective utilizes a discount rate that is generally much lower than cut-off discount rates used by private investors. In the case of cost-benefit analysis from the social perspective, the discount rate is called the *social discount rate*.

As with private discount rates, there are no fixed values for social discount rates. Some governments use set discount rates when they evaluate such things as big infrastructure projects. Such a social discount rate is generally derived from the cost of long-term capital. In industrialized countries, typical discount rates are 4 – 6%, but in developing countries the rates may be higher, in the range of 10 – 12%. Some economists argue that with problems with a long timeframe, like the problem of climate change, discount rates as low as 2% should be used. In social cost-benefit analysis, the depreciation period is often set equal to the lifetime of equipment, but fixed depreciation periods are also used.

To evaluate whether a project is attractive from the social perspective, decision makers make the same calculation: if the net present value is positive, the project is considered acceptable. A positive net present value means that the internal rate of return of the project is higher than the social discount rate.

Specific mitigation costs. Additional indicators have been developed to measure the economic attractiveness of a measure. The exact choice of the indicator depends on the target of the analysis. For instance, if one is interested in greenhouse gas emission reduction and wants to know how this can be done in the cheapest way, the specific cost of CO_2 mitigation is a useful measure. This is defined as the costs per unit of CO_2 emission avoided, and is usually calculated as the net annual costs of a measure divided by the annual CO_2 emission reduction. Capital costs are included in the annual costs and are calculated by multiplying the initial investment by the capital recovery factor α.

The following equations can be used to determine the specific cost of saved primary energy C_{spec} and the specific CO_2 mitigation costs $C_{spec,CO2}$. Similar equations can be given for other effects, such as for other emissions. Note that the equations presented here are only valid if annual costs and benefits are constant over the depreciation period.

$$C_{spec} = \frac{\alpha \cdot I + C - B}{\Delta E} \qquad [11.7]$$

$$C_{spec,CO_2} = \frac{\alpha \cdot I + C - B}{\Delta M_{CO_2}} \qquad [11.8]$$

where:
$\alpha \cdot I$	= annual capital costs
C	= annual operation and maintenance costs
B	= annual benefits
ΔE	= annual saved (primary) energy
ΔM_{CO2}	= annual amount of avoided amount CO_2 emissions

Once the specific CO_2 mitigation costs have been calculated for a range of projects, the projects with the lowest specific costs can be selected in order to obtain carbon dioxide emission reduction at the lowest costs for society as a whole.

External costs. An alternative way of treating avoided emissions is through the use of the concept of externalities, or external costs. A project causes externalities when it leads to costs for others than the one undertaking the project. Costs related to the negative effects of emissions are a well-known example of external costs.
If the external costs related to emissions could be precisely determined, they could easily be included in a cost-benefit analysis. For emissions of greenhouse gases, however, the estimates of the magnitude of the external costs differ widely, ranging from $5 - 125$ US$\$_{1990}$ per tonne of carbon ($1.4 - 34$ US$\$_{1990}$/t$CO_2$).

Indirect economic effects. So far we have only considered the direct costs and benefits of a specific project, either from a private or social perspective. However, when a project is carried out there are often indirect effects.

First, there are indirect effects on the level of the firm or sector. For instance, the project can be so costly or beneficial for a firm that its competitive position is greatly damaged or improved. In that case, the costs or benefits for the firm may be much larger than the direct costs or benefits. There may also be substantial net costs that do not affect the net result of the firm because all the costs can be passed on to the customers.

Next, there can be effects on national (or even international) level. For instance, a project may be costly, but have benefits like a better balance-of-payment for the country or higher employment. In such a case, the total net costs for society (in terms of effect on GDP or welfare) may be smaller than the direct costs. It should be obvious that calculation of the indirect costs is not easy and in general requires the use of sophisticated macro-economic or econometric models.

Box 11.1. Example of cost-benefit analysis calculations.

Your boiler is broken down and you have to select a new one. Your old boiler had a conversion efficiency of 90%. You can choose a conventional new boiler, with a conversion efficiency of 95%, or a condensing type, with a conversion efficiency of 107% (all LHV). The condensing boiler is 700 € more expensive, and maintenance will cost 20 € more per year. Your current boiler uses 2000 m³ natural gas per year; the natural-gas price is 0.6 €/m³, 32 GJ/m³. What are the net present value, the pay-back period, the internal rate of return, and the specific CO_2 mitigation costs of the investment in the condensing boiler, compared to a conventional one?

We only look at the difference between the two alternatives. Compared to the conventional boiler, the condensing boiler saves 212 m³ natural gas per year, or 127 € per year. We can also calculate that this avoids 380 kg of CO_2 emissions per year. For the NPV calculation, we assume a depreciation period of 15 years and a discount rate of 10% ($\alpha = 13.1\%$ per year). For the calculation of the specific CO_2 mitigation costs, a social discount rate of 4% is applied ($\alpha = 9.0\%$ per year).

$$NPV = -I + \frac{B - C}{\alpha} = -700 + \frac{(127 - 20)€ / yr}{13.1\% / yr} = -700€ + 816€ = 116 €$$

$$PBP = \frac{I}{B - C} = \frac{700€}{(127 - 20)€ / yr} = 6.5 \, years$$

IRR ≈ 13%   (determined by trial-and-error – from the NPV calculation one can already estimate that the IRR is somewhat higher than 10%)

$$C_{spec,CO_2} = \frac{\alpha \cdot I + C - B}{\Delta M_{CO_2}} = \frac{(9\% / yr) \cdot 700€ + (20€ / yr) - (118€ / yr)}{0.38t \, CO_2 / yr} = -92 \, €/tCO_2$$

As we already saw from the formula, the specific CO_2 mitigation costs can be negative.

11.6 Scale laws and learning curves

Information about the costs of new technology may not always be in a useful form. Some tools are available to convert costs to the desired form. Here scale laws and learning curves will be treated.

Scale laws. When the available information for equipment is for a scale different from the one required, one may use so-called scale laws. Such a scale law may have the form:

$$C = \gamma \cdot P^R \qquad\qquad [11.9]$$

where:
C = the cost of equipment
P = the capacity of equipment
R = a constant, the scale factor
γ = a constant

The scale factor depends on the type of equipment. Often a scale factor of 0.7 (or 2/3) is used, since the capacity for many types of equipment increases with the third power of the size (determined by volume) whereas costs only increase in a quadratic way (determined by surface area). One should be careful using this approach and consider whether the characteristics of appliances suggest a certain scale factor (for example, certain heat exchangers and photovoltaic systems have a scale factor closer to one as the costs increase in a more or less linear way with the throughput of the equipment).

Learning curves. A learning curve is a quantitative description of the process of technological learning: after a product is brought on the market and sales increase, the product improves, due to advances of technology, improvement of production processes, scaling up of individual units, and an increase of the scale of production. In many cases this leads to a steady decrease of the costs per unit of performance. This effect is often expressed in the form of a learning curve (also called an experience curve). A learning curve expresses that the *costs decrease by a constant fraction with each doubling of the total number of units produced.*

For instance, for photovoltaic systems it has been found that after each doubling of the cumulative production (generally expressed in MW of capacity), the costs per unit of electricity production capacity ($/W_p$) decrease by approximately 20%. The learning effect can be described by the following expression:

$$C_P = C_1 \cdot P^b \qquad\qquad [11.10]$$

where:
C_P = the cost per unit after the cumulative production of P units
C_1 = the cost of the first unit
b   = the experience index

The price of the product is reduced by the same percentage each time the cumulative production is doubled. This can easily be shown as follows by comparing the price after P units with the price after 2·P units. We take the ratio of these two price levels:

$$\frac{C_{2 \cdot P}}{C_P} = \frac{C_1 \cdot (2 \cdot P)^b}{C_1 \cdot P^b} = \frac{C_1 \cdot P^b \cdot 2^b}{C_1 \cdot P^b} = 2^b \qquad [11.11]$$

Hence, after each 'doubling', the price is multiplied with a factor 2^b. This factor is defined as the progress ratio. The parameter b is generally negative, so 2^b is smaller than one. The reduction fraction after each doubling is $1 - 2^b$.

In Figure 11.1, the development of the price of a fictitious product with a progress ratio of 0.8 is given. The price thus drops by 20% for each doubling. When both the price and the cumulative production are depicted on a logarithmic scale, the learning curve becomes a straight line.

In most cases the costs of the first unit is unknown, or not well defined; in that case we can write equation [11.10] as:

$$C_{P2} = C_{P1} \cdot \left(\frac{P_2}{P_1} \right)^b \qquad [11.12]$$

where:
P_1, P_2 = the cumulative production at different moments in time
C_{P1} = the cost of one unit after the cumulative production P_1
C_{P2} = the cost of one unit after the cumulative production P_2

Note that in the learning curve equation there is no relation between price and time. This means that the actual price development will only depend on the rate of deployment of the new technology.

Empirical evidence indicates that for most technologies, the progress ratio is somewhere between 0.7 and 0.95. In Figure 11.2 the price development of wind turbine technology is given.

Learning curves are a useful tool for making projections of the cost price development of new technology, but the approach has its limitations. It is not a 'law', just an empirical finding. Cost price reduction may accelerate and slow-down and decrease again (see Figure 11.2). Technological breakthroughs and the market situation will also influence costs and prices.

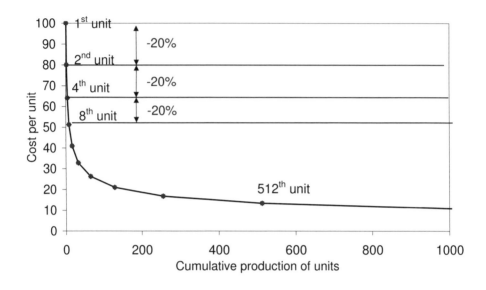

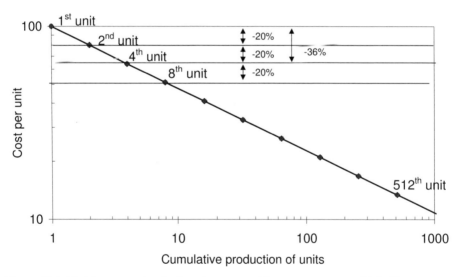

Figure 11.1. Fictitious example of a learning curve with a progress ratio of 0.8. The top picture has two linear axes, the bottom figure represents the same data, but with two logarithmic axes.

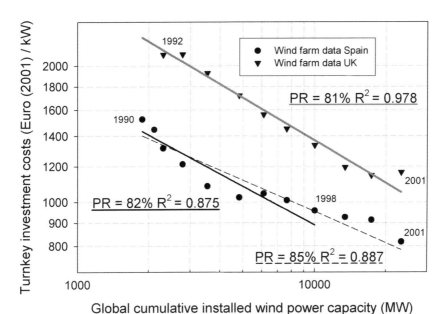

Figure 11.2. Learning curves for wind energy in Spain and the United Kingdom. Prices in the UK were higher because on average smaller wind turbines were used there than in Spain. Source: Junginger, 2005.

Further reading

R.A. Brealey, S. Myers: Principles of Corporate Finance, McGraw-Hill, Boston, 2003.

E. Gruber, M. Brand: Promoting Energy Conservation in Small and Medium-sized Companies, Energy Policy, 19 (1991) pp. 279-287.

M. Gillissen, J.B. Opschoor, J.C.M. Farla, K. Blok: Energy Conservation and Investment Behaviour of Firms, Vrije Universiteit Amsterdam, 1995.

M. Junginger, A. Faaij, W.C. Turkenburg: Global Cost Curves for Wind Farms, Energy Policy, 33 (2005) pp. 133-150.

M. Junginger: Learning in renewable energy technology development, PhD thesis, Utrecht University, 2005.

L. Neij: Use of Experience Curves to Analyse the Prospects for Diffusion and Adaption of Renewable Energy Technologies, Energy Policy, 23 (1997) pp. 1099-1107.

International Energy Agency: Experience Curves for Energy Technology Policy, IEA/OECD, Paris, 2000.

International Energy Agency: Comparing Energy Technologies, IEA/OECD, Paris, 1996.

K. Train: Discount Rates in Consumers' Energy-Related Decisions: a Review of the Literature, Energy the International Journal, 10 (1985) pp. 1243-1253.

Final achievement levels

After having studied Chapter 11 and the exercises, you should:
- be aware of the important elements in energy technology analysis;
- be able to discuss the usefulness of various sources of energy technology information;
- be familiar with the concept of time preference and discount rates and their role in the different perspectives of cost-benefit analysis;
- know the concepts net present value, internal rate of return, pay-back period, and specific emission mitigation costs and be able to calculate these;
- be able to apply scale laws; and
- be familiar with the concept of technological learning and be able to work with learning curves.

Exercises Chapter 11

11.1. Profitability of compact fluorescent lamps
How much money is saved per year if we replace a conventional lamp with a compact fluorescent lamp (CFL). And how long will it take until the investment is paid back? And what is the internal rate of return?
Assume that a 15-Watt CFL costs €5 and that it will replace a normal light bulb of 60 W. The CFL will burn 500 hours per year and has a lifetime of 10 years. The price of electricity is €0.12 /kWh. Neglect the cost savings of the non-purchase of conventional lamps.

11.2. Economic analysis of a wind farm
A 100 MW offshore wind farm is built. The investment amounts to 1500 €/kW. Annual costs for operation, maintenance and insurance are 3% of the investment. The equivalent operation time is 3500 hours per year, and the wind turbines run for 20 years. Assume that the electricity produced can be sold for 0.04 €/kWh.
a. What is the net-present value of the wind farm from a social-cost perspective (use a social discount rate of 4%)?
b. What are the specific CO_2 mitigation costs of the wind farm?

11.3. The production cost of electricity
a. Calculate the cost price of electricity for the power plants listed in Table 4.3. Use the 'best available efficiencies' listed. Use a discount rate of 10% and a lifetime of 25 years. Use current prices for coal and natural gas.
b. What difference would it make if you switch to a discount rate of 15%?
c. Also calculate the cost price of electricity for the offshore wind farm in the previous exercise.

11.4. Solar water heaters
In the Netherlands, 10,000 solar water heaters have been installed. The price is currently € 1600 each. The goal of the government is to have 300,000 solar water heaters installed in 5 years. What will the price of a solar water heater be in 5 years if the progress ratio is 0.95 and 0.85, respectively?

11.5. Net present value and specific CO_2 mitigation costs
If the NPV of an investment that reduces CO_2 emissions is positive, what does this tell about the specific CO_2 mitigation costs? Assume that the same discount rate is used in both cases.

11.6. Scale effects of CHP plants
A CHP (gas turbine) installation with an electricity production capacity of 100 MW costs 70 million Euro. The scale factor is 0.8.
a. What will a 10 MW CHP installation cost?
b. And how much is the price per kWh higher than for a 100 MW plant?
c. At what capacity of the gas turbine will the production costs be below 3 Eurocent per kWh?
Use the following information:
The electrical efficiency of the turbine is 34%, the thermal efficiency is 48% (assume that this is independent of size). Efficiency of the boiler that is replaced: 90%. Price of natural gas: 3 Euro per GJ. The gas turbine is in use for 7000 hours per year. Operation and maintenance costs are 3% of the investment. Interest rate is 15%.

11.7. Impact of external costs
A price range of 5 – 125 $/tC was mentioned for external costs of CO_2 emissions. Calculate the effect on the prices of coal, natural gas and electricity if these values were translated to a carbon tax. Do this, both in relative and absolute terms, for both small and large consumers of energy. Use the energy prices from Chapter 5, and make additional assumptions you need yourself.

12

Determining potentials

Some questions arise repeatedly: How much energy could be saved through energy efficiency improvement? What could the contribution of renewable energy sources be in 2020? What role can power sources with low CO_2 emissions play in the electricity sector? In all cases, these questions could be re-phrased: What is the potential of .....?

The previous chapter paid attention to the analysis of individual projects, and in this one the focus is on the combined contributions of a technology or groups of technologies.

12.1 Different types of potentials

Several types of potential can be distinguished:
* Theoretical potential
* Technical potential
* Economic potential
* Profitable potential
* Market potential
* Enhanced market potential

The theoretical potential describes what can be achieved (e.g. the amount of energy that could be saved), taking only physical limits into account. For instance, thermodynamic analysis can tell us the minimum energy use for a certain industrial process. Renewable resources are limited by the natural energy flows available, and fossil fuels are limited by the available stocks.

The technical potential is the contribution that could be made by the technologies in a certain (future) year. To determine the technical potential, one generally takes into account constraints like the regular turnover rates of capital stock. While the theoretical potential remains constant, the technical potential will probably increase, as a result of ongoing technological developments.

The economic potential is the part of the technical potential that is economically attractive from a social perspective (e.g., the options that show a positive net present value at a social discount rate).

The profitable potential – or business economics potential – is the part of the technical potential that is economically attractive from the point of view of private investors (firms, households or other institutions). Only economic barriers and stimuli for adopting new technology are taken into account when determining the profitable potential.

The market potential or implementation potential is the part of the technical potential that is likely to be implemented, taking into account all barriers and stimuli for adopting new technology (including all non-economic barriers and stimuli). In some cases, the market potential may be influenced by policies directed at energy efficiency improvement, stimulation of renewable energy, etc. If the effect of policies is included, we can talk about the *enhanced market potential.*

It should be clear that the potentials will generally decrease in the order listed except for the enhanced market potential, which will logically be larger than the market potential. The enhanced market potential can even be larger than the profitable potential or the economic potential – provided that the policies or other incentives are strong enough.

12.2 Reference levels

Apart from the range of technologies that are to be included when calculating these potentials, the reference situation needs to be clear. Potentials are always determined with respect to some (future) reference situation. Two reference levels are often used when dealing with potentials:
- the frozen-technology situation, and
- the business-as-usual situation.

The so-called frozen-technology level is often used as a reference level. This is the hypothetical situation in which no changes in energy supply and demand technology occur. For instance, frozen-efficiency energy use for a future year would be the hypothetical amount of energy used if energy efficiency remains constant while other development proceeds 'as usual'.

Another reference is referred to as business-as-usual, non-intervention or autonomous development. Contrary to frozen-efficiency, likely or expected autonomous technology changes are included in this reference situation. These may include some autonomous improvement of energy efficiency, a certain fuel shift, some adoption of the cheapest renewable energy sources, etc. Business-as-usual often excludes the effect of policy intervention (or assumes there will be no new policy intervention – i.e., 'policies-as-usual'), and assumes there are no important changes on the energy market.

In Figure 12.1, both reference levels and various possible developments are depicted.

When potentials are presented as a percentage or as reduction of the specific energy use, for analytical reasons this is generally done with frozen efficiency as a reference. When the saved energy or the avoided emissions are calculated in absolute terms, the business-as-usual level is more useful as the reference. In most cases, the potentials based on a business-as-usual reference level are more relevant to policy.

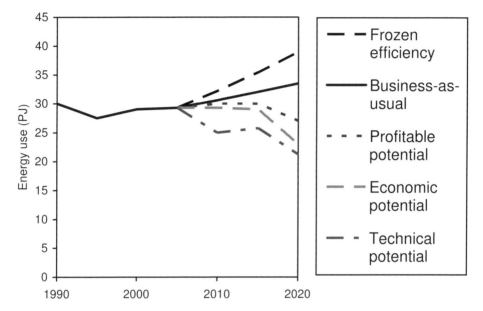

Figure 12.1. The development of energy use according to the various potentials (compared to both the frozen-efficiency level and the business-as-usual level).

12.3 Cost-supply curves

A convenient way to represent technical and economic potential is the so-called cost-supply curve. The cost-supply curve presents how much potential is available below a certain cost level. Cost-supply curves can be developed for all kinds of impact categories, but it is currently very common to develop cost-supply curves for CO_2 emission mitigation. Such a cost-supply curve can be constructed if an overview of all the options to reduce CO_2 emissions is available. The procedure is as follows:

- organise the various options according to increasing costs (e.g., specific CO_2 mitigation costs, see Section 11.5);
- depict the various options in a diagram where the horizontal axis gives the cumulative emission reduction and the vertical axis the specific costs of the last measures.

Figure 12.2 shows how a cost-supply curve can be built up from data about individual options. Cost-supply curves can also be the output of complex energy models.

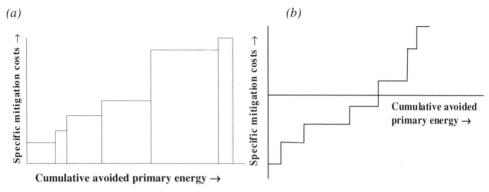

Figure 12.2. (a). Construction of a cost supply curve of emission mitigation technologies. Each rectangle represents one technology. The width of a rectangle reflects the amount of emission reduction, the height the specific cost. (b). Aggregate supply curve. If there are benefits as well the specific emission mitigation, costs may become negative.

Cost-supply curves can be constructed at various levels, e.g. for individual companies, for sectors, for countries, and groups of countries. The supply curves can be used to determine the amount of mitigation that can be achieved below a certain price. Alternatively, the marginal costs can be determined that should be allowed to achieve a certain CO_2 emission reduction or mitigation. See, for example Figure 12.3.

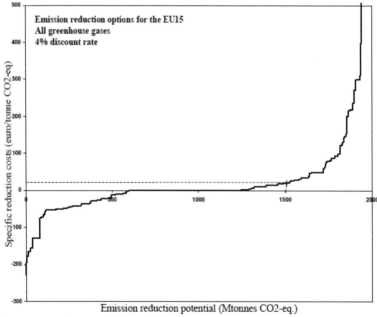

Figure 12.3. Cost-supply curve for the emission reduction of greenhouse gases in the European Union, 2010. The reference level of emissions is frozen technology. Total emission reduction required compared to this level is 1500 Mtonne CO_2-eq. From the diagram, one can conclude that such reduction is possible with measures that show social costs below 20 € per tonne of CO_2. Source: Blok et al., 2001.

12.4 Methods to determine potentials

Several approaches have been developed to determine potentials, especially to explore possibilities for energy efficiency improvement and – in connection with this – to project future energy use.

Thermodynamic methods

In thermodynamic methods, the current level of energy use for specific processes is compared to the minimum thermodynamic energy use. Furthermore, the magnitude and the character of the energy losses are determined (see Section 7.3). Though thermodynamic methods are only suitable for determining the theoretical potential, they may also serve as a starting point for further analysis.

Technical studies

In technical studies, the concrete technical possibilities which might limit (specific) energy use are used to determine the technical potential. The focus is not so much on individual technologies as on the combined impact that all available technologies might have. Technical studies were carried out for various countries in the late 1970s and early 1980s.

Techno-economic analysis

A step further is techno-economic analysis, also known as bottom-up analysis. The reason for techno-economic analysis is – of course – that information on costs is required. However, a concomitant effect is that the focus is much more on the individual technologies. Although techno-economic analysis was first used in the1980s, it became more popular in the 1990s. Techno-economic models permit the technical, economic and profitable potential to be calculated. As techno-economic analysis has become a widely-used method it will be discussed further in Section 12.4.

Trend extrapolation

Historically, energy efficiency improvement is an ongoing process and a certain trend can be distinguished. For instance, the autonomous rate of reduction of aggregate specific energy use is often estimated at 1% per year. This figure results from long-term multi-sector analysis, but for short time periods and individual sectors the development may be very different. Long-term trends are sometimes used for making future projections. At best, trend extrapolation is useful to determine business-as-usual market potentials and associated energy use development.

Economic models

Econometric approaches are also based on historical data. These approaches can include more variables than just time in the analysis. Price effects, in particular, can easily be taken into account (for a further discussion of this approach, see Section 13.3).

With the help of economic models (often, but not always, based on econometric results), it is possible to determine business-as-usual developments. Moreover, these models can calculate the effect of prices and taxes without the need for specific technology information. Indirect costs and benefits of certain developments can also be calculated in many cases.

From this overview of methods, two main classes can be distinguished:
- bottom-up or engineering approaches (techno-economic analysis), which are based on the individual technologies and determine the potentials through aggregation; and
- top-down or economic approaches (economic analysis), which look at the system of energy use (and energy users) from the outside to determine the expected behaviour of the system.

In the past there has been substantial debate between the bottom-up and top-down schools. It is important to realize that the approaches determine different types of potentials. A recent development is the incorporation of results from techno-economic analysis in economic models (combining top-down and bottom-up approaches).

In many cases it is desirable to determine the effects of specific policies or policy packages (the enhanced market potential). Techniques to analyse the expected impact of a broad range of policies are still being developed (for further discussion, see Section 15.4).

12.5 Techno-economic analysis

Techno-economic analysis, the bottom-up approach, is suited to a detailed and comprehensive overview of the potential for energy efficiency improvement, for example on the national level.

Techno-economic analysis of potentials for energy efficiency improvement generally consists of the following steps:
- Breakdown of energy use by sector, energy function and process steps;
- Technology identification, technology characterisation and data storage; and
- Data processing.

First of all, a country's energy consumption has to be broken down into parts that can be treated individually (see Figure 12.4), at least to the level of energy function and, for energy functions that consist of many processes, to the level of process steps. Of course a full breakdown is not always possible, and residual categories will always remain.

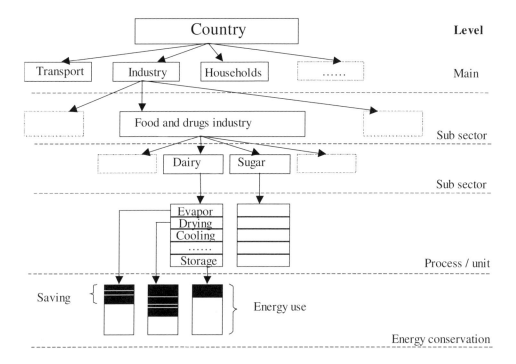

Figure 12.4. Schematic description of the approach generally followed in techno-economic analysis.

Second, technologies that can improve energy efficiency are identified and characterized for each of the selected categories. To carry out a techno-economic analysis for a country as a whole, one generally has to depend on secondary sources, like existing sector studies for the country, extrapolations of sector studies from other countries, technology databases, case studies and practical experience described in the literature, as well as consultation with experts. The main challenge is to compile the information from these diverse – and often incomplete – sources to a common set of characteristics for all the sectors. The characteristics generally consist of technology performance and cost information, though information relevant for implementation and policy analysis may also be included.

The composition of some sample datasets is presented in Table 12.1. The data are generally included in a spreadsheet, database or other information system. In order to cover a full range of energy efficiency improvement options, such information systems need to be quite large, and the databases typically contain data for hundreds or even thousands of technologies. Once the information system is completed, the information can be used to carry out calculations of technical, economic and profitable potential.

Table 12.1. Overview of parameters included for each technology for techno-economic information systems for Germany, The Netherlands and the United Kingdom. Source: Blok et al., 1999.

Country	Germany	The Netherlands	United Kingdom
Name of information system	IKARUS	ICARUS	ENUSIM
Institute	Fraunhofer Gesellschaft ISI, Karlsruhe	Utrecht University	AEA Technology, Culham
Technologies for which data are included	20 branches 1000 processes 4000 technologies (both reference and efficient)	25 branches 200 energy efficiency technologies	378 devices (= unit operations) 4291 technologies and technology combinations (both reference and efficient)
Data included for each technology	Energy consumption (specific, absolute, fuel mix data) Annual output Investment (capital cost, annual fixed cost, variable cost, investment period) Penetration rate Operation time Emissions (CO_2, SO_2 and NO_x, CH_4, NMVOC)	Sector/sub-sector Part of sector for which measure is relevant (%) Saving on fuel or electricity Saving potential (%) Investment (NLG/GJ) O&M costs (NLG/GJ) Lifetime equipment	Devices Name SEC Typical annual output Max. annual output Build time Operating lifetime Capacity profile Fuel mix Technology combinations Name Capital cost Discount rate multiplier[1] Investment period Annual fixed cost Variable cost Specific energy consumption Penetration curves and momentum Fuel mix data

There are a number of problems that have to be addressed when developing and using bottom-up energy efficiency information systems:

- There may be competition between various technologies. For instance, a conventional household boiler can be replaced with either a condensing boiler or a heat pump.

---

[1] A base discount rate is set by the scenario, but this multiplier allows individual technologies to be assigned a different discount rate.

- Overlap may occur with respect to the energy savings of various technologies. For instance, installing a condensing boiler reduces the energy saving effect of wall insulation and vice versa.
- Even for specific technologies and a specific group of energy users, the cost of technologies may vary. This can be caused by differences in local circumstances or differences in the scale of application.
- Costs and performance of technologies are not fixed. Performance may improve and costs may decrease thanks to learning effects. This means that technology characteristics are to some extent dependent on the degree of implementation.
- Stocks of existing capital are gradually replaced in time. Technology characteristics may differ hugely between retrofit situations and completely new plants. In the latter case, the range of applicable technologies is generally wider. This means that capital stock replacement and expansion need to be taken into account.

These problems have to be taken into account in one way or another, either by using sophisticated models or by using ad hoc corrections in such a way that the final calculations are correct. Even if these problems are treated adequately, the approach still has its limitations. For the longer term (>15 years) the overview of technologies becomes incomplete – depending on the way the analysis is performed. Beyond 25 – 30 years in the future techno-economic analysis has limited use.

12.6 Problems with the concept of potentials

Unfortunately, the concept of potentials has some problems. One peculiarity of the technical potential should be mentioned. When energy analysts determine the technical potential, they always limit the options that are included. For instance, completely demolishing the existing building stock and replacing it with super-efficient buildings is generally not included as an option, nor is building insulation with a thickness of 100 cm. For this reason, some analysts argue that technical potential is not a useful concept. They argue that there are always economic considerations involved when determining a technical potential. Nevertheless, many studies determine the technical potential for energy efficiency improvement. In such a case, it is wise to report the 'practical' limitations that have been applied. For example, the normal turnover rate of capital is commonly taken into account when determining technical potential.

For some options, including several renewable energy options, the technical potential is very large, but it is obvious that in many cases it would be impossible to realize these large potentials in a short timeframe, such as a decade. There are no generally accepted methods to deal with these practical limits to technology adoption. In potential studies on renewable energy, ad hoc constraints are often introduced.

Most of the potentials quoted (theoretical potential, technical potential, economic potential and profitable potential) can in principle be determined on the basis of technical or techno-economic analysis. It should be noted, however, that these calculations never have (or never should have) the character of a forecast or projection. In contrast, the market potential, and the construction of business-as-usual developments (or policy-intervention developments) do have the character of a projection. In order to make such projections, in addition to the techno-economic information, assumptions have to be made about the behaviour of the actors involved.

Further reading

Technical studies on energy efficiency:
A.B. Lovins: Soft Energy Paths, Penquin Books, New York. 1977.
G. Leach, C. Lewis, A. van Buren, F. Romig and G. Foley: A low Energy Strategy for the United Kingdom, Science Reviews Ltd., London, 1979.
International Energy Agency: Energy Conservation in IEA Countries, OECD/IEA, Paris, 1987.
J. Goldemberg, T.B. Johansson, A.K.N. Reddy and R.H. Williams: Energy for a Sustainable World, John Wiley, New York, 1988.

Techno-economic studies on energy efficiency and carbon dioxide emission mitigation:
K. Blok, J. Vis, H. Bradke, A. Haworth: Economic-Engineering Studies for Western Europe – a Review, Proceedings of the IEA International Workshop on Technologies to Reduce Greenhouse Gas Emissions: Engineering-Economic Analyses of Conserved Energy and Carbon, Published on www.iea.org/acti.htm, 1999.
K. Blok, D. de Jager and C.A. Hendriks: Economic Evaluation of Sectoral Objectives for Climate Change – Summary for Policy Makers, European Commission, 2001.
J.G. Koomey, C. Atkinson, A. Meier, J.E. McMahon and S. Boghosian: The Potential for Electricity Efficiency Improvement in the US Residential Sector, Lawrence Berkeley National Laboratory, Berkeley, CA, USA, 1991.
J.G. de Beer, M.T. van Wees, E. Worrell and K. Blok: ICARUS-3 – The Potential of Energy Efficiency Improvement in the Netherlands up to 2000 and 2015, Department of Science, Technology and Society, Utrecht University, 1994.

Final achievement levels

After having studied Chapter 12 and the exercises, you should:
-   know the definitions of the various types of potentials;
-   be able to work with the concepts frozen-technology/frozen efficiency and business-as-usual/autonomous development;
-   be able to construct cost-supply curves; and
-   know how techno-economic analysis works and be able to analyze the outcomes of a techno-economic analysis.

Exercises chapter 12

12.1. Energy conservation in a company
A company has an energy use of 1000 TJ per year. Several energy conservation measures are possible, see the table:

Measure	Energy savings (TJ/yr)	Investment (€)	O&M (€/yr)	Lifetime
A	50	300,000	10,000	5
B	50	30,000	30,000	20
C	50	750,000	30,000	20
D	100	750,000	20,000	20
E	50	1,500,000	40,000	20

a. Calculate the technical potential and the profitable potential (criterion for the latter: payback period of 5 years).
b. Construct a cost-supply curve, using a discount rate of 15%.
Use a uniform energy price of € 3 per GJ.

12.2. Energy conservation in a house
The natural gas consumption for a house is 100 GJ per year. Three different types of energy conservation measures are considered: wall insulation, roof insulation, and window insulation. The investments for these options are, respectively, 20, 30 and 200 € per m^2. The relevant areas are 40, 60 and 10 m^2. The annual energy savings are 600, 300 and 1000 MJ per m^2 respectively. The natural gas price is 15 Euro per GJ. Use a discount rate of 10% and a depreciation period of 30 years. Operation and maintenance costs can be neglected.
a. Can you explain why the saving per m^2 of insulated area is less for roof insulation than for wall insulation (insulation thickness and material are the same)?
b. Construct an energy conservation cost supply curve for the house.
c. Can you explain why the most costly measure is applied most? What can one do to let cost-supply curves give the right impression of the attractiveness of measures?

In addition, a condensing boiler is added to the package of options. A condensing boiler has an additional investment of 1000 Euro and saves 15% of the natural gas demand. The additional operation and maintenance costs are 30 Euro per year.
d. Construct an energy conservation cost supply curve in which the three options mentioned above and the condensing boiler are included.

12.3. The potential of efficient lighting
A country has 10 million households. On average, the households have 25 lamps. Of these lamps, 20% is on for 1000 hours per year, 20% is on for 500 hours per year, 20% is on for 100 hours per year, and the remaining 40% are on for 50 hours per year.
So far, only incandescent lamps are used in the country. Electricity can be saved through the use of compact fluorescent lamps (CFLs). Assume that incandescent lamps consume 60 W and CFLs use 15 W. The cost of a CFL is €5. The CFL has a lifetime of 10,000 hours (hours in use). Neglect the avoided costs of the conventional incandescent lamp. The price of electricity is 0.15 €/kWh. In the calculations, use a social discount rate of 5% per year.

a. Determine the technical and economic potential for electricity saving by efficient lighting (compared to a frozen-efficiency baseline). Use a realistic level for the lifetime of the light bulbs.
b. Construct a cost-supply curve for CO_2 emission mitigation by energy-efficient lighting (assume that per kWh saved 0.5 kg CO_2 emission is avoided).

12.4. Reference levels

In the previous exercise the potential was determined against a frozen-efficiency baseline.
a. Why is this potential not very relevant for policy makers?
b. Determine the potentials against a business-as-usual baseline. Assume that households will adopt 80% of the CFLs with pay-back times less than 2 years, 40% of the CFLs with pay-back times between 2 and 4 years, and none of the CFLs with longer pay-back-times
c. So far, time was not taken into account. Discuss how time could be brought into the equation.

13

Volume, structure and energy efficiency

One of the key tasks of energy analysis is to provide a better understanding of the way the energy use of a firm, a sector, or a country develops over time. This chapter will be devoted to concepts and methods that may improve such understanding. Similar methods can be used to understand why countries or regions differ in energy use.

Energy efficiency – as discussed in Chapter 10 – is not the only factor that determines the level of energy use. The other factors are volume (total amount of human activity) and structure (type of human activity). After discussing these concepts (13.1), this chapter moves on to so-called decomposition methods that can disentangle these factors (13.2). Econometric analysis, which is another approach to analyse the historic development of energy use, will be discussed in Section 13.3.

13.1 Volume, structure and energy efficiency

In general, the development of energy use for a country, a sector and even for an individual firm or household can be broken down into separate factors:
- Volume: the total level of activities;
- Structure: the mix of activities; and
- Energy efficiency (expressed, e.g., as the energy use per unit of activity).

'Volume' describes total activity and is most often described in monetary terms. For a country as a whole, gross domestic product (GDP) is an indicator of total activity.

In economics, 'structure' is generally used to describe the breakdown of a national economy into sectors. Here, the word structure is used more generally to indicate any mix of activities. It is important to recognize that structure can be distinguished on various levels:
- First, the contribution of various main sectors (agriculture, manufacturing industry, commercial services) to GDP.
- Second, the breakdown of these main sectors into sectors. This is most important in manufacturing industry (food and drugs, pulp and paper, chemicals, basic metals, etc).
- Third, a breakdown of sectors into sub-sectors (e.g., dairy and sugar within food and drugs; iron/steel and aluminium in basic metals).

- Fourth, within a sub-sector various products can often be distinguished (e.g., primary and secondary steel, hot rolled steel and cold rolled steel).
- Finally, the character of specific products may be different (e.g., materials may have undergone different finishing operations – steel may be galvanized or not).

For the so-called non-productive sectors (households and transport), other breakdowns are useful: e.g., the mix of appliances used by households; or the so-called modal split in transportation, distinguishing transportation modes (passenger car, public surface transport, air transport, etc.).

The third factor that needs to be taken into account is energy efficiency or specific energy use – as was described in Chapter 10.

13.2 Decomposition of volume, structure and energy efficiency

One often wants to decompose the development of energy use into the three factors mentioned above: volume, structure and energy efficiency. The question then is: how does each of these factors affect energy use over time?
In general, energy use can be written as follows:

$$ E = V \cdot \sum_x \frac{A_x}{V} \cdot \frac{E_x}{A_x} \qquad [13.1] $$

where the following quantities are all a function of time:
E   = total energy use
V   = total volume of activities (in monetary terms)
A_x = volume of activity of type x (in monetary or physical terms)
E_x = the energy use associated with the activity of type x

In this expression we recognise the three factors:
- V represents volume
- the terms A_x/V together describe the structure (mix of activities)
- for each activity x, the term E_x/A_x describes the energy intensity (or specific energy use or EEI if A_x is in physical terms).

Although equation [13.1] formally describes the relation between energy use and the three factors, it does not help us to understand how each of these factors affects the development of energy use over time. There are various approaches we can use to determine the effect of each of the factors.

First of all, there are some *simple* approaches:

1. The effect of each of the factors is determined one-by-one. First, the effect of volume on energy use is determined by keeping the other two factors constant; then the same is done for structure and efficiency.

2. The effect of each of the factors is determined successively. First, the effect of volume on energy use is determined, by keeping the other two factors constant. Second, the joint effect of volume and structure is determined by keeping the energy efficiency constant; the effect of structure is the difference between the first and the second. Finally, the effect of energy efficiency changes is the difference between the actual energy use and the outcome of the second calculation.

Both of these simple approaches have disadvantages. In the first method, the effects of the three factors together do not necessarily add up to the total effect. In the second method, the order in which the three effects are determined has an impact on the effects calculated for each of the three factors.

These problems are manifestations of the problem of residuals (see Box 13.1). In the first method, part of the change in energy use is not allocated to any of the factors. In the second, no residual remains, but it is arbitrarily allocated to one of the factors (depending on the order in which the factors are analysed).

Next, there are formal *decomposition methods*, which have been developed by economists who wanted to decompose economic growth into the factors 'price effect' and 'volume effect'. The same methods are useful to decompose the development of energy use into several factors.

In fact, the first simple approach quoted above is a decomposition method, but suffers from too large a residual. In all decomposition methods, the expression $\Delta E = E_{t2} - E_{t1}$ is written as the *product* or the *sum* of (at least) three terms, each representing effects of changes in volume, structure and energy efficiency, and a residual. In general, the methods for which the development is written as the sum of the three elements provide most easily interpretable results. Such decomposition would look as follows:

$$\Delta E = a \cdot \Delta V + b_1 \cdot \Delta \left(\frac{A_1}{V} \right) + b_2 \cdot \Delta \left(\frac{A_2}{V} \right) + \ldots + c_1 \cdot \Delta \left(\frac{E_1}{A_1} \right) + c_2 \cdot \left(\Delta \frac{E_2}{A_2} \right) + \ldots + r \qquad [13.2]$$

$$\underbrace{}_{\text{volume effect}} \quad \underbrace{}_{\text{structure effect}} \quad \underbrace{}_{\text{efficiency effect}}$$

where:

Δx	= the change in variable x in year t_2 compared to t_1
$a, b_1, b_2, \ldots, c_1, c_2$	= functions of V, A_1, A_2, $\ldots$, E_1, E_2
r	= a residue in which product terms of the Δ-terms occur

Box 13.1 presents a simple two-factor decomposition. The problem of the residuals is not completely solved, but can be substantially reduced by a careful selection of the decomposition methodology.

Box 13.1. Residuals in decomposition analysis.

Let us consider the simple situation for which energy use E_t is only determined by volume V_t and energy intensity ε_t.

$$E_t = V_t \cdot \varepsilon_t \qquad [13.3]$$

$$
\begin{aligned}
\Delta E &= E_{t2} - E_{t1} \\
&= V_{t2} \cdot \varepsilon_{t2} - V_{t1} \cdot \varepsilon_{t1} \\
&= (V_{t1} + \Delta V) \cdot (\varepsilon_{t1} + \Delta\varepsilon) - V_{t1} \cdot \varepsilon_{t1} \\
&= V_{t1} \cdot \Delta\varepsilon + \varepsilon_{t1} \cdot \Delta V + \Delta\varepsilon \cdot \Delta V
\end{aligned}
\qquad [13.4]
$$

where:
$$\Delta\varepsilon = \varepsilon_{t2} - \varepsilon_{t1}$$
$$\Delta V = V_{t2} - V_{t1}$$

We see that it is possible to write the change in E as a sum of two terms that are proportional to the change in V and the change in ε. However, a residual $\Delta\varepsilon \cdot \Delta V$ remains that is related to both factors and that may be substantial if the changes are large in relative terms.

A simple trick can help to reduce the residual. Instead of using the situation in starting year t_1 as the basis for the decomposition, one could take the average of the situation in the years t_1 and t_2. In the case of a two-factor decomposition, this leads to a zero residual.

$$
\begin{aligned}
\Delta E &= V_{t2} \cdot \varepsilon_{t2} - V_{t1} \cdot \varepsilon_{t1} \\
&= \tfrac{1}{2}(V_{t1} + V_{t2}) \cdot \Delta\varepsilon + \tfrac{1}{2}(\varepsilon_{t1} + \varepsilon_{t2}) \cdot \Delta V
\end{aligned}
\qquad [13.5]
$$

Avoiding the residual completely is generally only possible when there are only two factors. For larger numbers of factors, several so-called divisia methods exist, each consisting of a specific set of formulas and assumptions. They generally differ in the significance of the residuals.

A decomposition of the development of industrial energy use for a number of countries is given in Table 13.1. This is a classic example in which three factors are considered (cf. equation [13.1]):
- total industrial production (expressed in total value added of industry);
- sector structure (the mix of industrial sectors within manufacturing industry); and
- energy intensity (energy use per unit of value added for each sector).

Table 13.1. Average annual rates of change in manufacturing energy use, and the degree to which changes in volume, structure and energy intensity contribute to such change. The percentages in the last nine columns show how much each of these factors contributed to the growth (+) or decline (-) of energy use in the period mentioned. Source: Unander et al., 2001.

Country	Changes in energy use			Effect on energy use of changes of total industrial production volume			Effect on energy use of changes in industrial structure			Effect on energy use of changes in energy intensities of individual industrial sectors		
	1973-1986	1986-1990	1990-1994	1973-1986	1986-1990	1990-1994	1973-1986	1986-1990	1990-1994	1973-1986	1986-1990	1990-1994
Australia	0.3%	3.3%	0.8%	1.1%	3.2%	1.9%	0.0%	0.6%	-0.4%	-1.2%	-2.1%	0.1%
Canada	N/A	0.7%	0.8%	2.0%	1.7%	1.4%	N/A	-0.1%	0.4%	N/A	-0.8%	-1.0%
Denmark	-1.1%	-3.3%	1.5%	2.1%	-0.6%	0.9%	-0.3%	-0.1%	0.0%	-2.9%	-2.6%	0.7%
Finland	1.7%	3.3%	1.8%	2.9%	3.2%	1.6%	-0.1%	0.3%	1.6%	-2.0%	-0.2%	-1.5%
France	-2.3%	1.3%	0.7%	1.2%	3.2%	-0.5%	-0.2%	0.1%	0.0%	-3.3%	-2.0%	1.2%
W. Germany	-1.8%	0.6%	-0.5%	1.1%	2.7%	-1.4%	-0.4%	-0.5%	1.0%	-2.6%	-1.6%	-0.1%
Italy	-1.8%	3.8%	-0.7%	3.4%	4.0%	0.2%	0.0%	0.2%	0.4%	-5.2%	-0.4%	-1.4%
Japan	-1.8%	3.5%	-0.1%	3.2%	6.3%	-0.4%	-2.0%	-0.2%	0.1%	-3.0%	-2.6%	0.2%
Netherlands	-4.0%	4.4%	0.0%	1.8%	2.8%	0.6%	1.1%	-0.4%	0.8%	-6.9%	2.0%	-1.5%
Norway	0.1%	-0.9%	1.5%	0.5%	-1.3%	2.0%	0.6%	2.2%	0.8%	-1.1%	-1.8%	-1.3%
Sweden	-1.4%	0.0%	0.0%	1.3%	1.5%	1.3%	-0.4%	0.3%	2.8%	-2.2%	-1.9%	-4.1%
UK	-3.6%	0.0%	-2.4%	-0.7%	3.9%	-0.2%	-0.4%	-0.3%	-0.5%	-2.6%	-3.6%	-1.6%
USA	-1.9%	2.9%	1.9%	2.0%	3.0%	1.8%	-1.1%	-0.5%	0.1%	-2.8%	0.5%	1.6%

In addition to changes between sectors, a structural effect within subsectors can also be considered. This structural effect has also been referred to as a *dematerialisation effect*, because it is defined as the decrease of the ratio of physical production to value added (P_x/A_x). This results in an extension of equation [13.1], in which the specific energy consumption (E_x/P_x) is included:

$$E = V \cdot \sum_x \frac{A_x}{V} \cdot \frac{P_x}{A_x} \cdot \frac{E_x}{P_x}$$ [13.6]

where the following quantities are all a function of time:
E = total energy use
V = the total volume of activities (in monetary terms)
A_x = the volume of activity of type x (in monetary terms)
P_x = the physical activity of type x (in physical terms, such as tonnes of product)
E_x = the energy use associated with the activity of type x

Figure 13.1 presents an analysis including structural changes at two levels of sectoral aggregation and dematerialisation.

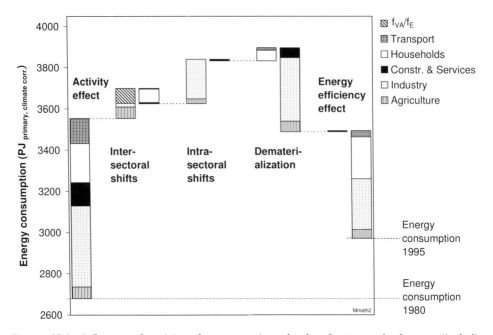

Figure 13.1. Influence of activity changes, various levels of structural changes (including dematerialisation), and energy efficiency on the total primary energy use in the Netherlands. The factor f_{VA}/f_E refers to the fact that the sectoral analysis does not cover the complete energy use and the complete value added of the Netherlands' economy. Source: Farla and Blok, 2000.

13.3 Econometric analysis

Prices of energy were not considered in the decomposition methods described above. In economics, prices are considered a central driver of developments in society, along with economic growth and technical change. Econometricians try to capture these impacts in mathematical relations. In this section, we treat a simple description of the development of energy use for a sector.

External factors that are considered important determinants of energy use are the price of energy (p) and the activity in the sector (A). Both p and A are time-dependent. Hence, the energy use in a sector can be written as follows:

$$E(t) = f(p, A) \qquad\qquad [13.7]$$

The exact form of the function f depends on assumptions about how the sector produces goods and services with the help of capital, labour and feedstocks. A function that is often used is:

$$E(t) = p^{\alpha} \cdot A^{\beta} \cdot \gamma \qquad\qquad [13.8a]$$

In this expression we recognize the price dependence of energy use, as was described in Section 5.7; the parameter α is the price elasticity. If the parameter β is 1, then the energy demand is proportional to sector activity. If β is smaller than one, then the energy use grows slower than the sector activity.

In econometric analysis, the parameters (in this case α, β and γ) are determined on the basis of historic time series for the variables $E(t)$, $p(t)$ and $A(t)$. The parameters α, β and γ are chosen in such a way that the equation shows a good fit. An approach that is often used is a linear least-squares solution of the following equation, which is equivalent to equation [13.8a]:

$$\ln E(t) = \alpha \cdot \ln p + \beta \cdot \ln A + \ln \gamma \qquad\qquad [13.8b]$$

Other elements can also be included in the equation, such as policies that affect energy use. Parameter estimates from econometric analysis can be used in economic models (see Chapter 14).

The strength of this approach is that no explicit analysis is necessary of what happens within a sector. A methodological weakness is that it is not easy to disentangle the effects of several correlated causes. For example, periods with high energy prices are also often periods with enhanced policy efforts aimed at reducing energy use.

Further reading

B.W. Ang: Sector Disaggregation Structural Effects and Industrial Energy Use – An Approach to Analyse the Interrelationship, Energy, 18 (1993) pp. 1033-1044.

B.W. Ang, F.Q. Zhang: A Survey of Index Decomposition Analysis in Energy and Environmental Studies, Energy, 25 (2000) pp. 1149-1176.

G. Boyd, J.F. McDonald, M. Ross, D.A. Hanson: Separating the Changing Composition of U.S. Manufacturing Production from Energy Efficiency Improvements: a Divisia Index Approach, The Energy Journal, 8 (1987) pp. 77-96.

J.C.M. Farla, K. Blok: Energy efficiency and structural change in the Netherlands 1980-1995, Journal of Industrial Ecology, 4 (2000) pp. 93-117.

M.G. Patterson: An Accounting Framework for Decomposing the Energy-to-GDP Ratio into Its Structural Components of Change, Energy, 18 (1993) pp. 741-761.

F. Unander, S. Karbuz, L.J. Schipper, M. Khrush, M. Ting: Manufacturing Energy Use in OECD Countries: Decomposition of Long Term Trends, in: New Equilibria in the Energy Markets, Energy Policy, 29 (2001) pp. 83-102.

J.M. Wooldridge: Introductory Econometrics – A Modern Approach, Thomson/South-Western, Mason, Ohio, 2002.

Final achievement levels

After having studied Chapter 13 and the exercises, you should:
- be able to explain how volume, structure and energy efficiency influence energy use;
- know how decomposition methods work and be able to discuss the role of residues;
- be able to carry out a simple decomposition, e.g. for one sector; and
- understand how econometric analysis proceeds.

Exercises chapter 13

13.1. Energy efficiency of refrigerators
In 1990, five million refrigerators were in use in a country, each using (on average) 300 kWh per year. In 2000, the number of refrigerators had increased to six million. The average energy use per refrigerator had decreased to 200 kWh per year.
a. How much energy was consumed by the refrigerators in 1990 and in 2000? What is the difference?
b. What would the difference have been if there had been no increase in the number of refrigerators?
c. What would the difference have been if there had been no change in the energy use per refrigerator?
d. Why is the sum of the results of questions b and c not equal to the difference determined in a?
e. When fully decomposed (residual reduced to zero), what is the effect of the volume increase and the energy efficiency improvement on the energy use?

13.2. Three factor decomposition
Write out the full decomposition in equation [13.1] to a sum of three terms, each including a change in volume, a change in structure, and a change in energy intensity, plus a residue. Hint: use the formalism as indicated in equation [13.4] in Box 13.1.

13.3. Decomposition of industrial energy use
Look closely at Table 13.2 for a number of countries.
What is usually the effect of volume, structure and energy intensity on the energy use? Check whether there are differences between the three periods considered. What do you notice? Can you think of an explanation?

13.4. Energy-efficiency indicators for metal manufacturing
For a certain country, the (physical) amounts of steel, copper and aluminium produced are shown in the table below. The total amount of energy used for the production of these metals is also given.

Year	Steel (tonnes)	Copper (tonnes)	Aluminium (tonnes)	Primary energy use (TJ)
1995	5,000	300	200	160
2000	6,000	350	180	170
2005	7,000	350	200	173

In the year 1995, the specific energy use for the production of steel was 20 GJ/tonne, for copper this was 80 GJ/tonne and for aluminium this was 180 GJ/tonne. Use these values as reference-SECs

a. Calculate the physical production index PPI for 2000 and 2005 (1995=100).
b. Also calculate the energy efficiency index EEI.
c. Explain why the ratio of PPI to total metal production can be considered as an indicator for the sector structure.
d. What is the relative difference between 1990 and 2000 with regard to volume (= total amount of metal produced), with regard to structure, and with regard to energy use?
e. Make a decomposition of the volume, structural and efficiency effects for the change from 1995 to 2005

13.5. Determining price elasticities
The following data are available for energy use in an industrial sector and the average price of energy for that sector, for a number of years:

Year	1996	1998	2000	2002	2004
Energy use (PJ)	103	100	102	95	88
Price (€/GJ)	3.1	3.0	3.5	4.0	5.5

Neglect the impact of activity change and technological development and determine the sole effect of the energy price by estimating α in the following equation: $E(t) = p(t)^{\alpha} \cdot \gamma$.
Hint: note that this equation can easily be made linear by taking the logarithm. Subsequently, you can estimate α either graphically or – if you have access to it – by a linear least-square approximation.

14

Building energy scenarios

Energy scenarios are developed in many ways, both national and international, short term and long term, and for a variety of purposes. Everybody working in the energy field will regularly encounter such scenarios. Therefore, it is important to have a good understanding of the reasons why scenarios are made, how they are constructed, and the pitfalls in constructing and interpreting them. What can scenarios be used for and what can they not be used for?

This chapter first gives a brief introduction to the scenario approach, including the various types of scenarios that can be distinguished (14.1). Next, ways of developing scenarios are discussed, both for the demand side (14.2) and the supply side (14.3). Subsequently, limitations of the scenario approach are discussed (14.4). Finally, an overview is given of some of the most frequently used scenarios (14.5).

14.1 The scenario approach

Scenario building can be defined as a technique that tries to provide a logical order of events in order to clarify how – departing from the present situation – a future situation (or a number of alternative future situations) can develop step-by-step. The outcome of a scenario exercise is often referred to as a *projection.*

A scenario may be developed for various purposes. The most well known are scenarios that are developed by governments as a tool for preparing, for example, energy or environmental policy. Non-governmental organisations (NGOs such as environmental pressure groups) develop scenarios, especially to draw attention to alternative policy options. Companies also use scenario analysis to estimate the market chances of their products, to assess risks, or to attain an optimum planning of their investments.

Scenarios can be classified in a number of ways:
a. Scenarios can explore or they can forecast. In general, the aim of scenario development is to explore the future, to work out which possible developments may occur and what the consequences of these developments might be. In some cases, a more deterministic starting-point is taken, and the emphasis is on prediction or forecasting. These two scenario types cannot be strictly separated. Explorative scenarios generally depart from certain regularities that determine the boundaries

within which one expects future developments to occur. This is necessary to attain consistent and realistic results, but by so doing it limits the forecasting value.

b. Scenarios can be explorative or normative. Explorative scenarios try to map different possible development paths towards the future, whereas normative scenarios try to indicate how a desired future outcome can be attained. This separation is also not strict, and explorative scenarios often turn out to contain implicit normative choices. In the case of normative scenarios, one generally tries to remain within the boundaries of the feasible (although they often explore whether these boundaries can be stretched).

c. In many cases, a whole set of scenarios is developed, with one of them serving as a so-called reference scenario: it is based on the existing trends within society, assuming there will not be major trend changes, big social changes, or enhanced government intervention. A reference scenario can be referred to as business-as-usual, baseline, non-intervention, trend or conventional wisdom. Such a reference scenario is contrasted with some alternative scenarios in order to show how different assumptions affect the outcomes.

Some scenario builders choose to use multiple baselines rather than selecting one specific scenario as the reference scenario, in order to leave the explorative character of their work as open as possible.

d. A distinction should be made between scenarios that describe the situation one year ('scene') in the future and scenarios that describe a series of years. Scenarios of the latter type are often developed using so-called vintage models, which explicitly model the building up of capital stock and the regular replacement of old capital stock with new stock.

e. It is important not to confuse a *scenario* with the tools that are used for constructing it. In scenario construction a *model* is often used to give a (quantitative) description of the relation between various quantities. Generally, such model is translated into a *computer program*. These three matters (models, computer code, and scenarios) are sometimes mixed up; however, a specific model or computer code can frequently produce a range of different scenarios.

Scenario development needs to satisfy two important criteria:

1. Internal consistency. When developing a scenario, one needs to take care that assumptions are not mutually conflicting and that the various assumptions are coherent.

2. Transparency. The construction of the scenario needs to be completely clear. For instance: what are the basic assumptions, both qualitative and quantitative, underlying the scenario development? What model relations are assumed? Which scenario characteristics are the outcomes of calculations and which are input assumptions?

14.2 Modelling approaches for energy demand

In the past, (long-term) energy demand scenarios were developed using trend extrapolation. For instance, the future demand for electricity was estimated by simply extrapolating the historical exponential growth of electricity demand.

Currently, most energy demand scenario construction takes into account all the elements that were discussed in Chapter 13, in one way or another: volume, sector structure and energy efficiency. This section will treat first volume and structure, and then energy efficiency; the next section will treat modelling of energy supply. However, in many energy models the separation is not that strict, and all components are treated in an integrated way.

Development of volume and structure

In order to develop a picture of future energy demand, one generally starts by constructing an image of how human activities will develop in the future, in general, based on how the future economy is expected to look. Not only is the total size of the economy important, expressed in macro-economic variables, such as GDP, income, and employment, but also how the activities are broken down across various sectors. The latter breakdown is especially important for energy scenario development, as the energy-intensity of the different sectors shows a wide variation.

A consistent image of the future economy is developed with help of a quantitative economic model. Such a model describes the growth of the economy based on such functions as the build-up of capital stock, technological development and external factors. It also describes the relation between the various sectors in the economy and how production and consumption, or savings and investments are related.

A number of model types are available, providing a comprehensive quantitative description of a complete economy, generally including the energy sector. Some characteristic approaches are:

- *General equilibrium models*[1] are the most commonly used nowadays. Based on neo-classical economic theory, the volumes of production and consumption and prices are determined through the equilibrium of supply and demand (see Box 5.1). The producing sectors are described by production functions that express output as a function of the inputs of capital, labour, and – depending on the application of the model – resources and energy. Consuming sectors can be described according to the price elasticities of the various commodities. On the basis of all these relations, a so-

---

[1] Besides general equilibrium models, we have *partial equilibrium models*. As the name suggests, they do not model the complete equilibrium in an economy, but only the equilibrium in specific markets, in the case of energy models in the various energy markets.

called computable general equilibrium (CGE) model is built, which can calculate all volumes and prices in society.

- *Macro-econometric models* model the economy on the basis of empirical relations between various variables that describe the economy. These relations can be determined with the help of historic data series (for a brief description, see Section 13.3). In the macro-econometric approach, the economy is not necessary always in full equilibrium.
- *Input-output models* are based on a full and detailed description of the relations between economic sectors as described in the national account statistics (see the description in Section 9.3). Input-output models are especially useful for a detailed analysis of the relations between the sectors of an economy.

In practice, most models are a mix of the various approaches. For instance, in CGE models, parameters can be partly derived from econometric analysis. Most models are multi-sectoral (though one-sector models are also used); such models need some kind of formal description of the intersectoral relations, as in input-output models.

Such a modelling environment allows a consistent image of the future economy to be developed. This still requires a variety of input assumptions, such as how the world economy will develop, whether international trade will grow strongly or not, how the emerging Asian economies will develop, and whether further integration of the European Union will occur. Expectations about national developments also need to be considered (for example, the development of part-time work, savings behaviour, the effects of ageing).

The amount of economic activity per sector is generally described in monetary terms, in terms of the value of output or in the value added, but these factors may be poor indicators of the energy use of a sector. For instance, the steel sector may realize a growth of value added, thanks to better steel qualities, while total steel production remains constant. In the consuming sectors (notably the residential sector and passenger transport), the relation between energy use and activity in monetary terms (like total household income) is equally weak. The weakness of the link between activity in monetary terms and physical terms represents an unsolved problem in energy modelling.

Energy efficiency and energy use

Once the level of human activities has been determined in sufficient detail, the next step is to determine final energy use. The most common approach is a so-called top-down approach. In this approach, energy use is determined as a function of (mainly) economic activities and energy prices; see, for instance, equation [13.8] in Section 13.3. Autonomous energy efficiency improvements are also frequently modelled by introducing a so-called autonomous energy efficiency improvement rate (AEEI). AEEI can be in terms of a percentage reduction per year.

In most of these models, determining energy use is not a separate step, but is an integral part of the total modelling exercise. In general equilibrium models, this is even necessary, as all markets, including energy markets, need to be in equilibrium in such models.

There are also models that include bottom-up information from techno-economic analysis, as described in Section 12.5. This can be done in various ways, by converting the results of the techno-economic analysis to a supply curve that can be integrated in the economic model, or by adding a module that explicitly models the adoption of energy-efficient technologies.

14.3 Modelling approaches for energy supply

An energy supply scenario describes how the extraction of primary energy and energy conversions can supply a certain final demand in energy. Both the various conversion processes and the connections between these conversion processes need to be described in an energy model. Such an energy supply system is generally described in physical terms, so that all inputs and outputs of energy extraction, conversion and final demand are described in terms of amounts of energy.

In comparison to energy demand scenarios, energy supply scenarios traditionally pay more attention to the description of individual conversion technologies. In doing so, assumptions need to be made about the future performance of these technologies, considering:
* conversion efficiency;
* specific investments (investment per unit of output or per unit of capacity);
* operational costs; and
* specific emissions (emissions per unit of output or per unit of input).

After making an estimate of future performance, one needs to determine which conversion routes will be used in the scenario. This is generally done by using modelling tools, of which economic optimisation is probably the most common. This selects the cheapest system (considering all possible components and routes selected for the model) under certain boundary conditions. Of course, the demand side and the supply side of an energy system influence each other. For instance, the composition of the electricity production system influences electricity prices, which affects electricity demand. This demand, in turn, affects the composition of the electricity production system. Many models place the supply side as an integral part of the total model.

A specific class of optimisation models is based on one specific optimisation algorithm, *linear programming*. In linear programming, all model relations are written as linear equations. This technique can optimise a certain goal function (e.g., minimizing the total costs of the system) within the boundaries set by the linear equations. In general, linear programming models are much richer in technological detail than most of the energy-supply models that are part of the economic models mentioned before. In most cases, however, the technological detail focuses predominantly on the supply-side of the energy system.

14.4 Pitfalls of the scenario approach

Energy scenarios are an important tool for obtaining a better understanding of possible future developments. However, they also present a number of problems including the following:

- The various components of the model do not always have a proper balance. For example, the treatment of the demand side and the supply side of the energy system may not be balanced, leading to results where options to reduce greenhouse gases appear more sizeable on the supply side than they do on the demand side (or vice versa).

- Assumptions about new technologies, such as efficiency or cost figures, can be either too pessimistic or too optimistic in comparison with existing technologies. This can lead to distorted outcomes in models that apply cost minimization. It is important to acknowledge that such models are often sensitive to small changes in cost assumptions: small changes in the assumptions can lead to substantial changes in outcomes, e.g. the adoption of certain technologies.

- New technological developments are often not sufficiently taken into account in long-term projections. For longer time periods, the assumed technological development is often limited to what can be currently anticipated. Since the foreseeable time period is limited to 15 – 25 years, long-term scenarios can be mistakenly pessimistic, as when estimating the potential for long-term energy efficiency improvements.

- Our perspective is limited. The assumptions used in scenario construction are essentially just an echo of current developments. A good example is the projection of world oil prices in the early 1980s: a dramatic increase was projected based on an extrapolation of recent trends. Instead, oil prices collapsed.

- Another problem is that the results of a scenario study can be incorrectly used or misinterpreted. For instance, a business-as-usual scenario is often considered as a forecast ('scenario X shows that energy demand will keep on growing'), or an investigation of the technical potential of a new technology is considered as a policy scenario.

- And, unfortunately, many energy scenarios do not satisfy the transparency requirement. In many cases, the assumptions underlying the scenarios are insufficiently reported. In some cases it is even not clear which data are assumptions made by the researchers and which are the results of model calculations. One of the reasons for lack of transparency is that computer models used for the development of energy scenarios have become more and more complex; therefore, it is always important to determine the right level of complexity for a specific problem.

14.5 An overview of some scenarios

Many agencies and research institutes produce scenarios for individual countries, economic regions, or the world as a whole. Some international scenario approaches are the following:

- The World Energy Outlook by the International Energy Agency (IEA) is published every year and provides energy projections for the world, broken down into ten regions, for 20 – 25 years ahead. The approach is typically top-down modelling of the demand side, using a separate least-cost optimisation model for the power generation sector. Special attention is paid to modelling oil supply. The published results mainly focus on developments at the supply-side of the energy system, but the attention for energy-efficiency options is increasing.

- The National Technical University of Athens develops energy scenarios for the European Commission, in cooperation with other research groups in Europe, using the energy model PRIMES. PRIMES is a partial equilibrium model, distinguishing about 20 sectors. It contains a fairly extended modelling of the energy supply sector, especially the electricity sector. The modelling of energy demand is derived from techno-economic analysis to some extent. This is a typical example of a model that combines bottom-up and top-down elements. Each member state of the European Union is modelled separately, and results are published about every five years, see the publications by Mantzos and Capros (2006).

- Markal (Market Allocation) is currently the best known example of a linear programming model for the energy system. National research groups in many countries apply Markal to their national energy systems, coordinated under the umbrella of the International Energy Agency. The supply side of the energy system is generally modelled in much technological detail, though more and more attention is being paid to the demand side. The applications of national Markal models can be very diverse, sometimes serving as the basis for national policy making. A typical application of the Markal model is to determine the least-cost composition of the energy system under certain constraints (e.g., a cap on carbon dioxide emissions).

- Very long-term scenarios (up to 2100) are being developed within the framework of the Intergovernmental Panel on Climate Change (IPCC), the scientific advisory committee on climate change to the United Nations. These scenarios explore the long-term development of the energy system and the associated greenhouse gas emissions. The models used by the IPCC are developed by various research groups and often have a top-down character, with different levels of technological detail. A new set of scenarios was presented in 2000 by Nakićenvović et al. The greenhouse gas emission scenarios serve as input to models of the Earth's climate system. The latter provide estimates of the changes in temperature and other changes in climate due to the enhanced greenhouse effect.

- An important forum for comparing and discussing energy scenarios is the Energy Modelling Forum[2]. The emphasis is on economic modelling.

---

[2] See: http://www.stanford.edu/group/EMF/.

- Several cooperating international experts have developed normative scenarios. An example is the study by Goldemberg et al. (1988) that – in relation to the report of the World Commission on Environment and Development – explored the feasibility of a sustainable development of the worldwide energy system. In 1992 Johansson et al. published a report on the feasibility of a large-scale penetration of renewables in the electricity and fuel supply system. Scenarios exploring the development of low energy end-use were published in the framework of the World Energy Council (Levine et al., 1995). The basic methodology in all these studies is techno-economic analysis of options, in combination with the use of appropriate models where necessary.

Further reading

K. Blok, D. de Jager, C, Hendriks: Economic Evaluation of Sectoral Emission Reduction Objectives – Summary Report for Policy Makers, European Commission, Brussels, March 2001, http://www.europa.eu.int/comm/environment/envcco/climate_change/sectoral_objectives.htm.

J. Goldemberg, T.B. Johansson, A.K.N. Reddy, R.H. Williams: Energy for a Sustainable World, John Wiley & Sons, New York, 1988.

L. Mantzos and P. Capros: European Energy and Transport Trends to 2030 – Update 2005, Office for Official Publications of the European Communities, Luxembourg, 2006.

L. Mantzos and P. Capros: European Energy and Transport Scenarios on Energy Efficiency and Renewables, Office for Official Publications of the European Communities, Luxembourg, 2006.

N. Nakićenović (ed.), Special Report on Emission Scenarios, Cambridge University Press, Cambridge, UK, 2000.

T.B. Johansson, T.B., H. Kelly, A.K.N. Reddy, R.H. Williams: Renewable Energy – Sources for Fuels and Electricity, Island Press, Washington D.C., 1993.

M.D. Levine, N.D. Martin, L.K. Price, E. Worrell (eds.): Efficient Use of Energy Using High Technology – An Assessment of Energy Use in Industry and Buildings, World Energy Council, London, UK, 1995.

B. Metz, O. Davidson, R. Swart, J. Pan (eds.): Climate Change 2001 – Mitigation, Cambridge University Press, Cambridge, UK, 2001.

V. Smil: Energy at the Crossroads – Global Perspectives and Uncertainties, MIT Press, Cambridge, Massachusetts, USA, 2005. (See especially Chapter 3: Against forecasting)

World Energy Outlook 200x, International Energy Agency, Paris, published annually.

World Energy Policy and Technology and Climate Policy Outlook (WETO), European Commission, Directorate-General Research, EUR 20366, Brussels, 2003.

Final achievement levels

After having studied Chapter 14 and the exercises, you should:
- know what scenarios are in general and energy scenarios in particular, and what they can be used for;
- be familiar the most important approaches to modelling energy demand and energy supply;
- be able to carry out a simple scenario exercise;
- have knowledge of the most important families of energy models; and
- be familiar with the main pitfalls of the scenario approach.

Exercises chapter 14

14.1. A simple energy scenario
Make calculations for a simple energy use scenario for an economy that consists of four sectors: Industry, Services, Transport and Households. In the year 2005, the energy use of these sectors is 1000, 200, 600 and 600 PJ, respectively. Industry and services each contributed 50% to the Gross Domestic Product (in 2005). In these four sectors, the volume of activity is increasing by 1, 3, 3 and 1% per year, respectively. The energy efficiency improvement (i.e., the decrease of the specific energy use) is 0,5% per year for the transport sector and 1% per year in the other sectors. Calculate the energy use after 10 years.
What is the effect of volume growth, changes in structure, and energy efficiency improvements on the energy use?

14.2. Analysis of a scenario
Take a look at the so-called World Energy Policy and Technology and Climate Policy Outlook (WETO) publication by the European Commission:
http://ec.europa.eu/research/energy/pdf/weto_final_report.pdf.
a. Can you characterize the scenarios in this publication (e.g., are they explorative versus forecasting? also consider other characteristics treated in Section 14.1).
b. What type of economic model is used in the scenario exercise?
c. Can you come up with one or two critical comments on these scenarios?

15

Policies for efficient energy use and renewable energy

There are numerous reasons to implement energy policies:
- Regulation of energy supply systems (especially for electricity and natural gas);
- Development of indigenous energy sources;
- Development of specific energy technologies (e.g., nuclear energy);
- Security of energy supply (especially limiting the dependency on oil),
- Conservation of energy sources;
- Limitation of environmental effects of the energy supply system;
- Liberalisation of the energy market; and
- Sustainable development.

Many governments consider energy conservation or improvement of the energy efficiency and the application of renewable energy sources as an important way to reach at least some of these targets.

This chapter is devoted to the types of policy instruments that can be used to improve energy efficiency and stimulate the application of renewable energy. Similar instruments can be used for a broader range of policy targets.

First, barriers to improving energy efficiency and implementing renewable energy will be discussed (15.1). Second, policy instruments will be discussed, first in general (15.2) and then with a focus on energy-related policies (15.3). Finally, ways of analysing the effectiveness of policy instruments is described (15.4).

15.1 Barriers for energy efficiency improvement

Various barriers to energy efficiency and renewables can lead an 'actor' (whether a company, institute, household or individual) *not* to pursue these options. These can be:
- Technical barriers. Options may not yet be available, or actors may consider options not sufficiently proven to be worth adopting.
- Knowledge barriers. Actors may not be informed about possibilities for energy efficiency improvement. Or they may know about certain technologies, but not be aware that the technology might be applicable to them.
- Economic barriers. The standard economic barrier is that a certain technology does not satisfy the profitability criteria set by firms. Another barrier can be the lack of

capital for investment. The fact that the old equipment is not yet depreciated can also be considered an economic barrier.

- Organisational barriers. Especially in non energy-intensive companies, there are no well-defined structures for choosing and carrying out energy efficiency investments.
- The landlord-tenant barrier. There is a group of barriers related to the fact that the one carrying out an investment in energy efficiency improvement (e.g., the owner of an office building) may not be the one who has the financial benefits (in this example, the user of the office building who pays the energy bill).
- Lack of interest. For the vast majority of actors, the costs of energy are so small compared to their total (production) costs that energy efficiency improvement is not even taken into consideration. The other barriers can then be considered as derived barriers: for instance, if energy costs are small, companies will not spend much effort learning about the options for energy cost reduction.

The use of the concept 'barriers' is common in energy analysis. Nevertheless, it has its limitations since it is based on the assumption that when enough barriers are taken away, measures will eventually be taken. However, even when all the barriers are removed, there may still be no real 'drivers' present for energy efficiency improvement, meaning that the associated measures are not adopted.

15.2 Policy instruments

Three basic mechanisms can be distinguished to influence the behaviour of an actor:
- Communication mechanisms: Transfer of information, providing knowledge. The basic assumption here is that people will change their behaviour when they are better informed.
- Economic mechanisms: Providing financial incentives to stimulate desired behaviour or financial penalties to discourage undesired behaviour. The basic idea here is that people will optimise their welfare.
- Normative mechanisms: Setting standards for what people are obliged to do or forbidding certain behaviour. The basic idea is that people will act on the basis of jointly adopted ideas about what is appropriate in certain situations.

Governments using these mechanisms to influence the behaviour of actors apply what we call *policy instruments*. In practice, policy instruments often use a combination of all three mechanisms. Of course, not only governments try to influence behaviour; other actors also try to influence each other's behaviour. Approaches to policy evaluation that take into account all these influences are called *network* approaches.

Government policy making can be described in a simplified way as a three-phase process (so-called rational-analytical approach):

1. In the *policy formulation* phase the policy problem is defined, the policy targets are set and the policy instruments are selected; this is often done by government and parliament. In this phase, all kinds of interest groups can be involved and exercise influence.

2. In the *policy implementation* phase, a government-designated agency translates the selected policies to actions that influence the individual actors. Examples of such intermediary agency are a municipality that enforces a building code, or an energy agency that carries out a subsidy programme. There are also interactions in this phase, generally between the government agency and individual actor.

3. In the final phase, policy *affects the behaviour* of the targeted actors (or fails to). The success of this phase may depend on the degree of interaction for example between a company and the implementing agency.

15.3   Policy instruments in the area of energy

To improve energy efficiency, the following policy instruments can be considered:
*   Energy or carbon taxation
*   Investment subsidies or fiscal incentives
*   Emission trading
*   Energy efficiency standards
*   Negotiated agreements
*   Energy efficiency labelling
*   R&D subsidies

To stimulate the production of energy from renewable sources, similar policies can be applied, the following can also be considered:
*   Feed-in tariffs
*   Renewable energy portfolio standards

We will now discuss these types of policy instruments in more detail.

In the case of an *energy tax*, energy users have to pay a levy on top of the market price when they purchase an energy carrier. When this levy is proportional to the carbon content of the energy carrier, the tax is called a *carbon tax*. Automotive fuels are taxed in most countries, but generally only small levies are placed on other energy carriers. Only a few countries in northwestern Europe have substantial carbon or energy taxes for fuels other than automotive fuels, and even in these countries, energy-intensive companies are generally exempted.

The appeal of a general tax is that it leads to an optimum outcome: if one wants to reach a specific aim (e.g., reduction of carbon dioxide emissions), taxation related to that aim (in this case, a carbon tax) will – at least in theory – produce the lowest possible costs for society as a whole. On the other hand, a serious disadvantage of an energy or carbon tax is that there may be negative effects for specific groups, in this case energy-intensive companies (especially if the tax is only introduced in a few countries), as well as on low-income households. Furthermore, to achieve the desired results, taxation levels have to be fairly high. One specific application of a carbon or energy tax is to raise funds for subsidy schemes.

Subsidies are often provided to encourage investments in energy-efficient or renewable energy technology. Part of the investment is refunded, either directly or in the form of tax reduction (fiscal stimulation). Investment subsidies are in place or have been in place in many countries, often refunding a fixed fraction of the investment. Another form of subsidy is the rebate: purchasers of equipment that is more efficient than average (e.g. efficient refrigerators, compact fluorescent lamps) get a fixed amount of money back.

General investment subsidies, which provide a fixed percentage of the investment as a refund, have the disadvantage of so-called free-rider effects: part of the subsidies (which can amount to 50% or more of the investment) are given to actors that would have made the investment anyway. The free-rider effect is greater when the subsidy is generic, applying to all technologies, whether highly profitable or unprofitable; but the free-rider effect tends to be smaller when the subsidies are directed at specific technologies. Investment subsidies can be effective, but in general the costs for the government are higher than for other policy instruments.

In order to stimulate the development of renewable energy, special *feed-in tariffs* can be provided for electricity from renewable sources that are delivered to the public grid. Normally, the revenues for electricity fed into the grid depend on the prevailing market price of electricity, but the production costs of renewable electricity are still higher than the wholesale price of electricity in many cases. Feed-in tariffs can take various forms, but the most common is a fixed rate per kWh delivered. Feed-in systems for renewable energy sources are in place in various countries, including Denmark, Germany and Spain, and have contributed greatly to the growth of wind and solar electricity production in Europe. In most cases the feed-in tariffs are paid via a surcharge on the electricity price. In comparison to investment subsidies, an advantage of a feed-in scheme is that payment is strictly dependent on performance: if no electricity is delivered, nothing is paid.

In the case of *emission trading*, each actor (in this case, a company) gets a certain number of emission allowances. The company needs to keep its emissions below this 'cap', but the emission trading system allows the companies to buy or sell their emission allowances. There are different ways the initial allowances can be set: the allocation of allowances can be made by the government, for instance based on historic emissions (this is called grandfathering), but the allocations can also be sold at auction.
Until recently, emission trading systems were rare. The oldest system of any significance is the emission trading system for SO_2 from power plants in the USA. However, in 2005 a large CO_2 emission trading system was introduced in the European Union, covering about

half of the Union's emissions (including both power plants and large industrial energy users).

Like emission taxation, emission trading theoretically leads to the lowest possible costs of total emission reduction. Furthermore, total emissions can be tuned exactly to a pre-determined level. The most important problem – apart from administrative issues – is making a fair initial allocation to the various companies.

Energy efficiency standards prescribe minimum technical requirements for energy conversion systems and energy end-use systems. Two main approaches are prescriptive standards, which impose requirements on specific components of equipment, and performance standards, which impose requirements on the overall level of (specific) energy use.

Most industrialised countries have standards for the energy efficiency of new buildings, both prescriptive (e.g., insulation values of walls and roofs) and performance standards. A number of countries (e.g., the USA and countries in South East Asia) have standards for the energy efficiency of household equipment. In 1975, the USA introduced the corporate-average-fuel-economy (CAFE) standard for passenger cars: the average specific fuel use of all new cars sold by a specific car company needs to meet a certain level.

Energy efficiency standards can be very effective in reducing or limiting energy use, but they are rigid and especially prescriptive standards do not allow much flexibility. Furthermore, legislative processes can take much time, and an adequate system of monitoring is necessary to enforce compliance. Finally, companies are not stimulated to go beyond the energy efficiency standards.

Renewable energy portfolio standards – also called renewable energy obligations – require that a certain part of the energy supplied originate from renewable sources. The obligation can be assigned to different parties, but in the case of electricity, the energy suppliers are often responsible (see Section 5.5). The suppliers are required to show that a certain percentage of the electricity they delivered to the final consumers comes from renewable sources. As there is only one grid, such a partial delivery is not possible in physical terms, so a system of certificates is introduced. When a unit of renewable electricity is produced, a certificate is created, which is redeemed when the electricity is delivered to the final consumer. This procedure avoids double-counting. In most systems, the certificates are tradable, and suppliers who do not comply, have to pay a penalty.

Renewable energy portfolio standards are in place in the UK and in several states in the USA. Though the instrument is still relatively young and experience is limited, it could induce more competition between technology suppliers and lead to lower costs; however, it also introduces more uncertainty for investors.

Negotiated agreements – or voluntary agreements – are agreements between governments and actors or groups of actors to limit or reduce energy use, usually specific energy consumption. Agreements can refer to the actors' own energy use, or the energy use of the equipment they produce. Voluntary agreements on the energy efficiency of industrial processes are in place in a number of European countries. The European Union has made voluntary agreements with car manufacturers and with selected household appliance manufacturers. For companies, an advantage of such voluntary agreements is that they can be formulated in a way providing maximum flexibility. From the point-of-view of the government, the advantages are better cooperation on the part of the companies and a generally faster achievement than with energy efficiency standards. In order to attain ambitious voluntary agreements, the government needs to have a good negotiating position and it should actively support the process of implementing the desired energy-efficiency measures. Regular monitoring and independent verification are also necessary.

Energy efficiency labelling. Labelling is a way of informing the buyers or users of the equipment about its energy performance. For example, in the European Union, the energy use of electric appliances and cars is clearly marked. Labelling has some effect on purchasing behaviour, but the effect is limited, as is often the case with information tools. Nevertheless, labelling is an important first step in policy development, and its effect can be enhanced when it is combined with other policy instruments, such as subsidies.

Instead of stimulating the use of energy efficient equipment that is already available, governments can also stimulate the development of new renewable energy technologies and new energy-efficient technology. This is usually done by providing *R&D subsidies*. In the past, the development of nuclear technology received much support and currently many countries are also supporting the development of renewable energy technologies; only a few countries provide substantial funding for R&D on energy efficiency.

Other policy instruments to stimulate the development of new energy technology include:
- Cooperative technology agreements: agreements on technology development between governments and private actors. An example is the Partnership for a New Generation of Vehicles, an agreement in 1993 between the US administration and US car manufacturers to jointly work on prototype cars to be ready by 2005 that would consume only one third of the fuel of cars produced in the early nineties.
- Technology procurement programmes: a government sets certain requirements for the equipment it purchases. The supplier that meets these standards best is rewarded, for instance, through a guaranteed purchase. This was applied in Sweden and led to the development of cheaper and more efficient heat pumps.
- Technology-forcing standards: a government may set energy efficiency standards for the long-term that cannot be satisfied with existing technology and requires additional technological development. An example is a requirement in California to have a certain fraction of zero-emission vehicles on the road in the year 2010.

15.4 Energy policy evaluation

Policy instruments can be judged on a number of criteria:

- *Effectiveness*. To what extent does the policy instrument contribute to reaching a specific goal? Before we can answer this, we must first determine to what extent the pre-set goal was achieved. This does not answer the question of effectiveness yet, since autonomous developments, other policies, or external factors, may have contributed to achieving the goal. The effectiveness of a policy instrument is the degree to which the policy instrument itself contributed to the achievement of the goal: to determine this, we must compare the achievement reached with the policy in place, with what would have been achieved had the policy not been in place.
- *Efficiency*. The efficiency indicates the effectiveness of the means required to reach the effect. In general, the means can be expressed in financial terms, determined for i) the government, ii) for the target group (those targeted by the policy who may need to invest), or iii) for society as a whole.
- *Side-effects*. Various negative (but also positive) side-effects may occur, like effects on employment rates, effects on income distribution, and effects on the country's balance of payments.

Policy evaluation can take place before a policy is implemented (*ex ante* evaluation) or after the policy has been implemented or has been in place for some time (*ex post* evaluation). Both types of evaluation have their own complexities:

- Ex ante evaluation generally requires two separate actions: to estimate what will happen if the policy is *not* introduced, and to estimate what will happen if it *is* introduced. The difference will represent the expected effect of the policy; of course, both estimates require some kind of modelling.
- In case of ex post evaluation, one is at least able to determine what has happened *with* the introduction of the policy instrument (although careful monitoring is required). In this case, though, an estimate needs to be made of what would have happened if the policy instruments had *not* been introduced.

Evaluating the effectiveness of energy efficiency improvement policies is more difficult than evaluating the effect of many other policies for two main reasons:

- First, autonomous developments and the effects of changes in energy prices can be very substantial. This makes the question "what would happen without the application of a policy instrument" difficult to answer, but highly relevant for the outcome of the evaluation.
- Second, the effects being measured are fairly small; in general, policies directed at energy efficiency improvement have an effect of one or at most a few percent per year. Especially when the policy is directed at a mix of options for energy efficiency improvement rather than individual technologies, it is difficult to measure the effects.

Ex ante policy evaluation can be done using the scenario building models discussed in Chapter 14. Some types of instruments, such as energy and carbon taxation, can be relatively easily simulated with these models, but the models are not always directly suitable for the evaluation of other policy instruments; then ad hoc assumptions have to be included in the analysis.

Two particular approaches for the *ex-post* analysis of the effectiveness and efficiency of policies can be mentioned, the first from economics, the second from policy science:

1. *Econometric approaches.* The effect of a policy instrument can be estimated by comparing situations with and without the policy instrument. These can be different periods in the same country, different regions within a country, or different countries. Ideally, econometric analysis will consider all the other relevant factors that can influence the development that the policy has targeted. Econometric analysis is especially strong in the case of economic instruments, but it can also be used for other instruments, for instance by introducing a variable that has a value 1 or 0 depending on whether the policy instrument is in place or not (a so-called dummy variable). Reliable econometric analysis is only possible when the available datasets are large enough.

2. *Theory-based evaluation.* Another useful approach is so-called theory-based programme evaluation. This assumes that policy instruments are based on an underlying 'theory' about how the policy is expected to work, or at least some implicit assumptions about the mechanisms of policy instruments. Theory-based evaluation does not only consider the outcomes, but also monitors the functioning of the underlying mechanisms. This monitoring can subsequently be used, not only to evaluate the policy instrument, but also to improve the understanding of actors' behaviour, ultimately improving the 'theory' and engendering more effective policies.

Examples of policy evaluation. There are many examples of both ex ante and ex post policy evaluation. A combination of the two is often used, and some examples are presented in Figures 15.1-3.

Many policy evaluations are carried out on a rather ad hoc basis, often at the request of government and government agencies, and they do not always have a systematic character. Further methodological development is necessary to come to better and more reliable evaluations of the effectiveness and cost-effectiveness of policy instruments.

Rebound and take-back effects. In one way or the other, policy instruments have indirect effects that can partly offset the effect of the policy instrument. We can distinguish:

*   The rebound-effect. Energy efficiency improvement may lead to savings, which may in turn be spent on other products or services that may generate additional use of energy.

- The take-back effect (sometimes also indicated as rebound effect). If energy efficiency increases for a specific energy function, the costs of this energy function become lower. The lower price of the energy function may lead to a higher use of the energy function. An example is the water-saving shower head. People with this equipment have lower costs for water and energy per unit of time, which may tempt them to shower longer or more often.

Take-back and rebound effects will be small, generally less than 10% of the intended energy conservation effect. Still, the effects may be substantial for specific types of equipment or specific sectors.

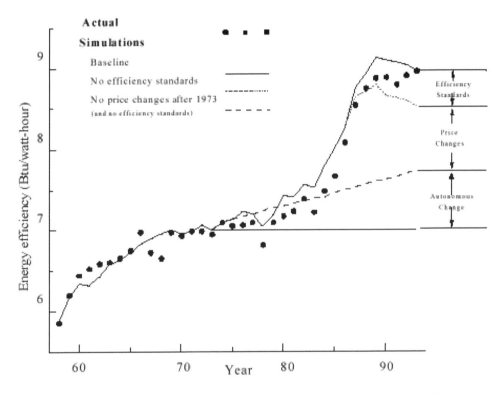

Figure 15.1. Evaluation of various effects on the energy efficiency improvement of room air conditioners in the USA. The dots describe the actual development of the average efficiency of air conditioners sold in the USA, on the basis of market surveys. The government tried to influence the efficiency by setting standards. At the same time, electricity prices increased over time.

The researchers had data available on 735 models of room air conditioners available on the US market, with information on a range of characteristics, including costs. They carried out econometric analysis on this data set to estimate the various effects: i.e., the relation between the characteristics of the room air conditioners and external factors, like time, energy prices and regulation. Next, these relations were used for the simulation depicted here. Though energy efficiency standards only came into effect in 1990, the authors allowed effects before that time in their analysis. Source: Newel et al., 1999.

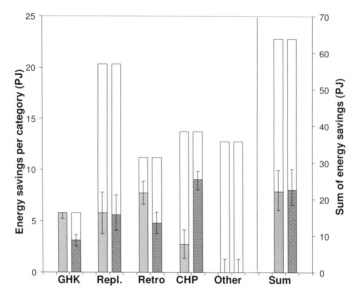

Figure 15.2. The effectiveness of voluntary agreements between the government and industrial companies in the Netherlands. The total energy conservation (compared to a frozen-efficiency-level) per category is represented by the total bars (data based on reporting by industry).

The researchers investigated which fraction of the conserved energy was induced by the voluntary agreements. They did this by category, using both expert estimates (the breakdown into categories was more detailed than that shown in the figure) and a survey among companies. The part of energy conservation that was induced through the voluntary agreements is shown in the shaded area of the bars. The rest is autonomous or caused by other policies (like the environmental action plans of the energy companies in the case of CHP stimulation). Source: Rietbergen et al., 2001.

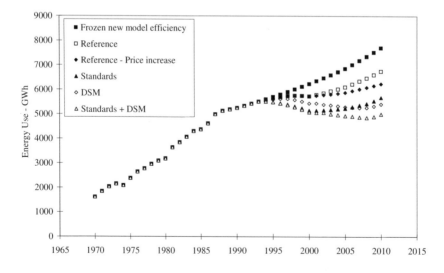

Figure 15.3. Ex ante evaluation of the effect of various policies on the introduction of energy-efficient lighting in the Swedish service sector.

In Figure 15.3, the researchers used a model simulating the adoption of technology by firms. This model represents the extent to which firms adopt new technologies, depending on the pay-back-period of the technologies. A vintage model is used to take into account the annual extension or replacement of part of the lighting systems. Energy-efficiency standards are simulated by assuming that full compliance occurs (or that undercompliance by some firms is compensated by overcompliance by others).

DSM = demand side management by the energy companies: the energy company provides the customer an incentive to invest in an energy efficiency measure, in exchange for a fraction of the energy savings paid via the electricity bill. Source: Swisher et al., 1994.

Further reading

K. Blok, H.L.F. de Groot, E.E.M. Luiten, M.G. Rietbergen: The Effectiveness of Policy Instruments for Energy-Efficiency Improvement in Firms: The Dutch Experience, Kluwer Academic Publishers, Dordrecht, The Netherlands, 2004.

C. Blumstein, S. Goldstone, L. Lutzenhiser: A Theory-Based Approach to Market Transformation, Energy Policy, 28 (2000) pp. 137-144.

C. Mitchell, D. Bauknecht, P.J. Connor: Effectiveness Through Risk Reduction: a Comparison of the Renewable Obligation in England and Wales and the Feed-in System in Germany, Energy Policy, 34 (2006) pp. 297-305.

S. Nadel: The Take-Back Effect – Fact or Fiction?, American Council for an Energy-Efficient Economy, Washington, 1993.

R.G. Newel, A.B. Jaffe, R.N. Stavins: The Induced Innovation Hypothesis and Energy-Saving Technological Change, Quarterly Journal of Economics, August 1999, pp. 941-975.
The figure is taken from: A. B. Jaffe, R.G. Newell, R.N. Stavins: Energy-Efficient Technologies and Climate Change Policies: Issues and Evidence, Resources for the Future, Washington D.C., 1999.

K. Ostertag: No-regret Potentials in Energy Conservation: An Analysis of Their Relevance, Size and Determinants, Physica-Verlag, Heidelberg, 2003.

On the rebound, Energy Policy, special issue 28 (2000) 351-500.

M.G. Rietbergen, J.C.M. Farla, K. Blok, Do Agreements Enhance Energy Efficiency Improvement? Journal of Cleaner Production, 10 (2002)153-163.

P.H. Rossi, M.W. Lipsey, H.E. Freeman: Evaluation – A Systematic Approach, SAGE Publications, Thousand Oaks, California, 7th edition, 2003.

S. Sorrell, E. O'Malley, J. Schleich and S. Scott: The Economics of Energy Efficiency: Barriers to Cost-Effective Investment, Edward Elgar Publishing Ltd., Cheltenham, UK, 2004.

J. Swisher, L. Christiansson, C. Hedenström: Dynamics of energy efficiency lighting, Energy Policy, 22 (1994) pp. 581-594.

Final achievement levels

After having studied Chapter 15 and the exercises, you should:
- be able to describe barriers for energy efficiency and renewable energy and be able to illustrate these with concrete examples;
- know the three basic mechanisms through which behaviour can be influenced;
- know the various policy instruments in the area of energy and be able to illustrate these with concrete examples;
- know the criteria for policy evaluation, know the various approaches to policy evaluation, and be able to apply these in a concrete situation; and
- be able to explain what rebound and take-back effects are.

Exercises chapter 15

15.1. Policy instruments and mechanisms
For each of the nine policy instruments (section 15.3), consider in what way communicative, economic and normative elements play an influencing role. Often more than one type may have an effect.

15.2. Ecotax
In the Netherlands, there is an energy tax in place. This tax was originally introduced to promote energy savings and the introduction of renewable energy. In 2005, the energy tax in the Netherlands for small users amounted for:
Natural gas € 0.15/m^3 (price without tax for small users is € 0.35/m^3);
Electricity € 0.07/kWh (price without tax is € 0.11/kWh);
a. Calculate the amount of tax in Euros per tonne CO_2.
b. What is the relation of the level of this tax compared to the external costs of energy use (with regard to climate change)?
c. Estimate the effect of the tax on the energy use of households (see Section 5.7).

15.3. Free-rider effect of subsidies
For a company, 15 measures to save energy are available. The investments are 4, 8, 12, 16, 20, ..., 56 and 60 k€, respectively. They all save 1 TJ per year. Neglect costs for operation and maintenance. The energy price for the company is 7 €/GJ. The company uses a pay-back time criterion of 3 years.
a. Which investments will be done without subsidies?
b. Which investments will be done with a 25% subsidy?
c. What is the free-rider effect of the subsidy for this company (which part of the subsidy has no effect on the investment behaviour)?
d. Do the same for a subsidy of 50%. Is the efficiency of the subsidy (from the viewpoint of the government) higher now?

15.4. Effects of subsidies
A subsidy not only affects the cost-benefit analysis companies make, but can also have other effects. Think of three mechanisms through which a company, via a subsidy, can be stimulated to take energy efficient measures.

15.5. The choice of policy instruments

Consider the policy instruments mentioned in Section 15.3, and investigate in what way these instruments can be applied for the following concrete goals:
1. Promoting energy efficiency in industry; and
2. Promoting the use of heat pumps in industry.

Make a table in which you show each of the policy instruments, and judge these instruments with regard to effectiveness, efficiency and side-effects.

15.6. Replacement of the energy premium

As of the year 2000, the Netherlands' government gave subsidies to buyers of energy-efficient electric appliances (refrigerators, freezers, washing machines, etc.). Each year 2 million of these appliances are sold. These appliances typically use 200 – 300 kWh per year (electricity costs for households are 0.20 Euro per kWh). The subsidy amounted to 50 Euro for equipment that is 15% better than what is sold without the subsidy. Under the subsidy scheme, about 80% of the people chose energy-efficient appliances (assume that there are only two types of equipment on the market: standard and energy-efficient).
a. Discuss why the measure has free-rider effects.
b. Discuss the take-back and rebound-effects associated with the measure.

In 2003, the subsidy scheme was stopped because of the increasing budget deficit of the Netherlands government. Despite the lack of resources, the Netherlands' government wishes to continue with the stimulation of the market penetration of efficient appliances. You are asked to give advice to the Netherlands' government. Consider alternative policy instruments that make use of each of the following mechanisms:
c. communicative
d. economic
e. normative

For each of these mechanisms, describe an alternative policy instrument that is based on the mechanism. Give an estimate of the expected effectiveness of each policy instrument. Be as quantitative as possible.

Appendix 1. List of abbreviations

k	kilo (10^3)
M	mega (10^6)
G	giga (10^9)
T	tera (10^{12})
P	peta (10^{15})
E	exa (10^{18})

AC	alternating current	J	joule
AEEI	annual energy efficiency improvement	kV	kilovolt
bbl	barrel	kWh	kilowatt-hour (= 3.6 MJ)
BTU	British-thermal-unit (= 1.055 kJ)	LCA	life-cycle assessment
CAFE	corporate average fuel economy	LHV	lower heating value
CDU	crude distillation unit	LPG	liquefied petroleum gas
CED	cumulative energy demand	Markal	market allocation
CFL	compact fluorescent lamp	NO_x	nitrogen oxides (NO and NO_2)
CHP	combined generation of heat and power	NCV	net calorific value
COP	coefficient-of-performance (of heat pumps)	NPV	net present value
DC	direct current	OECD	Organization for Economic Cooperation and Development
EEI	energy-efficiency index	O&M	operation and maintenance
EMAS	Eco-Management and Audit Scheme	OPEC	Oil Producing and Exporting Countries
ERE	energy requirement for energy	OTC	over-the-counter
EU	European Union	PBP	pay-back period
FCC	fluid catalytic cracker	PER	process energy requirement
GCV	gross calorific value	PFCs	perfluorocarbons
GDP	gross domestic product	PPI	physical production index
GER	gross energy requirement	ppm	parts per million
GJ_e	gigajoule electricity	PPP	purchasing power parity
GJ_p	gigajoule primary energy	PV	photovoltaic
GWP	global warming potential	R&D	research and development
HFCs	hydrofluorocarbons	SEC	specific energy consumption / specific energy use
HHV	higher heating value	SI	*Système Internationale*
hp	horse-power (= 0.7457 kW)	TFC	total final consumption
hrs	hours	tce	ton of coal equivalent (= 28.6 GJ)
HVAC	heating, ventilation and air conditioning	toe	ton of oil equivalent (= 41.868 GJ)
IEA	International Energy Agency	TPES	total primary energy supply
IFIAS	International Federation of Institutes for Advanced Study	UK	United Kingdom of Great Britain and Northern Ireland
IIASA	International Institute for Applied Systems Analysis	USA	United States of America
IPCC	Intergovernmental Panel on Climate Change	VDU	vacuum distillation unit
IRR	internal rate of return	W	watt
ISO	International Organisation for Standardisation	Wyr	watt-year (= 31.5 MJ)

Appendix 2. Unit conversion factors

For conversion factors for units of energy, see Table 2.1.

1 inch	= 2.54 cm
1 foot	= 30.5 cm
1 yard	= 0.91 m
1 mile (statute)	= 1.6 km
1 ounce	= 28.3 g
1 pound (lb)	= 0.4536 kg
1 short ton	= 907 kg
1 metric ton	= 1000 kg
1 pint	= 0.47 litre
1 gallon (US liquid gallon)	= 3.79 litre
1 pound (force)	= 4.45 N
1 ha	= 10,000 m^2
1 acre	= 4,047 m^2
1 atm	= 101.325 kPa
1 bar[1]	= 100 kPa
1 mm of mercury at 0 °C	= 0.133 kPa
1 pound per square inch (psia)	= 6.895 kPa
1 BTU/hr·ft^2· °F	= 5.682 W/m^2·K

Temperature conversion: $c = (5/9) \cdot (f-32)$
(c in °C; f in °F) $f = (9/5) \cdot c + 32$

Fuel use of cars: If fuel use in mile per gallon (mpg) is x, then fuel use in litre/100 km is 236.25/x (and vice versa)

---

[1] Often bar(a) and bar(o) are distinguished. The unit bar(a) = bar(absolute) is used in the case of absolute pressure whereas the unit bar(o) indicates excess pressure compared to atmospheric pressure.